Anne Hardy

Where to Eat in Canada

FORTY-EIGHTH YEAR

18-19

We acknowledge the support of the Government of Canada through the Canada Book Fund for our publishing activities.

ISBN 978 0 7780 1446 1

Front cover by Paul Cézanne

Printed in Canada by Coach House Printing

PUBLISHED IN CANADA BY OBERON PRESS

HOW TO USE THIS GUIDE

The restaurants recommended in this guide have been arranged alphabetically by location, from Abbotsford in British Columbia to Yellowknife in the Northwest Territories. Each entry begins with the name of the city, town or village in which the restaurant is located, followed by the name and address of the restaurant and its telephone number. Next comes the entry itself, printed in roman type, followed by two or three lines, in italic type, indicating the hours during which the restaurant is open for business. The entry ends with a quantity of other useful information: does the restaurant have a full liquor licence or is it licensed for beer and wine only? What credit cards does it take? If the restaurant is in an urban centre, does it have free off-street parking? Do you need to book a table? Is there wheelchair access to the front door and the washrooms?

If you already know what restaurant you want to go to, look up the restaurant in the guide, selecting first the name of the centre and then the name of the restaurant. You will find a heading like this:

LAKE LOUISE, Alberta   **MAP 95**
THE POST HOTEL   ☆☆☆
200 Pipestone Road   **$325 ($750)**
(800) 661-1586

At left, you will find the name, address and telephone number of the restaurant, all arranged under Lake Louise. The first line on the right means that Lake Louise is represented by Map Number 95. Look for Number 95 on the map of Alberta. Once you've found it, consult your road-map for the most convenient route to Lake Louise. Often a quick check of the entry in the guide will help you to find your way. The second line indicates how many stars the restaurant has earned. The maximum is three, and there are only 26 restaurants in the guide that have earned this rating. Another 86 have earned two stars and 136 have earned one. We consider a further 85 restaurants to be good buys, which doesn't necessarily mean that they are unusually cheap, though it usually does. They are indicated by a pointing finger.

The third line indicates the price. The first (and often the only) figure indicates the average cost of dinner for two with a modest wine, applicable taxes and a tip of 15%. Dinner for two is taken to mean two appetizers, two main courses, one sweet, two coffees and three glasses of an open wine. Where a restaurant has earned two stars, the cost of half a bottle of wine is included. Where a restaurant has earned three stars, the cost of a full bottle is part of the estimated price. The wines chosen are not the cheapest the establishment has to offer, nor are they the most expensive. Where, as in the case of the Post Hotel, a second figure in parentheses follows the first, this second figure indicates the average cost of dinner, bed and breakfast. The presence of this figure means that we recommend not only dinner but also, if convenient, an overnight stay.

If you don't know where you want to go, turn to the maps. Find yourself on the map that shows the province you are in. Select the nearest number and then look it up in the Index. Under the number you'll find all the centres represented by that number. Let's suppose that the nearest number is 204, which stands for the city of Toronto. Look up Toronto in the Index to Southern Ontario and you'll find that there are two other centres with the same number, each enclosed in parentheses. This means that these centres are both in the immediate vicinity of Toronto, too close to be given a number of their own. They are Creemore and Markham. Now look up Toronto in the main body of the guide, where you'll find all 32 restaurants that we recommend in the city itself. If you then look up the other two centres, you will find three more restaurants in the area that we also recommend.

I

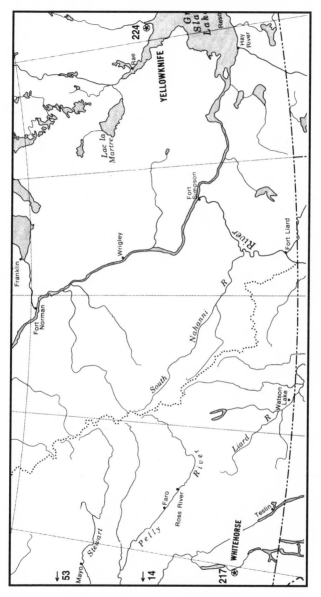

YUKON & NORTHWEST TERRITORIES

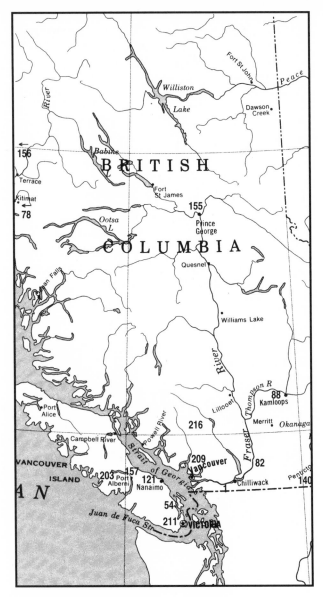

BRITISH COLUMBIA

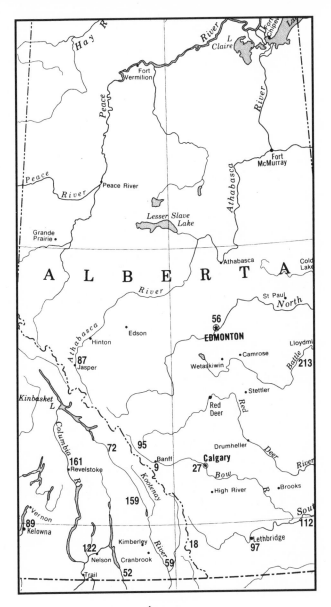

ALBERTA

SASKATCHEWAN

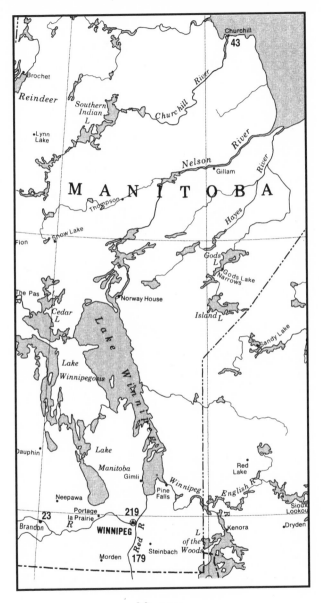

MANITOBA

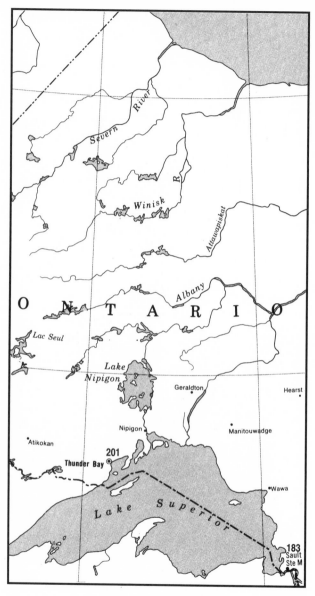

Severn River

Winisk

R

Attawapiskat

O N T A R I O

Albany

Lac Seul

Lake Nipigon

Geraldton

Hearst

Nipigon

Manitouwadge

•Atikokan

201

Thunder Bay

•Wawa

Lake Superior

183
Sault
Ste M

NORTHWESTERN ONTARIO

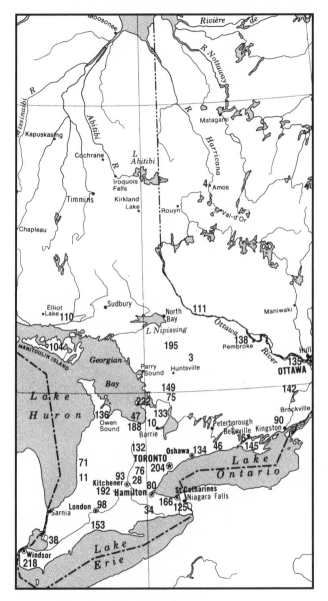

SOUTHERN ONTARIO

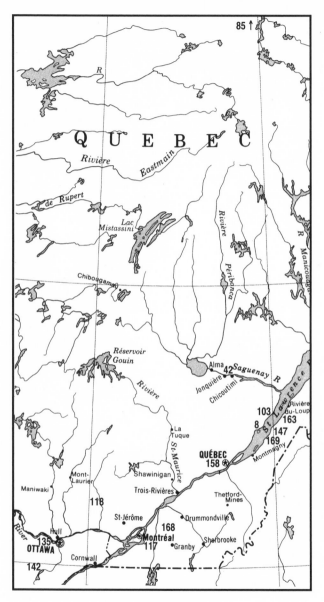

CENTRAL QUEBEC

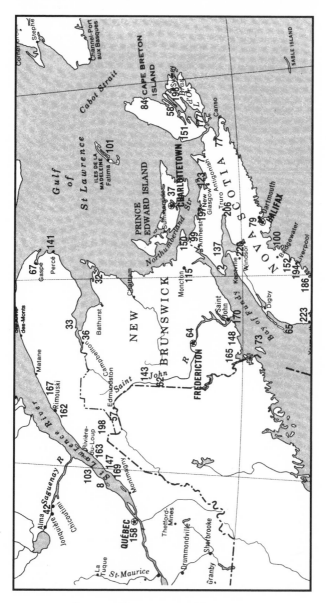

EASTERN QUEBEC & THE MARITIMES

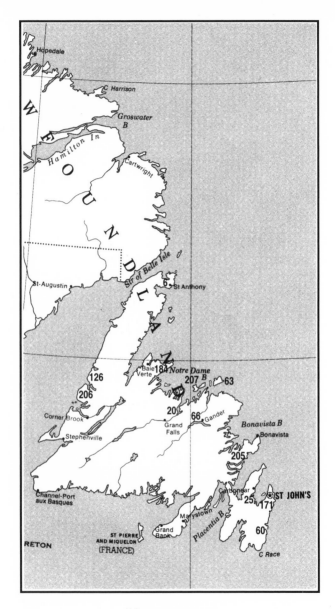

NEWFOUNDLAND

INDEX TO MAPS

MANITOBA

23 Brandon
43 Churchill
179 St. Pierre-Jolys
219 Winnipeg

NORTHWESTERN ONTARIO

183 Sault Ste. Marie
201 Thunder Bay

SOUTHERN ONTARIO

3 Algonquin Park
4 Amos
10 Barrie
11 Bayfield
16 Belleville
(16) Brighton
28 Cambridge
34 Cayuga
38 Chatham
46 Cobourg
47 Collingwood
71 Goderich
75 Gravenhurst
(75) Bracebridge
76 Guelph
(76) Morriston
80 Hamilton
(80) Ancaster
(80) Burlington
(80) Dundas
90 Kingston
(90) Ivy Lea
93 Kitchener
(93) Waterloo
98 London
104 Manitoulin Island
110 Massey
111 Mattawa
125 Niagara-on-the-Lake
132 Orangeville
133 Orillia
134 Oshawa
135 Ottawa
(135) Chelsea
136 Owen Sound
138 Pembroke
(138) Petawawa
142 Perth
145 Picton
(145) Bloomfield
(145) Wellington
149 Port Carling
153 Port Stanley
166 St. Catharines
(166) Beamsville
188 Singhampton
192 Stratford
(192) St. Marys
195 Sundridge
204 Toronto
(204) Creemore
(204) Markham
218 Windsor
(218) Kingsville
222 Wyebridge

150 Port Elgin
151 Port Hood
(151) Glenville
(151) Northeast
Margaree
152 Port Medway
158 Quebec
(158) Ile d'Orléans
162 Rimouski
(162) Le Bic
163 Rivière du Loup
165 St. Andrews
167 Ste.-Flavie
169 St.-Jean-Port-Joli
170 Saint John
177 St. Peter's
186 Shelburne
(186) Clark's Harbour
194 Summerville Beach
196 Sydney
(196) North Sydney
197 Tatamagouche
198 Témiscouata-
sur-le-Lac

206 Truro
220 Wolfville
(220) Grand Pré
223 Yarmouth
(223) Middle West
Pubnico

NEWFOUNDLAND &
LABRADOR

6 l'Anse-aux-Meadows
(6) St.-Lunaire-Griquet
20 Botwood
25 Brigus
60 Ferryland
63 Fogo Island
66 Gander
126 Norris Point
171 St. John's
(171) Portugal Cove
184 La Scie
205 Trinity
206 Trout River
207 Twillingate

ABBOTSFORD, B.C.

CLAYBURN VILLAGE STORE
34810 Clayburn Road
Clayburn
(604) 853-4020

MAP 1

$55

Bryan and Trish Haber are busy. Bryan is a practising barrister as well as a storekeeper, and Trish does all the baking and preserves—chutneys, pickles, scones, sticky toffee pudding and sticky gingerbread cake. They have no time for a social life, but they close the store every four months—in January, in May and in September—and take off for foreign parts, perhaps to a food festival in California, perhaps back to Trish's native England. Wherever they go, they look for new supplies, new ideas and new recipes for soup—Hungarian gulyassuppe for instance, or Guinness beef and barley. In 2013 the recipe for their coconut-and-carrot soup was published in *Bon Appétit*. The current store favourite is Thai coconut and squash. Tea is also a big feature. Fortnum and Mason worked with them on their Queen's Blend tea. Almost as elegant is the Earl Grey cream tea that Sloane of Toronto (alone in North America) imports from Britain. Clayburn offers the only clotted cream tea this side of Victoria. Bryan is also keen on British ales, which he buys from Samuel Smith's Yorkshire Brewery in Tadcaster (Trish's hometown). There's Imperial Stout, Nut Brown and Teddy Porter, and he now has an organic ale and an organic cider as well. There's always an assortment of British candies on the candy counter, all sold from big glass jars, the way they were in the nineteen-thirties. But they didn't have a frozen-yogurt machine then. He has one now that lets him choose whatever flavour the customer fancies.
Open Tuesday to Saturday 10 am to 4 pm. Closed on Sunday and Monday, and in January, May and December. Licensed. Master Card, Visa. &

This is a guide to Canadian restaurants from coast to coast—the first ever published and the only one of its kind on the market today.

ADVOCATE HARBOUR, N.S.

WILD CARAWAY
3721 Highway 209
(902) 392-2889

MAP 2
☆☆☆
$120 ($220)

Wild Caraway has always been one of our favourite restaurants. It may be four hours from Halifax, but it's worth every minute once you arrive, from the warm comfort of the old house and the stunning views of the harbour to the wonderful food. The menu is constantly changing. It starts with dulse and caraway biscuits and goes on to fresh vegetables grown in their own garden or foraged nearby. The flavours are not to be believed. They have five kinds of squash, served in a salad with a dressing of molasses and balsamic vinegar. They have a sunchoke salad, served with a reduction of burnt maple and yellow-birch oil. There are seared scallops with Keralan pickles, spiced chickpea fritters and Malaysian curried noodle soup with coconut milk, sprouts, mint and cilantro. There are housemade krauts with soy and sesame. They are equally inventive with their sweets, offering decon-structed lemon-meringue pie, peanut-butter-and-honey ice cream and banana *pain perdu*. It goes on and on, and it's spectacular.

Open Monday and Thursday to Sunday 11 am to 8 pm from the middle of May until late October. Closed on Tuesday and Wednesday. Licensed. Master Card, Visa. Book ahead. ♿

ALGONQUIN PARK, Ontario

AROWHON PINES
Highway 60
(866) 633-5661

MAP 3
☆☆
$200 ($625)

The cooking at Arowhon Pines this year has been some of the best we've ever experienced. Major investments have been made in the property—a new kitchen, a new dining-room entrance and a new front office—and they've richly paid off. The chefs may be working from established recipes—Eugene and Helen Kates put everything into the computer—but there's a liveliness and variety to the meals that we haven't seen before, and the dessert buffet is more elaborate than ever. The menus are all planned a week in advance so no guest will get the same meal twice. As you enter the huge hexagonal dining-room you're confronted by a big buffet table loaded with soups (perhaps lobster bisque with truffle cream), pâtés, salads and things like crispy duck in moo-shu pancake, shrimp dumplings and scallops with watercress. You can eat as much of any or all of these as you like. When you sit down—first come, first served—you have the choice of four entrées, one of which will be fish (baked halibut, say, in a parmesan crust) and another vegetarian. If you're hungry, ask for a second helping (they're free). If you're not, ask for a half-portion. You can even get a different second entrée—if you don't want to choose between the fish and the lamb you can just have both. The dessert bar has too many choices to list, but among them should be maple mousse, fruit salad, blueberry tart, carrot cake and the resort's famous butter tarts. And once again, you can help yourself to as much as you like. The price in parentheses at top right is for a room for two with three meals a day, plus all the recreational facilities—like canoes—that are available.

Open daily 12.30 pm to 2 pm, 6.30 pm to 8 pm from 3 June until Thanksgiving. Bring your own bottle. Master Card, Visa. Book ahead. &

ALGONQUIN PARK **MAP 3**
BARTLETT LODGE ☆
Highway 60 **$185 ($495)**
(866) 614-5355

No-one forgets their first visit to Bartlett Lodge. The Lodge is on Cache Lake about fifteen miles east of the West Gate. You drive to the far end of the car park, where you'll find a free telephone to the Lodge. A boat comes to pick you up in about two minutes. (In fine weather they come in a custom-built Giesler; if it's raining, they come in a covered pontoon boat.) On the far side, you'll be offered a four-course prix-fixe menu that includes a cheese and charcuterie board, five appetizers, five main courses and five sweets. Dinner might start with something like crispy spiced fish cake, butternut squash bruschetta or bacon-braised lentils, and go on to a main course of beef tenderloin, lamb shank, rainbow trout or rockfish. There are always vegetarian and gluten-free options. To finish there's a lemon cake, perhaps a fudge pie with chocolate ganache, a cheesecake and, if you're at the right time of year, a warm pumpkin bread pudding with caramel sauce and cinnamon whipped cream. Coffee is on the house.

Open daily 6 pm to 8 pm from early May until late October. Bring your own bottle. Master Card, Visa. You must book ahead.

AMHERST, N.S.
See LORNEVILLE.

AMOS, Quebec   MAP 4
LE FLINGOU   ☆☆
100 1 avenue o   **$140**
(819) 732-8271

We remember when a correspondent told us that Amos, a remote town 75 miles northeast of Noranda, had one of the best kitchens in northern Quebec. As Jean-Victor Flingou put it, a chef could hardly choose a more difficult place to work. Now, after 30 years in the kitchen of what used to be called Le Moulin, he's turned it over to his son, Maxime, who has renamed the restaurant Le Flingou. Maxime still makes things like French onion soup and bavette of beef, but he also has dishes of grilled octopus with chorizo and wapiti with huckleberry sauce. And he doesn't take any shortcuts. If he can't get fresh fish locally he imports it, six hours by truck, from Montreal. He prefers lamb to pork, but pork is on the menu now, with potato purée and two mustards. The sweets are familiar: if you don't fancy another crème brûlée, ask for the feuilleté of strawberries. It's delightful.

Open Monday to Wednesday 11 am to 2 pm, 5 pm to 9 pm, Thursday and Friday 11 am to 2 pm, 4.30 pm to 10 pm,

Saturday 5 pm to 10 pm. Closed on Sunday. Licensed. Amex, Master Card, Visa. Book ahead. &

ANCASTER, Ontario   (MAP 80)
THE MILL
548 Old Dundas Road   **$135**
(905) 648-1828

The Mill is one of the most conservative restaurants in its ownership group, which also includes Earth-to-Table Bread Bar in Hamilton (see below). But the chef, Jeff Crump, helped to found the Ontario chapter of the slow-cooking movement, and has long been an advocate of local organic produce, most of which comes from the restaurant's Earth-to-Table farm in Flamborough. He has some interesting appetizers, among them a roasted cauliflower soup, spaghetti squash and bison terrine. The most interesting of his main dishes is the confit duck leg, with moist flesh and crisp skin—a great dish. There's also roasted halibut with steamed mussels in a coconut curry sauce, a striploin steak and pork tortellini. Sweets—which are generally pies—depend largely on the time of year. Our favourite is the apple pie with maple syrup. The champagne Sunday brunch at 51.00 is as good as any in this part of the country.
Open Tuesday to Friday 11.30 am to 10 pm, Saturday 5 pm to 10 pm, Sunday 9.30 am to 2.30 pm (brunch), 5 pm to 9 pm. Closed on Monday. Licensed. Master Card, Visa. Free parking.

L'ANSE-AUX-MEADOWS,   MAP 6
Newfoundland
THE NORSEMAN   ☆☆
(877) 623-2018   **$155**

Adrian Noordhof loves his life in Newfoundland, but every winter he travels to Europe to study other cuisines. His wife Gina Hodge and her mother have been at The Norseman, which is a cafe and art gallery right next door to the Viking Settlement, for more than twenty years. They have always been known for keeping an open door for travelers of all sorts. Adrian still does most of the cooking himself, using all the resources at his doorstep. The fish plant in St. Anthony has given him tremendous support over the years. Their lobster, cod and shrimp are all perfectly fresh, and every morning Adrian makes them into a chowder with onions, saffron and port wine. The giant mussels come from just down the road, as does the snow crab. But you don't have to have seafood. You can ask instead for chicken, duck confit or Welsh lamb—which they find better than local. Adrian and Gina recently took over the bed-and-breakfast next door, which used to be run by her mother. They also own two state-of-the-art cottages on the seashore, which they bought from the author, Annie Proulx. One of them was built in 1890, and may be the oldest house in Newfoundland.

Open daily noon to 9 pm from 25 May until 20 September. Licensed. Diners, Master Card, Visa. Book ahead if you can. &

L'ANSE-AUX-MEADOWS
See also ST.-LUNAIRE-GRIQUET.

ANTIGONISH, N.S.	**MAP 7**
GABRIEAU'S BISTRO	☆☆
350 Main Street	**$170**
(902) 863-1925	

Gabrieau's has a wonderful wine-list, offering such things as Rothschild's petit mouton, several barolos (all properly aged) and, at the other end of the list, two or three from Luckett, among them the celebrated Phone Book. There are all the usual crabcakes and raw oysters, as well as perfectly fresh Atlantic salmon, Berkshire pork and lovely local lamb. Most remarkable of all is the sushi menu with its tuna sashimi and its shrimp tempura. You can order à la carte or ask for a sushi platter, which is loaded with Nigiri sushi of all sorts. There's also a tapas menu, normally only offered at the bar but available by request in the dining-room, with a wide selection of Asian choices like miso scallops and Thai green shrimp curry. This is an amazing restaurant.

Open Monday to Thursday 11 am to 9 pm, Friday 11 am to 9.30 pm, Saturday 4 pm to 9.30 pm. Closed on Sunday. Licensed. All cards. &

BAIE ST.-PAUL, Quebec   MAP 8

Baie St.-Paul is such an important centre on the north shore that we're taking a chance on one or two suggestions. A La Chouette at 2 rue Leblanc (telephone (418) 435-3217) is the best place to stay. It's bright and colourful, with seven bedrooms and stunning breakfasts. Ginette Guérette puts a lot of thought and energy into the planning and preparation of the meal, offering four varieties of toast, all made from local flour. For lunch and dinner, everyone's favourite is the Mouton Noir at 43 rue Ste.-Anne (telephone (418) 240-3030). It has a spacious deck overlooking a sleepy river and the restaurant is decidedly picturesque. We ourselves haven't had much luck with the kitchen, but other travellers have been more fortunate. It's open every day in season for both lunch and dinner. It has a licence and takes most cards.

BANFF, Alberta   MAP 9

Banff has a number of surprisingly good inexpensive restaurants. The Balkan at 120 Banff Avenue (telephone (403) 762-3454) was opened in 1982 by a Greek couple who had a lot of old family recipes. The cooking has always been completely authentic and the prices are as low as ever. The thing to have here is the so-called arni-psito, which is a version of lamb Greek-style, and it's a splendid dish. A few years ago, they decided to try something new, so they brought in a belly-dancer, and every Tuesday and Thursday invited customers to throw their plates on the floor. If you come with your family, try the Greek Platter: hummus and kopanisti dips, horiatiki salad, beef and pork souvlaki, lamb lollipops, moussaka, spanakopita, baked tomato with feta, tzatziki, rice and lemon-roasted potatoes. Baklava is made in house. The Balkan is open all day every day, has a licence and takes most cards. The Block at 201 Banff Avenue (telephone (403) 985-2887) is a tiny spot offering Thai-influenced fusion cuisine. We like the duck spring rolls, the red curry of mussels, the deep-fried chicken satays and the bison short-ribs. It's open all day every day, but only takes reservations from Sunday to Thursday (weekend lineups can be long). Eddie Burger and Bar at 137 Banff Avenue (telephone (403) 762-2230) is a hole in the wall that seats about 30 people. The best seats are at the bar, which features a good selection of B.C. and Alberta craft beers. There's a fabulous range of burgers, not cheap at 20.00 but delicious. The Eddie Classic is their best seller. Children like the Eddie Mac burger with poutine. You can even design and build your own custom burger. It's a likeable place: Eddie's website says, "I like burgers more than most, and just as much as you." Reservations are a must even though they're open fourteen hours a day, from 11.30 am to 1.30 am. They have a licence and take Master Card and Visa. The Three Ravens at 107 Tunnel Mountain Drive, on the top floor of the Sally Borden building at the Banff Centre (telephone (403) 762-6300), is a much more ambitious kitchen. If you can't afford Eden (see below)—and who can?—it offers contemporary Canadian cuisine, good service and stunning views. There's Arctic char, roasted sablefish, smoked and seared tuna served under a dome and grilled bison steaks. It's not cheap, but everything is perfectly cooked and elegantly presented. They're open daily from 5 pm to 9 pm, have a licence, take all cards, and are wheelchair accessible. Book ahead if you can.

BANFF	**MAP 9**
EDEN	✩✩✩
Rimrock Resort Hotel	**$400**
30 Mountain Avenue	
(888) 746-7625	

Eden is built into the side of Sulphur Mountain, and it's a very beautiful place. Even those who complain about the high prices admit that the view from the dining-room is amazing. And the presentation and the service are beyond compare. There are six sommeliers and their wine pairings—drawn from 90,000 bottles from all over the world—are inspired. There's nothing pretentious about the cooking, whether it's a tasting menu that features only seafood, or the vegetarian menu, which has a number of their best dishes (try the herb flan and you'll see what we mean). The game dishes have always been highly regarded: there's partridge carved at your table, there's duck and rabbit with nuts, wild berries and foraged wild mushrooms. We have, in fact, nothing to criticize, except perhaps the prices, which make it impossible for anyone but the very rich to dine here.

Open daily 6 pm to 9.30 pm from 1 June until 30 September, Wednesday to Sunday 6 pm to 9 pm from 1 October until 31 May. Closed on Monday and Tuesday in winter. Licensed. All cards. Book ahead.

BANFF MAP 9
NOURISH
211 Bear Street **$75**
(403) 760-3933

Nourish is a stylish farm-to-table bistro. The menu is vegan, with the exception of the wild mushroom ravioli, which succumbs alone to butter and cream. It is also, they will tell you, GMO free, organic, gluten-free, local, seasonal and compassionate. After all that, it's surprising how good everything tastes. Try the galaxy nachos topped with "cheeze" (cashew cheddar), legumes and fruit, the sautéd garlic greens and the wild mushroom ravioli. The daily special may be something like a vegetable Korma and is usually reliable. Dishes can come in any order, so it's best to share. There aren't many wines, but they're reasonably priced.

Open daily (including Christmas) 11.30 am to 4 pm, 5 pm to 9.30 pm. Licensed. No cards.

BARRIE, Ontario MAP 10
THE CRAZY FOX
135 Bayfield Street **$150**
(705) 737-5000

Coos Uylenbroek and the Crazy Fox have been here in Barrie for more than 30 years. Uylenbroek is no longer young, but for all his white hair he's still cooking as if he was. For instance, he's now offering tuna sushi, boldly flavoured with sesame. He still has liver on the menu, with double-cooked bacon and caramelized onions. The pasta is made in-house and the beef tenderloin well sauced with green peppercorns. There's an ample list of bottled wines, draft beers and a number of single-malt whiskies. The best buy is the flight of three two-ounce glasses of wine, which is yours for a song.

Open Tuesday to Friday 11.30 am to 11 pm, Saturday 5 pm to 11 pm. Closed on Sunday and Monday. Licensed. Amex, Master Card, Visa. Free parking.

BAYFIELD, Ontario   **MAP 11**
THE BLACK DOG   ☆
5 Main Street N   **$175**
(519) 565-2326

The Black Dog is still our first choice in Bayfield, but if they're full you can take a look at the Little Inn at 26 Main Street N (telephone (800) 565-1832)—the building is almost as old, the staff are professional and the menu is interesting. The Black Dog was built in 1850, and is now the oldest shop on the street. Ted McIntosh has an award-winning wine-list, twenty beers on tap and a host of Scotch single malts and Irish whiskies. The menu follows the seasons, but it also watches the fashions—you may find bone-marrow butter on your steak, pernod in your bouillabaisse and fenugreek in your lamb kofta. There are a number of vegetarian options, including a broccoli salad with chickpeas and quinoa and a vegetable curry with sweet potatoes and cauliflower. The patio is lovely in summer, the restaurant inside warm and cheerful in winter.

Open daily 11 am to 5 pm (lunch), 5 pm to 9 pm (dinner) from 1 May until Labour Day, Wednesday to Sunday 11 am to 5 pm, 5 pm to 9 pm from Labour Day until 30 April. Closed on Monday and Tuesday in winter. Licensed. Amex, Master Card, Visa. Book ahead if you can. ♿

We accept no advertisements. We accept no payment for listings. We depend entirely on you. Recommend the book to your friends.

BAY FORTUNE, P.E.I. (MAP 37)
THE INN AT BAY FORTUNE ★★
758 Highway 310 **$250**
(902) 687-3745

The Inn at Bay Fortune is walking on air these days. Michael Smith's celebrity is filling the rooms of the Inn, which is ably managed by his wife Chastity. The dining-room, now called Fire Works, has a huge open hearth, a rotisserie, a grill, a smoke-house and an oven. You are told that you will "discover live fire at every turn, and taste why we are so passionate about wood, flame and smoke." Smith even calls his kitchen staff the Fire Brigade. He's developed a so-called feast format, featuring local produce from the Inn's marvellous organic gardens and adjoining farmlands. Dinner is served informally at several butcher-block tables. There's a gin-and-tonic station, an oyster station, a sausage station and a station offering smoked salmon with a lemon-caper aioli where you can meet your neighbours cocktail-party style. It all takes three or four hours, and most people have been impressed by both the cooking and the presentation. Everything Smith serves—and there's a lot of it, the feasts are huge—comes from farm to table. The garden salad alone has dozens of different greens, herbs and flowers. The steaks are cooked *à point* and the butter-basted halibut and the charcuterie board have both been widely praised. The old house, built by Elmer Harris in 1913, is still beautiful, the bay at the foot of the garden still lovely.
Open daily 6 pm to 9 pm from the middle of May until the end of September. Licensed. All cards. Book ahead.

BEAMSVILLE, Ontario (MAP 166)
AUGUST ★
5204 King Street **$105**
(905) 563-0200

As we've said before, we can't imagine how a town of 12,000 can support a restaurant as good as this. Beth Ashton and Clayton Gillie have always been very serious about buying locally, and preparing everything they could themselves. Your Reuben sandwich at lunch will feature their bread, their corned beef and their sauerkraut. They smoke their own fish and bake their own sweets. And they make their own pasta: try the gnocchi with wild-boar bacon in a tomato-and-red-pepper sauce. Or there's a flat-iron steak rubbed with garlic and herbs and a seafood stew filled with shrimp, scallops and fish in a mango curry. Start with crispy duck rolls and peach-and-cayenne marmalade. We always wind up with the sticky toffee pudding. The wines are all from Niagara, but you can bring your own bottle on Wednesdays and Fridays with no corkage fee.

Open Tuesday to Saturday 11.30 am to 3 pm, 5 pm to 9 pm, Sunday 9 am to 3 pm (brunch). Closed on Monday. Licensed. Master Card, Visa. &

BEAVER CREEK, Yukon   MAP 14
BUCKSHOT BETTY'S
Highway 1   **$65**
(867) 862-7111

Betty is one of those people of whom one says, "They don't make them like that any more." Her real name is Carmen Hinson and nothing has changed here since we first wrote about her—except that she has added two more cabins (to make seven) and stopped renting rooms in her own house. One of the cabins has a fine view and all of them are very quiet. Carmen still works far too hard. She has some help in the summer, but all winter she works by herself, taking an occasional hour or two off to chop wood. There are about 45 seats inside and 45 on the wraparound deck outside. Carmen does all her own baking— bread, cookies, brownies and hamburger buns, and whatever else she feels like making. That might be pecan pie, carrot cake or apple strudel. Her homemade soups are full of flavour and her sandwiches are like no others. Beaver Creek is an ideal place to stop after the magnificent but scary drive from Whitehorse.

Open daily 6.30 am to 10.30 pm (or later) from mid-April until mid-October, daily 7 am to 1 pm, 4 pm to 9 pm from mid-October until mid-April. Licensed. Master Card, Visa. ♿

BELFAST, P.E.I. (MAP 37)
POINT PRIM CHOWDER HOUSE
2150 Point Prim Road   **$125**
(902) 659-2187

Point Prim was a reference point for navigation in the old days. The Point Prim lighthouse is built of brick, which is rare in Canada; it was begun in 1845. The Chowder House stands a few yards away, just above high tide, and it's open all summer long. Two years ago a fierce wind off the Northumberland Strait threatened to blow the place down, but in 2016 the season began with renovations that made the restaurant more secure and more comfortable. The menu has always been dominated by seafood, and they have a fine variety of chowders, lobster rolls and local mussels, along with several excellent sweets, among them a great blueberry bread pudding. The setting sun over the ocean is a remarkable sight.
Open daily 11 am to 8 pm from mid-June until the end of September. Licensed. Master Card, Visa.

BELLEVILLE, Ontario   MAP 16
AUBERGE DE FRANCE   ☞
304 Front Street   **$80**
(613) 966-2433

Downtown Belleville is not where you'd expect to find an authentic French bistro run by a chef from Avignon. But Jean-Marc Salvagno has been here for more than ten years now, and the Auberge is as popular as ever. It's made up of a café, a patisserie and a gourmet shop that sells charcu-terie, condiments, coffees and a range of frozen meals. The café is open all day, serving breakfast, lunch and patisserie. Lunches are housemade soups, salads, sandwiches and quiches, but the patisseries that follow are more important: croissants, pains au chocolat, compotes, but-tercreams, mousses and ganaches. Once a month they offer a chef's table, with a three-course menu that costs only 40.00 a head (but book well ahead, it usually sells out).

Open Monday to Friday 10 am to 6 pm, Saturday 9 am to 6 pm. Closed on Sunday. Licensed. All cards. Book ahead if you can. &

BELLEVILLE
See also BRIGHTON.

LE BIC, Quebec	**(MAP 162)**
CHEZ SAINT-PIERRE	☆☆
129 rue du Mont St.-Louis	**$225**
(418) 736-5051	

Colombe Saint-Pierre has three children, but that hasn't kept her away from her kitchen, which has become the passion of her life. She and her partner, Alexandre Vincenot, who is in charge of the front of the house, specialize in Laurentian cuisine. They've built working relationships with sixteen local farms and suppliers, each of whom concentrates on different meats, fish and vegetables, and they have a dedicated forager—sorrel grows wild on the shoulders of most roads in the area. Her menu is very short, but each dish is carefully considered. A favourite appetizer is ravioli with cashew miso in a consommé of gingered squash with a coconut and keffir lime mousse. She might go on to scallop gravlax with wild pepper, or lamb in a sunflower crust with wild thyme arancini. For sweet try the wild blueberry tart with baby basil and white chocolate tuile, or perhaps a plate of local cheeses. There are two tasting menus: one takes four hours for seven courses for 95.00, the other three hours for five courses for 75.00. The restaurant is on a back street facing a parking-lot, and you'll probably have to ask your way. But Colombe Saint-Pierre is cooking as well as anyone in Quebec. Don't miss this place; you must book ahead.

Open Wednesday to Sunday 5 pm to 9.30 pm from 29 April until 30 June, Tuesday to Sunday 5 pm to 9.30 pm from 1 July until 31 August, Wednesday to Sunday 5 pm to 9.30 pm from 1 September until 31 October, Friday and Saturday 5 pm to 9.30 pm from 1 November until 31 December. Closed on Monday and

Tuesday in the spring and fall, on Monday in the summer, Sunday to Thursday in the early winter. Licensed. Master Card, Visa. Book ahead.

BLAIRMORE, Alberta   MAP 18
51 R.T.   ☆
12337 20 Avenue   **$60**
(403) 753-2000

We used to recommend the Highwood in Blairmore. Their Indian menu was wonderful, but their Canadian food wasn't and they have since disappeared. This year we're recommending a Chinese restaurant, and it's very, very good. It's new, but so far everything on the menu is absolutely fresh, and the helpings are immense. The shrimp stir-fry is irresistible and so is the ginger beef, which comes with fresh slices of ginger. The won-ton soup is full of flavour, with just a hint of sesame. We find it hard to believe that a restaurant of this quality can survive in a place as remote as this. Send us your reports.
Open Monday to Saturday 11 am to 8.30 pm. Closed on Sunday. Licensed. Amex, Master Card, Visa.

BLOOMFIELD, Ontario   (MAP 145)
THE HUBB AT ANGELINE'S   ☆
433 Main Street   **$130 ($325)**
(613) 393-3301

Angéline's is a small hotel on the outskirts of Bloomfield, and its dining-room, The Hubb, was serving good bistro food long before Prince Edward County became a tourist destination. A few years ago the restaurant was reorganized by the chef Elliot Reynolds and his wife Laura Borutski (who is in charge of the wines and spirits). Reynolds has a sure, light touch in the kitchen, and even the simplest dishes are carefully considered. Appetizers may include lobster sausage with a daikon-and-apple salad, or roasted foie gras served with a sweet-potato pancake. To follow try the duck confit with chanterelles and gnocchi or the spicy chowder of scallops, clams and octopus. We like the jelly roll with lemon curd, pecans and meringue for sweet. There's a good selection of local wines, and for hotel guests an excellent breakfast buffet the next morning.

Open Thursday to Saturday 5 pm to 10 pm. Closed Sunday to Wednesday, and for the months of January and February. Licensed. All cards. &

BOTWOOD, Newfoundland   MAP 20
DOCKSIDE
243 Water Street   **$140**
(709) 257-3179

Jim Stuckless is back in the kitchen at Dockside after more than twenty years away. Most people think he's already offering some of the best cooking in central Newfoundland. They're now closed on Sunday, which means good-bye to their famous roast-beef dinner. But the breast of chicken stuffed with savoury and served with orange and Grand Marnier is almost as good. Jim Stuckless is self-taught, and he cooks what he likes to eat himself. He took over the place when it was an old hardware store, and turned it into a restaurant, learning to cook as he went. You can always count on fresh local greens in season— keep an eye out for the strawberry-spinach salad, which is one of their favourites. The beef is all triple-A and comes from Alberta, and people tell us they've never had better. There are often steamed mussels with garlic or scallops wrapped in bacon. And there's always fresh cod and farmed salmon (poached or grilled). Cod is usually served with sea urchins, but if you like you can have it with three cheeses instead. Stuckless doesn't make the apple torte or the partridge-berry kuchen. Botwood is handy to the Trans Canada—only twenty minutes by Highway 350.

Open Tuesday to Sunday noon to 2 pm, 5 pm to 8 pm. Closed on Monday. Licensed. All cards. &

The map number assigned to each city, town or village gives the location of the centre on one or more of the maps at the start of the book.

BRACEBRIDGE, Ontario   (MAP 75)
RIVERWALK
1 *Manitoba Street*   **$150**
(705) 646-0711

Riverwalk overlooks the falls from the foot of Manitoba Street. Dinner starts with foie gras, followed by crackling-skin chicken, duck, trout or a fine New York striploin. The trout comes with pickles, for which they have a weakness, but you can add good mashed potatoes if you ask—and you should. The sweets can be rather ordinary, but the flourless-chocolate cake and the homemade ice-cream are better than the crème brûlée. The atmosphere is warm and comfortable, the service attentive and friendly. Now that One Fifty-Five has closed, this is the best restaurant in Bracebridge.

Open Tuesday to Sunday 11.30 am to 2.30 pm, 5.30 pm to 8.30 pm (shorter hours in winter). Closed on Monday. Amex, Master Card, Visa. Book ahead if you can.

BRACKLEY BEACH, P.E.I.   (MAP 37)
THE DUNES   ☆
(902) 672-2586   **$145**

Emily Wells, who cooked here for many years, has left to open her own restaurant in New Glasgow, P.E.I. (see below). A number of visitors, however, have been excited by the work of her successor, Norman Day. Already he's won an award for his seafood chowder. But he has many other good ideas as well: slow-braised lamb shanks, fresh Atlantic salmon with yellow curry and a splendid chocolate torte. His wine-list is short, but there's always plenty of good drinking on it—Edna Valley chardonnay for one. The coffee is excellent.

Open daily 11.30 am to 4 pm, 5.30 pm to 10 pm from 15 June until 15 October. Licensed. Amex, Master Card, Visa. Book ahead. ♧

If you use an out-of-date edition and find it inaccurate, don't blame us. Buy a new edition.

BRANDON, Manitoba

BLUE HILLS BAKERY
1229 Richmond Avenue
(204) 571-6762

MAP 23

$45

This little bakery comes from another age. It has seven or eight tables, no decorations, and a soup and sandwich that cost exactly 10.17. Kelly and Becky, who run the place, go from strength to strength. They've made no compromises and people like their food. Both owners are Hutterites and both are passionate about fresh organic produce. They buy all their grains and vegetables from nearby organic farms. They make all their own granola and their own bread and serve them for breakfast until eleven o'clock on weekdays and one o'clock on Saturdays. Every noon they offer old-fashioned soups and chicken chowder, as well as sandwiches and salads. The coffee comes in fresh from Salt Spring Island.

Open Monday to Saturday 7 am to 5 pm. Closed on Sunday. No liquor. Master Card, Visa. &

BRIER ISLAND, N.S.
See FREEPORT.

BRIGHTON, Ontario

THE GABLES
14 Division Street N
(613) 475-5565

(MAP 16)

☆
$160

Dieter Ernst is still in charge at the Gables, but after almost 50 years he thinks he deserves a rest. From our point of view, this is a loss. Everyone thinks that every dish is one of the best they've eaten in their lives. He's a master chef, and he even makes his own pastries—his apple strudel is famous in these parts. If you're nearby between Wednesday and Saturday, call and see if he's still on the job. And if he answers, drop by right away before it's too late.

Open Wednesday to Friday 11.30 am to 2 pm, 5.30 pm to 9 pm, Saturday 5.30 pm to 9 pm. Closed Sunday to Tuesday. Licensed. Amex, Master Card, Visa. Book ahead. &

BRIGUS, Newfoundland

MAP 25

THE COUNTRY CORNER

14 Water Street

$60

(709) 528-1099

There's been a lot going on at the Country Corner. It all started when the restaurant, which had been in the same family for nearly 25 years, changed hands at the beginning of 2017. Almost at once the new owners began to maximize their investment. The original tiny café now leads into a bright, modern addition with huge windows looking out over Water Street that seats another 30 people. And with a view to filling those extra chairs, a deep fryer was brought in to add things like fish and chips and fried chicken to the original short menu of soup, sandwiches and sweets. There's even a ten-ounce striploin on Friday and Saturday nights and live music every weekend. Fortunately, the owners have taken great care through all this upheaval to keep safe the reasons they bought the business in the first place. All the ingredients are still fresh and local, the sandwiches on housemade bread are still made to order with gluten-free options, and the cod chowder and the famous blueberry crisp are never leaving the building. Brigus is on Conception Bay, built around a sheltered harbour and surrounded by hills. It was established in 1612 and looks much as it did before Confederation, one of the few towns in the province that does. *Open Wednesday and Thursday 11 am to 7 pm, Friday and Saturday 11 am to 9 pm, Sunday 11 am to 7 pm from the beginning of May to the end of December. Closed on Monday and Tuesday. Licensed. Master Card, Visa.*

BURLINGTON, Ontario

(MAP 80)

BLACKTREE

✫✫✫

Roseland Plaza

$175

3029 New Street

(905) 681-2882

Matteo Paonessa has worked with some of the best chefs in Canada, including Marc Thuet, Susur Lee and Michael

Stadtländer, and his restaurant is a testament to Italian nouvelle cuisine. The à la carte menu has now been changed to a prix fixe: six courses for 80.00 (plus an optional seventh course of foie gras for an additional 20.00). It starts with what Paonessa calls a Soup Taste, which doesn't have much to do with soups as we know them. It might be caramelized asparagus with banana espresso or a superb chilled pineapple-cilantro citrus rind with mushrooms. Next there's the Little Salad, which you know by now won't have much to do with salads either: our favourites have been the beet and octopus carpaccio with a white-bean fritter, crispy kale, oyster mushrooms, candied Brussels sprouts and peppercorns, and the coconut-milk arancini with rapini two ways, potato purée, turnip, blueberry and chocolate. The third course is a meat or fish appetizer: try the burnt lobster orange with enoki mushrooms, carrot, orange, and torched Hollandaise sauce, or the duck confit croquette with white beans, brie two ways, cured duck and cran-berry-crusted foie gras. The fourth (pasta) course is all gnocchi, which Paonessa makes small, light and fluffy. His treatments combine various kinds of cheese with astringents like olives and lemons, and they all work well. The fifth course is the main course, meat or fish: we like the macadamia-crusted halibut with candied grapefruit, coconut avocado, apricot jam, yellow-bean sauce and sweeet pickled asparagus, and the New Zealand red deer with kale, daikon, Jamaican sweet potato and raisins soaked in plum juice. And finally there's the sweet course, filled with interesting combinations like apricot panna cotta with ginger, cocoa, chocolate and passion fruit, and soft strawberry milk cake with black-peppercorn-brittle ice cream, strawberry mousee, Earl Grey cream and strawberry paper. Dinner wraps up with a glass of grappa or limoncello and a piece of Paonessa's mother's fudge, and it's certainly good value. Blacktree is still, without any doubt, the best restaurant in this part of the country. *Open Wednesday and Thursday 6 pm to 9 pm, Friday and Saturday 6 pm to 10 pm. Closed Sunday to Tuesday. Licensed. Master Card, Visa. Book ahead. Free parking.* &

BURLINGTON (MAP 80)
PANE FRESCO 🖐
414 Locust Street **$50**
(905) 333-3388

The breads here are superb, and a steady stream of people come in to take them home. The bakery business is in fact becoming large enough to threaten the café, but it hasn't so far. The famous red pepper soup has lost none of its savour. (There's always a second soup as well, but we've never been willing to give up the red pepper to try it.) What else you get depends on the day of the week: Wednesday is chicken parmigiana, Thursday is meatballs on a rustic baguette, Saturday is prime rib on a toasted ciabatta. Everyday there are quiches, paninis, salads and pizzas. There are a number of pastries to follow but we prefer the chocolate bread pudding.
Open Monday 8 am to 4 pm, Tuesday to Thursday 8 am to 6 pm, Friday and Saturday 8 am to 7 pm, Sunday 8 am to 4 pm. No liquor, no cards. ♿

BURLINGTON (MAP 80)
SPENCER'S AT THE WATERFRONT ☆
1340 Lakeshore Road **$135**
(905) 633-7494

The menu at Spencer's now focuses on seafood, which means that you start your meal with shrimps, Alaska king crab, lobster (with avocado salad), oysters (with a spicy mignonette) or a hearty haddock chowder. Sometimes they serve ceviche with lime and cilantro instead of the chowder, but they're all superb. To follow there's a great variety of fish—skate, monkfish, black cod, Ahi tuna, organic Scottish salmon and red snapper with scallions, ginger, soy and white wine. Best of the sweets is now the vanilla pot de crème with maple syrup. Their Sunday brunch is a feast for 49.00; it has an amazing selection of seafood, as well as prime rib of beef and local lamb.
Open Monday to Thursday 11.30 am to 4 pm, 5 pm to 9 pm, Friday and Saturday 11.30 am to 4 pm, 5 pm to 9.30 pm,

Sunday 9.30 am to 2.30 pm (brunch), 5 pm to 9 pm. Licensed. Master Card, Visa. Free parking. &

CALGARY, Alberta   MAP 27
ANJU   ☆☆
344 17 Avenue SW   **$125**
(403) 460-3341

Roy Oh was born in Edmonton to Asian parents, and he created Anju to celebrate modern Asian cooking—which means east-meets-west fusion cuisine. He likes to bathe milk-poached halibut in a golden curry, to glaze his mac'n'cheese with gochujang and chili-dusted panko, to serve his braised beef cheeks with maitake mushrooms and *pommes purée*. He even makes a sweet-potato trifle with spicy Korean pears. Things can get messy, sticky and spicy, but chances are you won't mind. Add a little soju or sake (or beer or wine) and you may become another convert to the Modern Asian movement.
Open Monday to Friday 5 pm to 1 am, Saturday and Sunday 11 am to 1 am. Licensed. Amex, Master Card, Visa. Book ahead. &

CALGARY   MAP 27
BLINK   ☆☆
111 Stephen Avenue SW   **$175**
(403) 263-5330

Housed in one of Stephen Avenue's historic sandstone buildings, Blink straddles the old and the new with ease. The room has been beautifully restored, with exposed sandstone and brick, a long bar, banquettes and creaking wood floors. Leslie Echino has owned and operated Blink for ten years now, and made it into one of Calgary's top restaurants. Her menu is modern Canadian: grilled lamb sirloin with polenta and sunchokes; squid with andouille, pickled shiitakes and a balsamic reduction; blood-orange and cardamom yogurt; roasted pears with tarragon cream and toffee. The ice creams and sorbets are all made in house, and they're superb. The wine-list is extensive and well-chosen, featuring small estate wines from California, the Pacific Northwest and Europe. And the prices, for the meal you are getting, are reasonable.

Open Monday to Friday 11 am to 2 pm, 5 pm to 10 pm, Saturday 5 pm to 11 pm. Closed on Sunday. Licensed. All cards. Book ahead. &

CALGARY   **MAP 27**
BRIDGETTE BAR   ☆
739 10 Avenue SW   **$125**
(403) 700-0191

Calgary has a penchant for converting old warehouses into stylish restaurants, and Bridgette Bar is the latest example. The building used to be filled with sacks of flour; now there are plants in macramé, Eames chairs and a Scandinavian suspended fireplace. The menu of small and large plates is created over a wood-burning stove, and its signature smoke colours many of the dishes, such as the grilled octopus with orange and fennel and the pork chop with Calabrian chilis. If you're of two minds about smoke, try the heirloom tomato salad with crispy shallots, coriander vinaigrette and saffron mayonnaise. It takes tomatoes to a whole new place. The avocado toast is similarly transformed by a sunflower vindaloo crunch. For sweet, there's a bananas Foster cream pie with a pretzel crust and rum custard. And the bar, of course, wants for nothing.

Open Tuesday and Wednesday 11 am to 11 pm, Thursday and Friday 11 am to 1 am, Saturday 2 pm to 1 am, Sunday 2 pm to 11 pm. Closed on Monday. Licensed. All cards. Book ahead. &

CALGARY   **MAP 27**
CHARBAR   ☆☆
618 Confluence Way SE   **$140**
(403) 452-3115

A couple of years ago, Charcut (see below) took over a big space in the Simmons Building in the East Village and opened Charbar, an Argentinian-style restaurant.

There they installed a parilla, which is a traditional Argentinian grill that requires some skill to operate—chef Jessica Pelland went all the way to Buenos Aires to apprentice. Essentially, the meat is cooked over embers while the chef moves the grill plate up and down to manage the heat. The dry-aged and grass-fed Longhorn beef that they cook this way is fabulous. But unlike Charcut, Charbar is not just about meat. There's a strong vegetarian presence on the menu and they have some impressive seafood—particularly the ceviche and the calamari with chimichurri. Try them—you'll be surprised. From the rooftop terrace there's a celebrated view of the city.

Open Monday to Wednesday 11.30 am to 10 pm, Thursday and Friday 11.30 am to midnight, Saturday 10 am to midnight, Sunday 10 am to 10 pm. Licensed. All cards. &

CALGARY　　　　　　　　　　　　　　　　**MAP 27**
CHARCUT　　　　　　　　　　　　　　　　☆☆
899 Centre Street SW　　　　　　　　　　**$150**
(403) 984-2180

Charcut is all about meat. Not just the usual tenderloins and T-bones, but things like flame-grilled lamb sirloin, juicy, house-ground burgers and a pig's head stuffed with mortadella. They bring in the whole animal, butcher it in-house and throw almost nothing out. There is a classic prime rib for dinner though, which gets made into a popular sandwich for lunch. Surprisingly, the vegetables are also very good, particularly the beet salad and the Brussels sprouts (admittedly, the sprouts have been fried in duck fat).

Open Monday and Tuesday 11 am to 11 pm, Wednesday to Friday 11 am to 1 am, Saturday 5 pm to 1 am, Sunday 5 pm to 11 pm. Licensed. All cards. Book ahead if you can. &

The price rating shown opposite the headline of each entry indicates the average cost of dinner for two with a modest wine, tax and tip. The cost of dinner, bed and breakfast (if available) is shown in parentheses.

CALGARY   MAP 27
COTTO   ☆
314 10 Street NW   **$100**
(587) 356-4088

Cotto is the latest creation of Guiseppe di Gennaro, who
previously ran Capo and Borgo. Capo was tiny and
expensive, Borgo was large and affordable, and now
Cotto has been set squarely in the middle. The food is
comfortable and full of big flavours: try the amazing
funghetto of eggplant in tomato-and-basil sauce with
soft goat cheese, or the sautéed calamari with tomato, garlic, chili and olives. Even the spaghetti carbonara has
clarity and bite. The sweets stay traditional—housemade
sorbetto or gelato, tiramisu, lemon-filled cannoli—but
it's a long time since they've been made like this. Finish up
with a glass of grappa.
Open Tuesday to Thursday 11.30 am to 2 pm, 5 pm to 9 pm, Fri-
day 11.30 am to 2 pm, 5 pm to 9.30 pm, Saturday 5 pm to 9.30
pm, Sunday 5 pm to 9 pm. Closed on Monday. Licensed. All
cards. Book ahead. ♿

CALGARY   MAP 27
DEANE HOUSE   ☆
806 9 Avenue SE   **$140**
(403) 264-0595

Following his success with the River Café, Sal Howell
bought and restored this fine old Victorian house at the
junction of the Bow and Elbow rivers across from Fort
Calgary. It used to be the home of Richard Deane, super-
intendent of the North-West Mounted Police. Jamie
Harling has added a contemporary Canadian spin to
the menu: sprouted farro risotto, Berkshire pork loin
with charred cabbage, duck-confit perogies, juniper-and-
beet-cured trout. This is farmhouse cooking elevated to
a whole new level. His weekend brunches are a treat: try
the smoked Arctic char benedict on buttermilk biscuits,
or a croque madame made with prosciutto and cheddar
and a duck egg. There's a fine selection of whiskies and

craft beers.

Open Tuesday to Friday 11 am to 10 pm, Saturday and Sunday 10 am to 10 pm. Closed on Monday. Licensed. All cards. Book ahead.

CALGARY

MAP 27

FOREIGN CONCEPT ☆☆☆

1011 1 Street SW **$160**

(403) 719-7288

The most important restaurant opening in Calgary last year was Foreign Concept. Duncan Ly, formerly of Hotel Arts, is serving here what he calls Alternative Asian cuisine. He brought Raw Bar executive chef Jinhee Lee over with him from the hotel, as well as chef de cuisine Michael Nop from the Chef's Table at the Kensington Riverside Inn. That's a lot of talent. Their version of trout cha ca la vong with dill and persimmon (a Western update of a regional Vietnamese dish) won the top prize at Calgary's Gold-Medal Plates in 2016. What more can one ask? At Foreign Concept, Ly has covered the walls with lovely hand-painted lotus-flower murals. Antique moon-cake moulds line one wall and a charcuterie bar lines another. This is a very special restaurant.

Open Monday to Friday 11.30 am to 10 pm, Saturday 5 pm to 10 pm. Closed on Sunday. Licensed. Book ahead. &

CALGARY

MAP 27

THE GUILD ☆

200 8 Avenue SW **$150**

(403) 770-2313

When Oliver & Bonacini decided to open a restaurant in Calgary, they picked one of the city's most iconic buildings: the Bay in the heart of downtown. The Guild occupies one half of the old main floor—the former lingerie department, in fact. It's been turned into a large and elegant dining-room and Canadian Culinary Championships winner Ryan O'Flynn has taken over the newly-created kitchen. What the menu offers first and foremost is large quantities of meat: a 28-ounce porterhouse, a 32-ounce striploin and a whole roasted pig's head. We couldn't face the pig's head, but people who did have told us that the meaty jowls and cheeks below the skin and fat were well worth the effort. The beef is among Alberta's best, from Beretta Farms. There's also a hearty prairie paella of smoked barley with octopus, bacon, clams and roast chicken. If you have room, you can round things off with a caramelized pumpkin tarte tatin.

Open Monday 11 am to 10 pm, Tuesday to Thursday 11 am to midnight, Friday and Saturday 11 am to 1 am, Sunday 11 am to 10 pm. Licensed. All cards. Book ahead if you can. &

CALGARY　　　　　　　　　　　　　　　　**MAP 27**
MODEL MILK　　　　　　　　　　　　　　　☆☆
308 17 Avenue SW　　　　　　　　　　　　**$150**
(403) 265-7343

The art-deco Model Milk building has had a number of tenants since the dairy left for larger quarters 50 years ago. But when Justin Leboe opened his restaurant here in 2012, he came to stay. Later that year Model Milk placed second on EnRoute's list of best new restaurants, for its contemporary treatment of shrimps with hominy, pork with Tokyo turnips and fricassee of calamari. One visitor told us the shrimp and grits were the best he'd had north of the border. Their cheese still comes from the Drunken Cow, and their apple crisp is made with hand-picked apples.

Open Monday to Saturday 5 pm to 1 am, Sunday 5 pm to 10 pm. Licensed. Amex, Master Card, Visa. Book ahead if you can. &

CALGARY　　　　　　　　　　　　　　　　**MAP 27**
THE NASH
925 11 Street SE　　　　　　　　　　　　**$195**
(403) 984-3365

The Nash is Michael Noble's latest venture. The name comes from the old National Hotel, of which the restaurant occupies the ground floor. The stylish renovation has created a sunny, warm space featuring a wood-burning rotisserie and a charcoal Josper oven. The menu starts with things like Ahi tuna poke and marinated squid, and goes on to pan-roasted duck breast with Bing cherries, grilled lamb sirloin with chickpeas, and charcoal-grilled ribeye with mushroom and potato ragout. The lemon cream with blackberries is a splendid sweet. The wines are expensive, and the best buy is probably the Tawse, even at 12.00 a glass.

Open Tuesday and Wednesday 11.30 am to 10 pm, Thursday 11.30 am to 11 pm, Friday 11.30 am to midnight, Saturday 11 am to midnight, Sunday 11 am to 9 pm. Closed on Monday. Licensed. Amex, Master Card, Visa. Book ahead if you can. &

CALGARY   **MAP 27**
NOTABLE   ☆
4611 Bowness Road NW   **$150**
(403) 288-4372

When Michael Noble was building this restaurant people thought he was crazy. "A restaurant on Bowness Road? Impossible." They were wrong. Notable has been packed since it opened, because most people like what it has to offer: things like chicken ravioli, merguez lamb meatballs, rotisserie features and burger inventions. It's the sort of satisfying food you'd cook at home if only you knew how. Michael Noble knows how, whether it's a marvelous spring salmon, beef tartar with house-made mustard or a skillful niçoise salad with Albacore tuna. He recently opened a second restaurant, the Nash (see above).

Open Tuesday to Friday 11.30 am to 11 pm, Saturday 11 am to 11 pm, Sunday 11 am to 9 pm. Closed on Monday. Licensed. Amex, Master Card, Visa. Book ahead if you can. &

CALGARY   **MAP 27**
OX BAR DE TAPAS   ☆
528 17 Avenue SW   **$125**
(403) 457-1432

This used to be a restaurant called Ox & Angela, but Angela left and Ox turned his talents to tapas. At the same time the owners knocked down some walls and refurbished the room, which has created a more open and attractive space. Ox offers the usual classics: spicy prawns, stuffed squid in its own ink, salt-cod-and-potato cakes, Iberico and serrano ham. The acorn-fed Iberico has been aged for thirty-six months—we usually settle for the serrano, which is half the age and half the price, and nearly as nice. If you want something larger, there's a fine seafood, chorizo and chicken paella. Or you can just sit back and order the Spanish Table, a long list of tapas costing 45.00 a person. The wines are mostly Spanish and there's a wide range of sherries.

Open Monday to Thursday 5 pm to 11 pm, Friday and Saturday 5 pm to midnight, Sunday 5 pm to 11 pm. Licensed. All cards. Book ahead. &

CALGARY	**MAP 27**
PIGEONHOLE	☆
306 17 Avenue SW	**$140**
(403) 452-4694	

Justin Leboe has been on EnRoute's list of top new restaurants three times: he came in third at Rush, second at Model Milk and finally first at Pigeonhole. Housed in the same former dairy as Model Milk, Pigeonhole is a bright, lively and noisy place that serves an attractive collection of small plates. The most popular dish on the menu is the superb charred cabbage with mimolette and jalapeno cream, but the lamb ragu with poached egg and grits and the Wagyu beef tartar with celeriac and cheddar aren't far behind. We also like the barbecued carrots with béarnaise and bone marrow—Leboe is a master of texture. There's a respectable cocktail list and a short selection of wines— and Stampede Park is right at the end of the road.

Open Monday to Saturday 5 pm to midnight. Closed on Sunday. Licensed. All cards. Book ahead. &

Every restaurant in this guide has been personally tested. Our reporters are not allowed to identify themselves or to accept free meals.

CALGARY   **MAP 27**
RIVER CAFE   ☆
Prince's Island Park   **$175**
(403) 261-7670

Surrounded by tall cottonwood poplars in the middle of
the Bow River, the River Café has the prettiest setting in
Calgary. Inside is a sunwashed room with bentwood
chairs and a huge stone fireplace. Behind the scenes, executive chef Matthias Fong is taking the kitchen to new
heights. The restaurant calls itself seasonally Canadian,
and they mean business. If it's on the menu, it has to have
something seasonal and Canadian to say: roasted mussels
with Granville Island sake and grilled rye sourdough;
wild boar served with farro, Honeycrisp apples and rye;
flatbread topped with Taber corn; maple wild-rice pudding with saskatoon-berry compote; Yukon birch-syrup
cookies. They even churn their own butter. And of
course the pick of the wine-list comes from the Okanagan
and Niagara.
*Open Monday to Friday 11 am to 10 pm, Saturday and Sunday
10 am to 10 pm. Licensed. All cards. Book ahead.* ೬

CALGARY   **MAP 27**
TEATRO   ☆☆
200 8 Avenue SE   **$195**
(403) 290-1012

Calgary seems to have a *penchant* for turning old bank
buildings into new restaurants. And it's true that they
make airy, elegant spaces that flatter most food. Such is
the case with Teatro, which occupies a Toronto-Domin-
ion Bank built more than a hundred years ago. The
owner, Dario Berloni, is Italian and took the restaurant's
name from the Arts Commons across the road. His menu
is Italian as well, specializing in ricotta gnocchi, marinated eggplant, sundried tomato, apple marsala and gi-
anciale. Try their seafood lasagne, the only dish to have
survived since opening day. And the wine-cellar happens
to be one of the best in the city.

Open Monday to Thursday 11.30 am to 2 pm, 5 pm to 10 pm, Friday 11.30 am to 2 pm, 5 pm to 11 pm, Saturday 5 pm to 11 pm, Sunday 5 pm to 10 pm. Licensed. All cards. Book ahead. ♿

CALGARY
See also CANMORE.

CAMBRIDGE, Ontario	**MAP 28**
LANGDON HALL	☆☆☆
1 Langdon Drive	**$290 ($630)**
(800) 268-1898	

It's easy to make fun of Langdon Hall. They're so determined to be top of the walk. Already they're a Relais & Chateau, they serve their sea scallops with caviar and champagne and you can't even think about wearing shorts into the dining-room, no matter how hot the weather. People who want to dress casually have to eat in Wilks Bar, an attractive small room with a wood-burning fireplace. In the main dining-room, they never relax their standards. The menu could be considered pretentious: venison with sumac, veal tartar with Jerusalem artichokes and nasturtium blossoms. But the chef is always up to his billing, and so are the servers. The wine-cellar has 1400 labels, many of them very grand indeed. Niagara is hardly good (or expensive) enough for such company, but there are 25 pommards, all premier-cru, on the list. If you want to spend a great deal more money to stay the night, the hotel now has 52 guest suites, all impeccably maintained. *Open daily noon to 2.30 pm, 5.30 pm to 9 pm. Licensed. All cards. Book ahead.*

CAMPOBELLO ISLAND, N.B.	**(MAP 73)**
FAMILY FISHERIES	☞🍽
1977 County Road 774	**$60**
Wilson's Beach	
(506) 752-2470	

The family sold up and left in June of 2016, but the new owners are as likeable and hard-working as the old. The helpings may be too large for some—two people could share a small Caesar salad—but that doesn't mean that the prices have risen. They haven't. It's a long menu, but we still think that the whole lobster is probably your best bet. Others prefer the lobster stew or the perfectly cooked haddock. The shrimp is very lightly battered, and the scallops, certainly, are the best on this shore. If you find every table full, just go to the carry-out window, where everything is the same as inside. Start with an appetizer of smoked salmon and end with blueberry or raspberry pie. (They pick the raspberries in their own garden and serve them with real whipped cream.) Everything is cooked to order and the service is slow, but sitting back and slowing down, as somebody once said, is one of the things you come to the Maritimes for.

Open daily 11.30 am to 9 pm from mid–April until Thanksgiving. Bring your own bottle. Amex, Master Card, Visa. ♿

CAMPOBELLO ISLAND   (MAP 73)
JOCIE'S PORCH   👌
724 Highway 774   **$30**
Welshpool
(506) 752-9816

Jocie's has a front porch 70 feet long, furnished with Adirondack chairs and a couple of swings. They have a lovely view of Friars Bay, which is filled with bald eagles and finback whales. The menu is short, but everything comes fresh from the kitchen. The service doesn't seem slow when you're watching somebody make your sandwich to order on the grill right in front of you. You can order old favourites like French onion soup or a ham-and-cheese sandwich, and think you've never tasted either one before. The bread is all homemade; they grind their own coffee, and the decaffeinated version is as good as the regular. The sweets are just out of the oven—keep an eye out for the lemon squares. On Friday nights there are jam sessions where local people come with their guitars and everyone joins in.

Open Monday to Thursday 9 am to 6 pm, Friday 9 am to 9 pm, Saturday 9 am to 3 pm from early June until late September. Closed on Sunday. No liquor. Amex, Master Card, Visa.

CANMORE, Alberta (MAP 27)
BLAKE ☆
810 Bow Valley Trail **$120**
(403) 675-3663

Blake is a new place in an old body shop, with great views of the mountains. It's owned by the father-son team of Norm and Blake Flann. Blake won the Gold Medal Plates competition in Calgary in 2017 with a typically global dish: gochujang-lacquered pork belly and prawns laid over garlic-butter prawn paper, soju pickled prawns, nori-dusted ramen, peanuts, yuzu, coal salt, sous-vide egg and micro-greens—a rich and creative mix of flavours and textures. It's on the menu at Blake now, along with curried cauliflower steak, ramen cacio e pepe, beef tartar with turmeric aioli and miso broccoli steamed buns. The service is as eclectic as the food, but it all means well. Drinks include nouveau cocktails, a respectable wine-list and craft beer. In summer look for Blake's double-decker Leyland bus out on Main Street, serving Asian-fusion street food.
Open daily 11.30 am to 11 pm. Licensed. All cards. No reservations. ♿

CANMORE (MAP 27)
CRAZYWEED ☆☆
1600 Railway Avenue **$150**
(403) 609-2530

Crazyweed is the grande dame of Canmore restaurants, but its cooking is still as creative and satisfying as ever. There's a sparkling Icelandic cod and prawn cake with a picada of lemongrass and turmeric, a spicy bibimbap of brown rice and vegetables and smoked camembert with pomegranate-habanero jelly and goji berries. The house-ground brisket burger is every purist's ideal. The wine-list is deep and well-selected from international vineyards: tannats, nebbiolos, arneis and even an Austrian rotgipfler. The Hrabec family have created an experience at Crazy-weed like no other for miles around: fine food, skilled service, memorable drinks—and a lovely view. Look for the odd building with a live grass roof.

Open Tuesday to Thursday 11.30 am to 9 pm, Friday and Saturday 11.30 am to 10 pm, Sunday 11.30 am to 9 pm. Closed on Monday. Licensed. All cards. Book ahead. &

CANMORE (MAP 27)
TAPAS
633 10 Street **$100**
(403) 609-0583

One of the best things about Tapas is that most of us can afford to eat there. The setting in a small unassuming house is comfortable; the service as friendly and prompt as you'd expect. You'll be told that two people should order five or six tapas plates, and you should—but if one of those plates is the splendidly rich figs and chorizo in sweet-and-sour sauce you'll never finish. The cheese and charcuterie board is always rewarding, if not cheap, but we prefer the patates Diablo with smoked onions and mayonnaise. The menu changes with the seasons, so that everything can be perfectly fresh. The sweets are rich and filling, and worth saving room for.

Open daily 5 pm to 10 pm. Licensed. Master Card, Visa. &

CAP A L'AIGLE, Quebec (MAP 103)
AUBERGE DES PEUPLIERS ☆
381 rue St.-Raphael **$185 ($350)**
(418) 665-4423

It's nearly 200 years since the Tremblay family came to Charlevoix, and 40 years since they turned their homestead into a small hotel that many of us grew to love. Ferdinand Tremblay himself began to modernize the house. He installed a new bar and enlarged the dining-room. The new bedrooms are small, but they're comfortable enough to bring people back year after year. Dominique Truchon, a local boy, was in charge of the kitchen for many years. Since he left to establish his own restaurant (Chez Truchon in La Malbaie, see below) there have been some weak moments in the cooking. But Gilles Bernard leaves most diners happy. We were sorry to see the bouillabaisse go, but his onion soup with Charlevoix beer and gratinéed cheddar is an interesting idea, and so are the roasted scallops with grapefruit and white butter. The menu used to be focused on fish, some of which we had hardly heard of. Now it's more inclusive. But the best of the sweets is still the local cheese. The wine-list is French, and has the virtues and vices that go with that. But for just 25.00 you can get three different glasses, one for each course.

Open daily 8 am to 10.30 am, 6 pm to 10 pm. Licensed. All cards. Book ahead. &

CARAQUET, N.B.   **MAP 32**
HOTEL PAULIN   ☆☆
143 boulevard St.-Pierre o   **$160 ($340)**
(866) 727-9981

We stopped writing about the Hôtel Paulin, because it didn't seem serious about taking non-residents. We're recommending it again now because it's the best place to stay in town and a good place to eat. Three generations of the Paulin family have made this one of the oldest family-run hotels in the country. Built in 1891, it's a good example of turn-of-the-century Acadian architecture. It's been completely redecorated inside, with three luxurious suites on the third floor, each of which has a lovely view of the Baie des Chaleurs. After running the place alone for 30 years, Gérard Paulin married Karen Mersereau and found himself with a first-class chef. She loves to cook and for about 50.00 guests get course after course of fascinating dishes. She changes her menu every day, always emphasizing regional produce. That of course means local seafood from the bay, local lamb and local cheeses, as well as hand-picked fiddleheads, chanterelles and strawberries. Everything is beautifully prepared. The service, however, is slow.

Open daily (if anyone is staying at the hotel) 7 pm to 8.30 pm. Licensed. Master Card, Visa. You must book ahead. &

CARAQUET   MAP 32
MITCHAN SUSHI   ☆☆
114 boulevard St.-Pierre o   **$95**
(506) 726-1103

You wouldn't expect to find a good Japanese restaurant in the heart of Acadian country, but there are those who think that Mitchan Sushi is the best restaurant of its kind in New Brunswick. Certainly, they have an enormous selection of sushi, sashimi, tempura, teriyaki and shrimp and pork dumplings. The sweets are quite ambitious. They make their own ice cream (green-tea, red-bean and black-sesame). The dining-room is attractive and the plating will remind you of a bouquet of flowers. The prices are all surprisingly low.

Open daily noon to 3 pm, 6 pm to 11 pm from early May until late November, by appointment only Wednesday 5 pm to 9 pm, Thursday and Friday 11.30 am to 1.30 pm, 5 pm to 9 pm, Saturday and Sunday 5 pm to 9 pm from late November until early May. Closed on Monday and Tuesday in winter. Licensed. Master Card, Visa.

CARLETON–SUR–MER, Quebec   MAP 33
LE MARIN D'EAU DOUCE
215 route du Quai   **$140**
(418) 364-7602

We've been coming to this old house by the sea for years. The place was built in 1820 overlooking the beach. There's a jetty at the back and a bright, cheerful dining-room. Mustapha Benhamidou is at his best with seafood, but he's also interested in adapting refined French cuisine to such local dishes as veal chops and merguez de canard, as well as cod and salmon. Sweets are not a big thing with him, but wine is, and most of his wines come, not from

Niagara or Prince Edward County, but from France or Italy. It's usually a good idea to order from the menu du jour, which always has some fish on it.

Open Monday to Saturday 5 pm to 9 pm. Closed on Sunday. Licensed. All cards.

CAYUGA, Ontario   MAP 34
THE TWISTED LEMON   ☆
3 Norton Street W   **$145**
(905) 772-6636

The Twisted Lemon hasn't missed a step since it opened back in 2009. Before long people were driving to the small village of Cayuga from as far away as Hamilton— 45 minutes each way. The menus are approachable, the portions are ample. Dan Megna learned a lot about produce from Mark McEwan, and nearly everything he uses comes from Haldimand County. Last year he established a huge garden of his own, which now supplies many of his needs. It's hard work, but you can taste the difference. Dinner starts with a complimentary bowl of lemon twists (dried slices of wonton seasoned with lemon and pepper) and you'll be left looking for more. Then there are panseared scallops in a blueberry-and-whisky sauce, gnocchi with sweet potatoes, deep-fried lasagne filled with the Megna family's "grumpy" sauce, confit of duck, stuffed chicken leg and trout with apple-ginger cream and greentea black rice. If you want to spend another ten or fifteen dollars you can try the top-end beef tenderloin and striploin, or even the pepper-rubbed wild boar. The wine-list offers an ambitious selection of wines from here and abroad, as well as several craft beers, most of them from Ontario.

Open Tuesday 5 pm to 9 pm, Wednesday and Thursday 11.30 am to 2 pm, 5 pm to 9 pm, Friday 11.30 am to 2 pm, 5 pm to 10 pm, Saturday 4.30 pm to 10 pm. Closed on Sunday and Monday. Licensed. Master Card, Visa. Book ahead. ♿

We accept no advertisements. We accept no payment for listings. We depend entirely on you.

CEDAR, B.C. (MAP 121)

CROW & GATE PUB
2313 Yellow Point Road **$70**
(250) 722-3731

In 1972 Jack Nash, an Englishman, built the Crow & Gate on ten acres of scenic property in Cedar, near Nanaimo. The Crow & Gate was the first neighbourhood pub in the province. The place is pure Yorkshire, with its low wooden ceilings, oil paintings and wood-burning fireplaces. There's no deep fryer here, no fish and chips. What they have is country-style meat pies, the best of which, of course, is the steak-and-kidney pie. There are other good things too, like the oyster stew, the crab-cake, the stilton quiche, the English trifle and the sticky toffee pudding. You order and pay up front and the food is brought to your table, so there's no waiting ever.
Open daily 11 am to 11 pm. Licensed. Master Card, Visa. &

CEDAR (MAP 121)

MAHLE HOUSE ☆☆
2104 Hemer Road **$150**
(250) 722-3621

Just ten minutes south of Nanaimo, the Mahle House is a tastefully restored heritage house standing in an acre of English-style gardens. Stephen and Tara Wilson have designed a menu that makes use of the vegetables and herbs they've grown themselves, supplemented by produce from local farms. Start with the calamari dijonnaise, or the legendary porcupine prawns in kataifi pastry, and go on to the deboned rack of lamb, the maple-brined pork tenderloin, or the seared tuna with sesame, miso and kimchi. For vegetarians there's a curried lentil and goat-cheese phyllo roll stuffed with cauliflower and chick peas. Naida Hobbs's sweets are all delightful, especially her celebrated peanut-butter pie with cinnamon crème anglaise. The wine-list features a number of choices from two of the top Cowichan wineries, Alderlea and Blue Grouse.

CHARLO, N.B.   MAP 36
LE MOULIN A CAFE   ☆
210 Chaleur Street   **$60**
(506) 684-9898

Christian Paquet gave this tiny place (eight tables in summer, five in winter) a huge reputation in the time he was here. People came from far and wide for his cooking. But now he is gone, and a new chef, Ashley McNair, who made something of a name for herself in Moncton, has taken over. Wisely she has started off by changing as little as possible. There are still five daily soups—including the outstanding seafood chowder of scallops, shrimp and lobster—still the same pizzas, Acadian dishes and fresh local fish. And Andrea Boudreau still makes all the bread-rolls and the fabulous berry pies—the strawberry is our favourite. You have to bring your own wine, but there's a long list of teas and coffees and everything is very cheap.
Open Tuesday to Sunday 10 am to 8 pm. Closed on Monday. Bring your own bottle. Master Card, Visa. Book ahead if you can.

CHARLOTTETOWN, P.E.I.   MAP 37

We always urge visitors to the Island to go to the Farmer's Market, which is held every Saturday morning. Most of the produce is organic, and you can snack on smoked salmon just inside the main door. Not far away, on a short stretch of Great George Street, there are several attractive restaurants. Leonhard's Cafe and Bakery at 142 Great George Street (telephone (902) 367-3621), has some of the best coffee in town. The young German owner also makes fine homemade bread and pastries, glorious Florentines, homemade stews and big, substantial sandwiches. This is a perfect place for lunch, but they aren't open for dinner and are closed on Sunday. Beanz at 138 Great George Street (telephone (902) 892-8797) has just been sold after 22 years. The new owner, Kaan Ulkan, is not about to make any changes.

He bought the place because he admired everything about it. Beanz is an espresso bar, but they also have soups, sandwiches and salads, and their squares, cookies and cheesecakes are all wonderful. They're open all day every day and take Master Card and Visa, but there's no liquor. Along the street from Beanz, at 144 Great George Street (telephone (902) 368-8886), is Shaddy's, a nice, comfortable Lebanese restaurant that has the only upright broiler in Charlottetown. The best thing they do is the shawarma with tabouleh. As for the falafel in a pita, one visitor thought it the best in the world. We ourselves admire the lamb kebabs and the kofta. The pastries all come from Montreal, where the chef spent ten years before coming here. Shaddy's is open all day Monday to Friday and all afternoon Saturday and Sunday, has a licence and takes Master Card and Visa. The Brickhouse at 125 Sydney Street (telephone (902) 566-4620) is a beautiful space with an open kitchen and counter, where you can sit and talk to the chef. But the cooking can be inconsistent. There's a choice of gluten-free dishes, and everyone likes the charcuterie and the blue mussels. They're now open all day every day, have a licence and take Amex, Master Card and Visa. The Pilot House at 70 Grafton Street (telephone (902) 894-4800) specializes in seafood, draft beer and scotch whisky. The menu lets you choose between pub food and such important things as chicken, pork, scallops and salmon. The scallops are served with a mushroom risotto, the salmon in a maple glaze. They also have a fine lobster sandwich and excellent fish and chips. To follow, try Old Sam's date pudding, a long-time local favourite. They're open all day every day but Sunday, have a licence and take all cards. Finally we should mention the Gahan House at 126 Sydney Street (telephone (902) 626-2337), right across the road from the Brickhouse. There are other Gahans in Halifax, Saint John and Fredericton, but this one (the first) still brews its own handcrafted beers, and they're good. Food runs to seafood chowder, lobster roll, calamari and fish and chips, and is very popular with both locals and tourists. They're open all day every day, have a licence and take Amex, Master Card and Visa.

🖎 This symbol means that the restaurant is rated a good buy. This ♿ means that there is wheelchair access to both the tables and the washrooms.

CHARLOTTETOWN　　　　　　　　**MAP 37**
BUONO MANGIA
12 Mount Edward Road　　　　　　　　**$115**
(902) 370-6676

Buono Mangia moved last year from Kent Street to larger premises on Mount Edward Road, but they're still cooking some of the best Italian food on the Island. Hooie and her partner, Ian, serve everything with homemade fettuccine or cannelloni, sometimes tagliatelle. Their fettuccine Alfredo is about the lightest we can remember. Every evening there are seven or eight main dishes, plus a nightly special. Those who should know say that Buono Mangia has the freshest food in town. Everything is local (even the cheese) and the ice cream is beautiful. The food is hot and cheap and there's a short wine-list that offers five reds and five whites.
Open Tuesday to Friday 11.30 am to 2.30 pm, 5 pm to 8 pm, Saturday 5 pm to 9 pm. Closed on Sunday and Monday. Licensed. Master Card, Visa. Book ahead.

CHARLOTTETOWN　　　　　　　　**MAP 37**
HIMALAYAN INDIAN CUISINE
Midtown Plaza　　　　　　　　**$100**
375 University Avenue
(902) 892-7450

Charlottetown has long needed an authentic Indian restaurant and this, at last, is it. It's owned by a Nepalese family and it opened in 2014. They serve a variety of Indian and Nepalese dishes, among them a few tandoori specialties. The big sellers are the kormas, the saags and the biryanis. Naan or rice comes with each of these and you can choose to have your food mild, medium or hot. The only sweet is mango sorbet and the best thing to drink is the mango lassi.
Open daily 11.30 am to 9.30 pm. Licensed. Master Card, Visa.

Nobody can buy his way into this guide and nobody can buy his way out.

CHARLOTTETOWN

MAP 37

TERRE ROUGE
72 Queen Street **$100**
(902) 892-4032

Terre Rouge was once a grocery store, but now it looks more like a French bistro or an old-style New York bar. The kitchen is interested only in produce that grows nearby—local oysters, pork, beef and lamb, fish and shellfish. The cooking is simple and straightforward. Arctic char, for instance, may be served with smoked potatoes, rotisserie chicken with lightly-whipped mash. Usually they offer at least three different varieties of beet. The waiters are young and eager and the service is always quick, though the cooking is not. At Terre Rouge they aim to provide good food, not fast food, and good food takes time to prepare.

Open daily 8 am to 10 pm. Licensed. Amex, Master Card, Visa.
&

CHARLOTTETOWN

See also BAY FORTUNE, BELFAST, BRACKLEY BEACH, GEORGETOWN, MONTAGUE, MURRAY HARBOUR, NEW GLASGOW, ST. PETERS BAY, SOURIS; SUMMERSIDE, VICTORIA-BY-THE-SEA, WEST POINT.

CHATHAM, Ontario   MAP 38

CHURRASCARIA
525 Grand Avenue E **$130**
(519) 355-1279

Churrascaria has succeeded in a town where many restaurants have failed because it takes pains to please as many people as possible. They serve three meals a day, quite different in style, and in the end there's something for everybody. Breakfast is the best in Chatham: it starts at 5.99 for two eggs with bacon and tops out at 13.75 for Norwegian salmon. In between there's a popular eggs benedict and Nutella French toast. By noon Brian Machado's menu has added a number of Portuguese specialties such as bacalhau (pan-seared fillet of cod), santola (crab-legs) and Portuguese free-range chicken. Both at noon and at night there's a wide variety of char-grilled steaks, most notably an organic New York striploin crusted with figs and finished with port for only 28.95. There's also fresh Atlantic salmon and Lake Erie pickerel. Dinner closes early, so don't be late.

Open Tuesday to Thursday 8 am to 2 pm, 5 pm to 8 pm, Friday and Saturday 8 am to 9 pm, Sunday 8 am to 2 pm. Closed on Monday. Licensed. Amex, Master Card, Visa. &

CHELSEA, Quebec (MAP 135)
LES FOUGÈRES ☆
783 route 105 **$100**
(819) 827-8942

Les Fougères has probably been in business longer than any other restaurant in the area. Of course, part of the reason for that is that they have never tried to stand still. The house was completely renovated a few years ago, and is now quite beautiful both inside and out. And the cooking just gets better, as if it's trying to keep up. Their dinner menu is innovative—smoked breast of duck with jalapeno and sweet-chili vinaigrette, Thai shrimp with chips, wild Arctic char with parsnip and ginger, quail in brown butter, Grand Banks salt-cod ravioli and Prince Edward Island mussels in seaweed. To follow there's baked Alaska, panna cotta with quince jelly and dark-chocolate terrine. On Sunday they put on a grand breakfast. Les Fougères is an easy drive from Ottawa, and there's even a shop by the front door where you can buy many of the restaurant's dishes to take away. Charles Part, who is in charge of the kitchen, and his wife, Jennifer Warren, who is in charge of everything else, deserve a lot of credit.

Open Wednesday to Friday noon to 10 pm, Saturday and Sunday 10 am to 4 pm (brunch), 4 pm to 10 pm (dinner). Closed on Monday and Tuesday. Licensed. Amex, Master Card, Visa. Book ahead.

CHEMAINUS, B.C. (MAP 54)
ODIKA
2976 Mill Street **$100**
(250) 324-3303

If you're on the Trans Canada Highway between Victoria and points east, this is where you should stop for lunch. The cafe uses fresh local ingredients to make dishes inspired by many different cultures. Murray Kereliuk is equally skilled with pan-seared scallops, strawberry salad, leek crème brûlée and curried lamb shanks African-style. We particularly like his Penang prawn curry, served with basmati rice and steamed bok choy. Grand Marnier crème brûlée is now a permanent part of the sweet list, and no wonder. In good weather it's fun to eat outside on the tiny roadside patio,

Open Tuesday to Thursday 11 am to 8.30 pm, Friday and Saturday 11 am to 10 pm. Closed on Sunday and Monday. Shorter hours in winter. Licensed. All cards. ♿

CHESTER, N.S. (MAP 79)
KIWI
19 Pleasant Street **$80**
(902) 275-1492

The Kiwi Cafe is located directly across the street from the Chester Playhouse and it's always busy. It's open all year, which makes it popular with the local residents. Their food is comfort food at its best. The all-day breakfast features scrambled eggs with lobster, eggs benedict with smoked salmon and beautiful omelettes. Then there are lobster rolls, grilled paninis, innovative wraps and an outstanding veggie burger. Specialty coffees and teas are always on offer, as well as beer and wine. The service is fast and friendly, and gourmet mustards and frozen soups can be bought to take away.

Open daily 8 am to 5 pm. Licensed. All cards.

Our website is at www.oberonpress.ca. Readers wishing to use e-mail should address us at oberon@sympatico.ca.

CHICOUTIMI, Quebec — MAP 42

LA VOIE MALTEE
777 boulevard Talbot
(418) 549-4141

$80

The Voie Maltée may be no Chez Amato. In fact it certainly is not. But unlike Amato it's packed with students, and they all think the food, the beer and the atmosphere are beyond compare. There are ten micro-brews, including a blond pilsener made on the premises from local ingredients. Several of the dishes are based on beer and the best of them is probably the beef stroganoff with ale. The cooks are fond of cheese and if you ask for the macaroni and cheese with crab or a cheeseburger made with foie gras you'll see why. There are at least two first-class appetizers (spiced shrimp and salmon Caesar) and one excellent sweet (tiramisu with beer). The food is all good and very cheap. A second Voie Maltée has now opened at 2509 rue St.-Dominique in Jonquière (telephone (418) 542-4373) and a third at 1040 boulevard Pierre Bertrand s (telephone (418) 683-5558) in Quebec. *Open Monday to Friday 11.30 am to 3 am, Saturday and Sunday noon to 3 am. Licensed. All cards. No reservations.*

CHURCHILL, Manitoba — MAP 43

GYPSY'S
253 Kelsey Boulevard
(204) 675-2322

$120

Tony Da Silva came here from Montreal to open Gypsy's as a bakery. More than 30 years later, the restaurant that grew out of that bakeshop is still very much the creation of the Da Silva family. Times have become difficult of late, with the decline in polar bear numbers cutting into the town's tourist revenues. But there are still a few bears to be found, and on the days when there aren't, you can take one of the new beluga-whale tours or a dog-sled trip. The menu at Gypsy's never changes: there's always Arctic char, Manitoba pickerel and a selction of Portuguese dishes like chicken marinated in white wine. Most of the breads and wines are also Portuguese. Gypsy's is an institution in Churchill .

Open Monday to Saturday 6 am to 10 pm from 1 March until mid-October, daily from mid-October until 30 November. Licensed. All cards.

CLARK'S HARBOUR, N.S. (MAP 186)
WEST HEAD TAKEOUT 🖝
81 Boundry Street **$45**
(902) 745-1322

About 800 people live in Clark's Harbour, which is the only settlement on Cape Sable Island. Everybody enjoys getting there and everybody admires the white-sand beaches, which are important for bird-watchers. There are many rare species to be seen, including 20% of the world's piping plovers, an endangered species. The West Head Takeout is a tiny building at the end of the town wharf, with a fish-processing plant on either side. This year they have a licence (or so they say) and tour buses are stopping at the door. The place looks like nothing from the outside and there's little to indicate what goes on inside. Still, the Takeout is busy from morning till night. It used to be called the Seaview, but if the name has changed the fish hasn't. It's easy to recommend the lobster roll, which is as good as any we've tasted. They also have a scallop burger for 4.25 and very fresh fish and chips for 8.95. Anyone who finds himself within 25 miles of this place and doesn't come in for a meal is making a mistake.

Open daily 10.30 am to 8 pm from late March until late September. Licensed. No cards. ⟨♿⟩

COBBLE HILL, B.C. (MAP 54)
PRIMA STRADA
1400 Cowichan Bay Road: Unit 14 **$110**
(250) 929-4655

You'll find Prima Strada in a small shopping-centre just off the Trans-Canada Highway. It seats 65 people, with a fine view of the Cowichan Valley. Like its sister restaurants in Victoria, it serves Neapolitan-style wood-fired thin-crust pizzas. There's a nice polenta starter featuring eggplant, peppers, fennel and sultanas, and a rich plate of polpette with shaved parmigiano, but after that the menu is all a matter of toppings. We like the Panna e Cotto (cream and ham) and the Rucola e Crudo (arugula and prosciutto) but more complicated choices run from the Caponata (eggplant, peppers, ricotta and arugula) to the Pollo Panna e Pancetta (cream, roast chicken, house-cured pancetta, garlic, red onion and lemon). The wine-list is small but choice, and quite cheap by the glass. Craft beers are locally brewed.

Open daily 11.30 am to 9 pm. Licensed. All cards. &

COBOURG, Ontario   MAP 46
WOODLAWN INN   ☆
420 Division Street   **$130 ($295)**
(905) 372-2235

It's now 30 years and more since the Della Casa family bought this fine old inn and installed Stephen Della Casa as sommelier, with a list of 300 wines and two dozen single malts. The cellar hasn't looked back, and nor has the kitchen. They buy everything they can from local suppliers, though their most popular dish has always been the Dover sole. It's carefully deboned at your table, and might be the best of its kind this side of Dover. Almost as good are the New York striploin and the Australian lamb. We like to start with the Hudson Valley veal tourtière or the salmon gravadlax on a crusty potato lattice. Cobourg is easily the most attractive town between Toronto and Kingston, and the inn is a beautiful place to stay.

Open Monday to Saturday 11.30 am to 2 pm, 5.30 pm to 8.30 pm, Sunday 11.30 am to 2 pm, 5.30 pm to 8 pm. Licensed. All cards. &

Where an entry is printed in italics this indicates that the restaurant has been listed only because it serves the best food in its area or because it hasn't yet been adequately tested.

COLLINGWOOD, Ontario   **MAP 47**

FISH & SIPS

206 Hurontario Street   **$40**

(705) 293-7477

Fish & Sips is a lot more than a fish-and-chip joint. For many diners, it's a destination—if only because it has quick and cheerful service, beautiful presentation and low prices. (At the moment, a lunch of fish, chips and a drink costs only 7.99.) The fish is always lightly battered and perfectly cooked. The fries are always hot and plentiful, and if you like you can start your meal with a plate of calamari, shrimp and scallops. There's a short, simple wine-list and several local micro-brews, as well as a cider or two. The restaurant is a first for the young couple who run the place, but the chef grew up in his parents' fish-and-chip shop in Toronto, and he knows his way around. *Open Monday and Wednesday to Sunday 11.30 am to 8 pm. Closed on Tuesday. Licensed. Master Card, Visa.*

COLLINGWOOD   **MAP 47**

GUSTAV'S CHOPHOUSE

Georgian Bay Hotel   **$125**

10 Vacation Inn Drive

(705) 445-9422

Two new steak houses have opened recently in Collingwood and Gustav's is the more promising of the two. The Georgian Bay Hotel has been entirely renovated and the owners have picked the best chef and the best pâtissière they could find. Both are at Gustav's now, and the pâtissière is certainly amazing. But they're still scanning local farms to find out where the best produce is to be had. The restaurant is too new for us to say in any detail just what the chefs are doing. Further reports needed. *Open Tuesday to Saturday 11 am to 11 pm, Thursday and Friday 11 am to midnight. Closed on Sunday and Monday. Licensed. All cards.* &

Nobody but nobody can buy his way into this guide.

COLLINGWOOD

MAP 47

SANTINI
61 Hurontario Street **$130**
(705) 443-8383

Andrea de Matteis didn't miss a step when he expanded his twelve-table liquor-free deli into a beautiful full-service restaurant seating 200 people. We still mistrust a menu of this length, but the chef has a winning simplicity of style when it comes to an arugula salad with lemon or even a plain chocolate mousse. He has wood-fired pizzas "as good as any in Italy," as his admirers like to say, as well as a remarkable branzino (European sea-bass) entrée. Everyone likes the carpaccio, the salads and the sweets—the tiramisu has as many fans as the chocolate mousse. The atmosphere is friendly and the service is the best in Collingwood.

Open Monday and Wednesday to Sunday 11.30 am to 10 pm. Closed on Tuesday. Licensed. Amex, Master Card, Visa. ᷤ

COOMBS, B.C. (MAP 157)

THE CUCKOO
2310 Alberni Highway **$130**
(250) 248-6280

The Cuckoo opened in 2011, offering authentic Italian food to travellers on their way to or from Pacific Rim National Park. It's an attractive place, in beautiful surroundings. The menu is quite ambitious, but the kitchen seems to have learned how to cope. There's a welcome number of gluten-free options: pizzas, pastas, foccacias—even a chocolate almond torte. A good start to dinner is the generous seafood antipasto platter, which is designed for sharing. The linguine pescatora tosses clams, mussels, shrimp and scallops with garlic, tomatoes and olive oil; the linguine granchio comes with sautéed local crab in a creamy rose sauce. Best of the risottos is the seafood Cinque Terre, followed closely by the Piemontese, filled with chanterelles, beef stock, parmesan cheese and truffle oil. There are also shared

"Paesano" platters for parties of four or more, which go well on the patio in summer.
Open daily 11.30 am to 3 pm, 5.30 pm to 10 pm. Licensed. All cards. Book ahead if you can. &

COWICHAN BAY, B.C. (MAP 54)
THE MASTHEAD ☆
1705 Cowichan Bay Road **$125**
(250) 748-3714

The Masthead is a charming restaurant, and Luke and Denise Helms are warm and welcoming hosts. The menu has few changes, though sadly dungeness crab and spot prawns recently disappeared, their prices driven up astronomically by export demand (they've been replaced by imported rock crabs and red tiger prawns). Everything else—fish, oysters, clams and weathervane scallops—is still local, and the beef (you don't have to have seafood just because you're at the water's edge) still comes from Alberta. We like the Masthead chowder of salmon and local shellfish, the scallops on a mushroom risotto, the sockeye salmon on pappardelle and the hazelnut crusted halibut. If you'd rather get away from the sea, try the peppercorn glazed duck breast or one of the grilled steaks. Everything comes with the restaurant's signature potatoes cooked in duck drippings, which are probably about as bad for your health as they are good to eat.
Open daily 5 pm to 10 pm. Licensed. All cards. Book ahead if you can. &

CREEMORE, Ontario (MAP 204)
CREEMORE KITCHEN ☆
134 Mill Street **$140**
(705) 466-2900

Creemore is an attractive village and it has the best-known of Ontario's craft breweries, Creemore Springs. Ignore all the negative rumours you hear about the kitchen. The fact is, it serves the best food in town. The menu is seasonal and changes every few weeks, and they use local suppliers whenever they can. Caesar Guinto (formerly the executive chef at the Royal Ontario Museum) flirts from time to time with Asian cuisine. For instance, he likes to offer steaks with kimchee fries. But he also likes to serve his burgers with housemade HP sauce, to say nothing of spaghetti bolognese or Eton Mess (until it recently disappeared). The soups and the fish are both reliable. The wine-list is small, but Creemore lager and pilsener are both on tap. Guinto and his partner Sam Holwell created the restaurant—which is right across the street from the Brewery—by linking two cottages together with a cathedral ceiling and hemlock walls, and the result, like the cooking, is at once traditional and modern.

Open Monday, Thursday and Friday 11 am to 2.30 pm, 5.30 pm to 9.30 pm, Saturday and Sunday 11 am to 2.30 pm (brunch), 5.30 pm to 9.30 pm. Closed on Tuesday and Wednesday. Licensed. Master Card, Visa. Book ahead. ♿

CRESTON, B.C.   MAP 52
REAL FOOD CAFE   ☆
223 10 Avenue N   **$130**
(250) 428-8882

The Real Food Café looks like an old house at the side of the road, but inside you'll find several dining-rooms and even a dog-friendly patio. Prices are modest, and the menu makes time for vegans, vegetarians and gluten-free diners. This is modern British pub food adapted to the Canadian experience. There's fish and chips (made with Alaska wild cod), a poutine covered in curry and—England's favourite dish—chicken tikka masala. Best of all is the shank of lamb, which has to be ordered a day in advance. The sticky toffee pudding is as British as the beers, but the wines, thankfully, are from the Okanagan. Service is excellent.

Open Monday to Friday 11 am to 2 pm, 4.30 pm to 8 pm. Closed on Saturday and Sunday. Licensed. Master Card, Visa. Book ahead if you can. ♿

Every restaurant in this guide has been personally tested.

DAWSON CITY, Yukon   MAP 53
THE DRUNKEN GOAT   ☆
950 2 Avenue   **$125**
(867) 993-5868

We used to underestimate the Drunken Goat. The fact is that it's a lot more than a friendly place offering big help-ings of Greek food. One reader swears that it's the best place to eat within 500 miles. The helpings are certainly large—that's true. But the Greek recipes are utterly authentic, and the grilled lamb is a masterpiece. The prices are high, even for the north, but nobody seems to complain. The Billy Goat bar has comfortable seating and a great open fireplace. In summer you can sit outside on the deck and enjoy a drink of wine or local beer under the midnight sun.
Open daily 4.30 pm to 11 pm (shorter hours in winter). Licensed. Master Card, Visa.

DUNCAN, B.C.   MAP 54
HUDSON'S ON FIRST   ☆
163 First Street   **$125**
(250) 597-0066

More than a year ago Dan Hudson left his award-win-ning restaurant, which was generally held to be the best place to eat between Victoria and Nanaimo. So far stan-dards have been maintained. At noon you should try the green salad with pan-seared red snapper, and at night there's a fine halibut with olive-crusted potatoes, roasted cauliflower and a piperade sauce. There are usually Salt Spring mussels on the menu, served either with white wine and garlic or with tomato, fennel and a housemade sausage. For sweet, have the Earl Grey panna cotta or the citrus posset with a compote of blueberries and lime. There's an interesting selection of wines from the Cowichan Valley.
Open Tuesday 11 am to 2 pm, Wednesday to Friday 11 am to 9 pm, Saturday 10 am to 9 pm, Sunday 10 am to 2 pm (brunch). Closed on Monday. Licensed. Amex, Master Card, Visa. Book ahead. ♿

DUNCAN

MAP 54

VINOTECA
5039 Marshall Road   **$120**
(250) 748-2338

When Vinoteca opened in 1996, it was the only winery restaurant with a licence in B.C. Chef Fatima da Silva continues to work her magic in this century-old family farmhouse on the Zanata Vineyard—the oldest on the Island. Da Silva cooks Italian in the country style, using ingredients grown on the family farm or nearby. Everything is locally sourced and everything is perfectly fresh. The menu is seasonal, and the dishes are all beautifully presented and served. She has a dab hand with lamb, served with vegetables from the Cowichan Valley, and spot prawns, clams and mussels, all from local waters, go well with tomato, basil and coconut sauce. Pasta plays a significant role on the menu—the spaghetti puttanesca is a classic dish, as is the ravioli stuffed with locally-foraged wild mushrooms. They carry only Zanata wines, which means that you can drink nothing but the bubbly or the pinot grigio, both of which pair well with Fatima's food. They have a pleasant brunch on Sunday, and offer a three-course Sunday dinner for only 27.50.

Open Wednesday and Thursday noon to 3 pm, 5.30 pm to 10 pm, Friday to Sunday 11.30 am to 3 pm, 5.30 pm to 10 pm. Closed on Monday and Tuesday. Licensed. All cards. &

DUNCAN

See also CHEMAINUS, COBBLE HILL, COWICHAN BAY.

DUNDAS, Ontario   **(MAP 80)**

QUATREFOIL   ☆☆
16 Sydenham Street   **$185**
(905) 628-7800

Quatrefoil opened in 2010. Fraser Macfarlane is still in charge of the kitchen; his wife, Georgina Mitropoulos, has left the front of the house to become a full-time mother. The service is as fresh and accomplished as ever, and the cooking is, of course, beyond compare. Meals start with sea scallops with corn and sweet pepper, poached (not grilled) Ontario white asparagus or a mushroom soup with potato-and-onion crumble and blue-cheese foam—a rare and delightful dish. Then there's Cumbrae's beef, European sea-bass, Pacific halibut or swordfish steak—which is much better than it sounds. Our favourite is the sea-bass, which comes with blue mushrooms and garlic in mousseline sauce. The best of the sweets is the chocolate blood-orange cake with Grand Marnier ice cream—"absolutely delicious," writes one diner, "and one of the most memorable sweets I've had in the past year."

Open Tuesday to Saturday noon to 2.30 pm, 5 pm to 10 pm. Closed on Sunday and Monday. Licensed. Amex, Master Card, Visa.

EDMONTON, Alberta MAP 56
ALDER ROOM ☆
10328 Jasper Avenue **$165**
(780) 244-3635

The Alder Room isn't a traditional restaurant. In fact they don't seem to regard themselves as a restaurant at all. A dinner here is presented as an evening of culinary theatre. You don't make a reservation; you buy a "ticket" for either the 5 pm "matinee" performance of ten courses for 100.00, or the 7:30 pm evening performance of fifteen to twenty courses for 160.00 (plus another 70.00 if you want to add wine pairings). There are only twelve people in the audience, and of course none of you know what you'll be having. You move slowly around the dimly-lit room, from the appetizer table, where the chef/owner Ben Staley explains your meal, to the main-course counter overlooking a grill manned by Staley's sous-chefs, and then back full circle to the appetizer table for sweet. In the evening the performance lasts three hours. The menu changes every day, but most of it is vegetable-based, with only very small roles for duck, pork and beef. We've been offered fire-roasted potatoes speared on tiny twigs, sunchokes roasted and filled with burnt cream, caramelized cabbage leaves on a bed of oak leaves (don't eat the oak leaves), crackling duck, vegetable-ash-covered quail eggs on charcoal (don't eat the charcoal) and 36-hour sous-vide pork belly with pickled green tomatoes, gherkins and freeze-dried onion blossoms. They were all interesting.

Open Tuesday to Thursday 5 pm to 11 pm (sittings at 5 pm and 7.30 pm), Friday and Saturday 5 pm to 2 am (sittings at 5 pm and 7.30 pm). Closed on Sunday and Monday. Licensed. All cards. You must book ahead. ♿

EDMONTON   MAP 56
BAR CLEMENTINE
11957 Jasper Avenue   **$125**
(780) 756-4570

Clementine really is a bar; it just happens to serve some excellent small plates with its cocktails. It seats only 28 people, ten of them at the bar, and with cool jazz on the soundtrack the noise level is refreshingly low. They stay open until midnight, but if you get there late the most popular dishes—like the kushi oysters in a shallot mignonette and the peking duck with shiitake and leek—tend to be gone. We also admire the slow-cooked rillons of pork with apple, lentils and shallots, the tobacco-smoked triple-cream brie with basil and plums, and the Atlantic lingcod poached in blue-cheese butter with fennel, bell peppers and salumi. There is of course no shortage of liquor of all kinds, but in addition to their creative cocktails they have a nice selection of craft beers and a small but carefully chosen list of natural wines.

Open Tuesday to Thursday 5 pm to midnight, Friday and Saturday 5 pm to 1 am, Sunday 5 pm to 11 pm. Closed on Monday. Licensed. All cards. You must book ahead.

If you wish to improve the guide send us information about restaurants we have missed. Our mailing address is Oberon Press, 145 Spruce Street: Suite 205, Ottawa, Ontario K1R 6P1.

EDMONTON   **MAP 56**
CHARTIER   ☆☆
5012 50 Street   **$180**
Beaumont
(780) 737-3633

Chartier is widely considered to be the best restaurant in
Edmonton, but it's not really in Edmonton at all. Beaumont is a small francophone village on the edge of the
city, and Chartier serves hearty, rustic French-Canadian
food. For lunch there's a rich and cheesy onion soup made
with duck and brandy broth, beef brisket with dijon mustard and mushroom croquettes with lemon yogurt. In the
evening there are both small plates and large, starting
with a classic poutine, pork jowl cakes braised with cinnamon and apples and mussels with andouille sausage, pickled onions and blue cheese. Larger plates include boeuf
bourguignon, blueberry perogies with sauerkraut and
duck, fried chicken with biscuits and mirepoix and even a
lobster poutine filled with a full pound of lobster meat
sautéed in garlic and butter. From Thursday to Sunday
there's a wild game daily special, and the wine-list features
a number of little-known European vintages.
Open Tuesday to Friday 11 am to 3 pm, 4 pm to 10 pm, Saturday
and Sunday 10 am to 2 pm, 4 pm to 10 pm. Closed on Monday.
Licensed. All cards. Book ahead.

EDMONTON   **MAP 56**
CORSO 32   ☆☆
10345 Jasper Avenue   **$190**
(780) 421-4622

Corso 32 is typically Italian—small and narrow and full
of the sound of people having a good time. The menu is
quite short and offers only three main dishes, but there's
an attractive selection of antipasti: things like the slow-
cooked short rib with shaved pear and arugula or the noce
di prosciutto with apple and parmigiano. Best of the
unusual pasta combinations is the parsnip agnolotti in
burnt butter with sage, amaretti, parmigiano and aged

balsamico. Everyone likes the game hen with charred radicchio, lardo, balsamico and pomegranate, but if you're hungry there's a berkshire pork shoulder with polenta and shaved brussels sprouts. To finish there's panna cotta and chocolate torte. The Italian wine-list is well chosen but expensive—the cheapest glass is 15.00.

Open Wednesday to Sunday 5 pm to 11 pm. Closed Monday and Tuesday. Licensed. All cards. Book ahead. &

EDMONTON   MAP 56
HAUS FALKENSTEIN   ☞
15215 111 Avenue   **$80**
(780) 483-5904

In 2015 Silke and Michael Hentschel moved their Haus Falkenstein from Lougheed to Edmonton, where they've settled into a mini-mall next to an adult store. But the waiters still wear lederhosen and dirndls, and the walls are still plastered with vintage Alberta licence plates. And they still offer 67 varieties of schnitzel. These are not Viennese wienerschnitzels, which are made with veal; they're traditional German schnitzels made of pork. Out of such a selection there must be many favourites, but we like the Falkenstein schnitzel, which comes with chanterelles in a cream sauce, and the pepper schnitzel with green peppercorns. If you want a change from schnitzels, you can try the Bayerische weisswurst, two white sausages with sauerkraut and sweet mustard. All the plates are large, and you may prefer a half-portion for about 15.00. Beer is what you drink with schnitzels, and the list at the Haus Falkenstein is long: Holsten, Erdinger, Bitburger, Krombacher, Radeberger and Warsteiner—among others.

Open Wednesday to Sunday 4 pm to 9 pm. Closed on Monday and Tuesday. Licensed for beer and wine only. All cards. &

This is a guide to Canadian restaurants from coast to coast—the first ever published and the only one of its kind on the market today. Every restaurant in the guide has been personally tested. Our reporters are not allowed to identify themselves or to accept free meals.

EDMONTON   **MAP 56**
LINNEA
Holland Plaza   **$100**
10932 119 Street NW
(780) 758-1160

Linnea is something different for Edmonton. For one thing, it bills its cuisine as French-Scandinavian fusion. For another, it serves breakfast five days a week. And what a breakfast: oeufs en cocotte with caramelized onion and pickled chanterelles in a sherry cream sauce; a buckwheat galette with oyster mushrooms, creamed leeks and apple-wood-smoked cheddar; a breakfast tart topped with a poached egg and filled with kuri squash, bacon, ricotta and fried sage. At night there's a house charcuterie board, perfect for sharing, with a selection of house-cured meats, pâtés and condiments, as well as gougeres, croquettes, scallops and beef tartar, followed by a whole seared rockfish, perhaps, or birch-glazed duck or even every teenager's first crush, a ten-ounce striploin steak au poivre. The restaurant runs its own bakery in-house, with a range of breads and sweets that can also be bought to take out. Try the London Fog panna cotta with orange shortbread crumble. Every Tuesday there's a set dinner menu of three courses for only 35.00.

Open Tuesday 5 pm to 10 pm, Wednesday to Friday 10 am to 2 pm, 5 pm to 10 pm, Saturday 9 am to 2 pm, 5 pm to 10 pm, Sunday 9 am to 2 pm. Closed on Monday. Licensed. All cards. Book ahead. ♿

EDMONTON   **MAP 56**
THE MARC
9940 106 Street   **$150**
(780) 429-2828

The Marc occupies the ground floor of a modern office block near the high-level bridge. Inside, it's all white with wide steel-and-glass windows. At noon they serve a hearty vegetable soup, followed by a galette of apple-wood-smoked chicken, croque madame on potato bread and a fish stew of prawns, scallops, clams and quenelles in a fumet of wine. The evening meal is more formal. Their signature main dish is Arctic char prepared in a variety of ways—our favourite is roasted, with a lovely crisp skin. We also like the confit of duck leg and the grilled octopus with chorizo. There's an interesting choice of wines by the glass and the bottle.

Open Monday to Friday 11.30 am to 2.30 pm, 5.30 pm to 10 pm, Saturday 5.30 pm to 10 pm. Closed on Sunday. Licensed. Amex, Master Card, Visa. Book ahead. ዼ

EDMONTON   **MAP 56**
XIX NINETEEN   ☆☆
5940 Mullen Way NW   **$190**
(780) 395-1119

Nineteen has earned a big reputation for both its lunch and its dinner. Lunch means crisp squid and beef-tender-loin sliders. Even better is the soy-glazed Mongolian beef sautéed with garlic and ginger. In the evening start with Thai noodles with Asian slaw and cilantro aioli or the sriracha-marinated octopus. Both are extremely popular. If you want to play it safe, just ask for the wild-mushroom soup with chives and truffles. The lamb-shank risotto makes a fine main course, as does the sous-vide breast of duck or the beef tenderloin with ponzu butter, wasabi and salmon roe. There's always plenty of pasta, the best of which is probably the Atlantic lobster ravioli with red chili, garlic and sambuca. After that, ask for the warm butter-cake with a compôte of fresh fruit. The restaurant recently opened a new location at 150 Bellerose Drive in St. Albert (telephone (780) 569-1819), which is getting great reviews. Nineteen is expensive in both locations, but between 3 pm and 6 pm it's cheaper. Go then.

Open Monday to Thursday 3 pm to 11 pm, Friday and Saturday noon to midnight, Sunday noon to 10 pm. Licensed. All cards. Book ahead. ዼ

If you use an out-of-date edition and find it inaccurate, don't blame us. Buy a new edition.

EDMONTON   **MAP 56**
PADMANADI
10740 101 Street NW   **$100**
(780) 428-8899

The most popular Asian restaurant in Edmonton is not
just vegetarian but vegan, which is surprising in the heart
of cattle country. The chef/owner Kasim Kasim came to
Edmonton from Indonesia, but his menu is a blend of
Indonesian, Chinese, Thai and Indian cuisines. The
kitchen makes extensive use of tofu and other vegetable
products to fill in for meat, even going so far as to offer
curried chicken, curried mutton and General Tso's
chicken, though no chickens or sheep are in the building.
The restaurant's two most popular dishes are the Chinese
eggplant quartered and stir-fried in chili sauce and the
ginger beef ("beef") with sweet red peppers and julienne
carrots. Kasim's religion unfortunately prevents him
from using any member of the allium family—onions,
garlic, shallots, leeks—in his cooking, and some things,
like the spring rolls, don't work well without them. Try
the deep-fried wontons or the cauliflower bites instead.
We also like the Thai yellow curry of vegetable chicken,
the spicy string beans, the oyster mushroom gaylan, the
spicy coconut eggplant and the extravagant Padmanadi
vegetable deluxe. There is no liquor, but they have excellent fresh-squeezed juices and Asian teas.
*Open Tuesday to Friday 11 am to 2 pm, 4 pm to 10 pm, Saturday
and Sunday 10 am to 2 pm, 4 pm to 10 pm. Closed on Monday.
No liquor. All cards. Book ahead.* ♿

EDMONTON   **MAP 56**
RANGE ROAD   ☆
10643 123 Street   **$140**
(780) 447-4577

Range Road is an unassuming place in an inconvenient
location. Inside it's equally plain. But it has interesting
cooking. You start with goose rillettes with crème fraîche
and caramelized fruit, or bison sausage with saskatoons or

perhaps beef tartar with onion curd. The main dishes are almost as surprising—there's pan-seared duck breast in black garlic, or roasted pig with five-spice pork belly and bean-and-apple jelly topped with Asian slaw and duck crackling. For vegetarians there's mushrooms and farro with leeks, goat cheese and sunchokes. They have a limited selection of wines by the glass from Niagara and the Okanagan. The service is outstanding.

Open Monday to Saturday 5 pm to 11 pm. Closed on Sunday. Licensed. Amex, Master Card, Visa. Book ahead.

EDMONTON   **MAP 56**
RED OX INN   ☆
9420 91 Street   **$175**
(780) 465-5727

If you're a stranger to Edmonton, the Red Ox Inn is hard to find. Head east on Whyte Avenue and turn north on 83 Street to a roundabout. The third exit from the roundabout is Connors Road. Turn right off Connors Road and find your way the few blocks to 91 Street. The Red Ox Inn has been completely redecorated and the menu, always innovative, now seems more exciting than ever. Currently they're offering things like smoked steelhead trout, pork belly, breast of duck, Alaska black cod, lamb shank, parmesan gnocchi, loin of lamb and beef tenderloin. The duck comes with farro risotto and roasted pears, the black cod with sweet-potato purée and panroasted fennel, the lamb with a chick-pea fritter and puréed cauliflower—an adventurous dish. Chantilly cream is the sweet of choice, with a generous selection of wines by the glass. Wine is in fact the real strength of the restaurant. If it's still on the list, ask for a half-bottle of Grgich Hills cabernet-sauvignon—it's expensive but worth every dollar.

Open Tuesday to Sunday 5 pm to 9 pm. Closed on Monday. Licensed. Amex, Master Card, Visa. ♿

We accept no advertisements. We accept no payment for listings. We depend entirely on you.

EDMONTON   **MAP 56**
SOLSTICE
10723 124 Street   **$140**
(780) 488-4567

Solstice has never looked like much, but the cooking is highly imaginative. Jan Trittenbach handles his palette of exotic flavours with verve and panache. Duck breast is wrapped maki-style in chard, set on a bed of baked polenta and served with red cabbage and honey-poached cranberries; black cod is marinated in miso and served with pilaf and root-vegetable noodles in a ginger-and-carrot emulsion. A small plate of beef belly is served with farrotto, kale and smoked onion remoulade on a purée of acorn squash; ahi tuna comes with beetroot, baby radish, fried capers and a coconut-curry cream. Apple strudel is paired with a cranberry compote and a sage crémeux. The wines are carefully chosen and reasonably priced—and half-price on Wednesday.
Open Monday to Saturday 5 pm to 11 pm. Closed on Sunday. Licensed. All cards. Book ahead if you can. &

EDMONTON   **MAP 56**
UCCELLINO
10349 Jasper Avenue   **$125**
(780) 428-0346

This is Daniel Costa's third restaurant, and it's just across the street from Corso 32. The menu here is simple and direct, concentrating on dishes from central and southern Italy. Start with panzanella, a Tuscan bread-and-tomato salad, or the bucatini cacio e pepe (pasta tossed with salty pecorino and black pepper), which is pure perfection. After that, you can't do better than the char-grilled leg of lamb with roasted eggplant and salsa rosa or the black cod brodetto, with chickpeas, tomatoes, capers and chilis. The crostinis are all good, expecially the polpette di pane (salami fritters) and the cottechino (pork sausage from Modena). The olive-oil cake and the chocolate budino are the two most interesting of the

sweets. The service is superb.
Open Wednesday to Sunday 5 pm to 11 pm. Closed on Monday and Tuesday. Licensed. All cards. Book ahead if you can. &

EDMONTON   MAP 56
ZINC
Art Gallery of Alberta   **$150**
2 Sir Winston Churchill Square
(780) 392-2501

Zinc is located in the Art Gallery of Alberta and tries to live up to its surroundings. The walls are all glass and steel, and the sun pours in the great west windows. It's a lovely place to be in fine weather. And David Omar is an artist in his own way in the kitchen: all his effects are carefully thought out and arranged. Try the miso marinated lamb chops with sweet-potato-and-ginger purée, asparagus, fried garbanzo beans and rhubarb jam, or the salmon fillet with citrus couscous, wild boar bacon, heirloom tomatoes and grilled lemon. Every Tuesday evening, when admission to the gallery is free, becomes Tapas Tuesday at Zinc. The only menu is a long list of small plates: Tea-cured duck breast, cauliflower and feta croquettes, sweet and spicy prawns, grilled romaine lettuce with parmesan and bacon, escargots with shallots, green peas and gorgonzola, grilled chorizo sausage with sauerkraut and bacon-roasted wild boar terrine with butter-poached onions, foie gras, Dijon aioli and onion jam. They're all reasonably priced from 7.50 to 18.00 (for the wild boar terrine). The wine-list is full of good buys like Cakebread chardonnay and Black Hills syrah.
Open Tuesday and Wednesday 11 am to 2.30 pm, 5 pm to 9 pm, Thursday to Saturday 11 am to 2.30 pm, 5 pm to 10 pm, Sunday 11 am to 2 pm. Closed on Monday. Licensed. All cards. &

This is a guide to Canadian restaurants from coast to coast—the first ever published and the only one of its kind on the market today. We accept no advertisements. Nobody can buy his way into this guide and nobody can buy his way out.

EDMUNDSTON, N.B.   MAP 57
CHANTAL'S STEAK HOUSE
721 C Victoria Street   **$90**
(506) 735-8882

We'd like to send you to the Lotus Bleu (see below), but maybe you'd like some meat with your meal—or even a linen napkin. In that case, you'll be glad to know about Chantal's. Chantal has had her problems in the past, but at the moment she seems to have the ship right on course. Her staff are perfectly professional, her fruits and vegetables are perfectly fresh, her meat is all cooked *à point*. Her menu may not break any new ground, but what she does she does well. Even her deep-fried cauliflower has gained a lot of admirers. She has no liquor license, so bring your own bottle. How a restaurant can survive without a license we don't know, especially as this one offers diners a complimentary appetizer.
Open daily 4 pm to 10 pm. B.Y.O.B. No reservations.

EDMUNDSTON   MAP 57
LOTUS BLEU   ☆
52 chemin Canada   **$45**
(506) 739-8259

This bright and cheerful little cafe will celebrate its tenth anniversary this summer, which is remarkable for a town that always refused to take its restaurants seriously. Costs have been rising recently though, and at the Lotus Bleu they've had to work harder than ever. In a town the size of Edmundston, it's always difficult to find qualified staff. A year or two ago we spoke highly of the curried vegetable stew, but the chef that made it was from Pakistan, where he soon returned. The next chef came from Columbia, and the one after that from Iraq. Learning from experience perhaps, the restaurant now offers a different hot dish every day of the week. The vegetables are all organically grown, and there are several attractive salads. The bread comes all the way from Première Moisson in Montreal, the wonderful bagels from St.-Viateur. The sweets are all made in-house, and there are 50 different leaf teas. Breakfast starts at 7.30 in the morning, and it's a fine meal.

Open Tuesday to Friday 7.30 am to 4 pm, Saturday 9 am to 4 pm. Closed on Sunday and Monday. No liquor. Master Card, Visa. &

ENGLISHTOWN, N.S.   MAP 58
THE CLUCKING HEN
45073 *Cabot Trail*   **$50**
(902) 929-2501

If you just got off the Englishtown ferry, chances are you'll drive right past this little place. But if you started the Trail at Baddeck you'll know that there aren't many places like it on the road ahead of you. The cooking at the Clucking Hen is simple, but the baking is special. Everything is freshly made. You place your order at the counter and it'll be delivered to your table. Everybody seems to like their pan-fried haddock, their fish chowder and their crab sandwich with tomato, red wine and mayonnaise, all on house-made bread. Oatcakes are a specialty of the house, and there are always cinnamon rolls, butter tarts and gingerbread with caramel. In warm weather you can sit outside and enjoy the garden.

Open daily 7 am to 8 pm from 1 July until 31 August (shorter hours in the spring and fall). Licensed for beer and wine only. Master Card, Visa. &

FERNIE, B.C.   MAP 59
THE CURRY BOWL
931 7 *Avenue*   **$80**
(250) 423-2695

You'll have to get in your car to visit the Curry Bowl, which is a short distance down Highway 3, but it's worth the drive. This is not, as you might expect from the name, an Indian restaurant. It's a curry restaurant. There are Indian curries, yes, but there are also Japanese curries and Thai curries. We like the Thai ones the best, particularly the panang curry with peanut sauce, though the green curry comes a close second. There are even several non-curry choices like nasi goreng, Vietnamese stir-fry and pad Thai. To start there are samosas, satays, deep-fried tofu, curried lentils and everyone's favourite, tom ka soup, filled with coconut milk, lemon grass and Thai ginger. They also have more than 50 beers on offer, many of them from cottage breweries.

Open daily 5 pm to 10 pm. Licensed. All cards.

FERRYLAND, Newfoundland   MAP 60
LIGHTHOUSE PICNICS   ☞
Highway 10   **$60**
(709) 363-7456

There are restaurants that are about the food, and there are restaurants that are about the occasion. Lighthouse Picnics is about the occasion. Not that there's anything wrong with the food, which is the sort of picnic our great-grandmothers are supposed to have made: home-made bread, homemade lemonade, salad, sweet. The bread is cut into thick sandwiches—we prefer the ham and brie, but there's also chicken with mango and various combinations of seafood—and the lemonade is served in a vintage Mason jar. You place your order in the light-house, and they give you a blanket and a little flag. Where you plant the flag and spread the blanket is up to you, but it's probably charitable not to go too far from the light-house, since one of the kitchen staff will have to carry your tray to you when it's ready, and that can involve quite a bit of climbing. (For you as well, since you have to carry it back.) The view is of course remarkable—all the way to Europe—a view is one thing you can usually count on at a lighthouse. Unfortunately so is a remote location: the Ferryland lighthouse is a thirty-minute walk from its parking lot, which is itself a difficult mile or so over a very rough surface from the signpost on Highway 10. But that's all part of the occasion—the bumpy drive, the long walk, the lighthouse looming up in front of you, the roar of the wind and the sea beyond, the climb up to the cramped parlour where you check in, the climb down to the ocean to plant your flag. And, of course, the long walk around the promontory afterward to wake yourself up for the drive home. Everyone likes Lighthouse Picnics, which is why you have to book weeks ahead (and hope for fine weather—you can eat inside if it rains but of course that's not the same thing at all, and they won't mind if you call and cancel).

Open Wednesday to Sunday 11.30 am to 4.30 pm from late May to early October. Closed on Monday and Tuesday. No liquor. Master Card, Visa. You must book ahead.

FIELD, B.C. (MAP 95)
TRUFFLE PIGS ☆
Kicking Horse Lodge **$150**
100 Centre Street
(250) 343-6303

There are only two places between Banff and Kamloops where we stop to eat—the Cedar House in Golden (see below) and Truffle Pigs in Field. You won't go wrong with either place, but you'll have more fun at Truffle Pigs. There are only 169 permanent residents in Field, but everyone who visits here remembers it. This is what people from the East think of when they think of Western Canada—a small town with a general store and mountains on all sides. The view from Truffle Pigs is spectacular. Inside there are ten tables and a modern kitchen. Everyone seems to have come for the mussels in white wine, dijon and cream or the seafood platter of smoked BC tuna, Pacific oysters, seared wild scallops and black tiger prawns. But there are many other good things, including, of course, quite a lot of pork: pork-belly nachos, pork-nam dumplings, a ten-ounce pork rack and even rainbow trout wrapped in double-smoked bacon (this dish is unfortunately called If Pigs Could Swim). If you've had enough of pork, there's a coffee-crusted striploin served on rosemary focaccia, confit of Brome Lake duck and a bouillabaisse of prawns, mussels and lobster. To drink there's the usual selection of local craft beers and BC wines.

Open daily 7 am to 11 pm from late May until the end of September (shorter hours in winter). Licensed. All cards. Book ahead. ♿

FLORENCEVILLE, N.B.   MAP 62
FRESH   ✩✩
9189 Main Street   **$185**
(506) 392-6000

Fresh has had a great year, which is very good news. One has to worry about a place as special as this. Sara Caines opened it some ten years ago, in the first of three antique railcars parked on the track next to the Shogomoc railway station in the former village of Bristol. Her plan was to sell nothing but fresh food cooked from scratch, changing her menu every six weeks. She had only enough space for two, and it's not every chef who can keep up with Sara Caines. In the spring of 2016, Jeffrey Patterson took over from James Freeman with no apparent difficulty. With his four burners and small oven he still offers a *menu surprise* that most visitors go for. You simply tell him what you like (or don't like) and he cooks it for you. He also has a regular menu that changes every few weeks. Last winter they had a pro-sciutto-and-pear salad that probably won't be there in the spring. They also had chicken Wellington and a very popular shrimp pad Thai. You can start with crab-cakes finished with caper cream or snails on quinoa with caviar and saffron. They butcher their own beef in house. The wine-list is ambitious, but the house wine is Jackson Triggs. *Open Tuesday to Saturday 5.30 pm to 10 pm. Closed on Sunday and Monday. Licensed. Amex, Master Card, Visa. Book ahead.*

FOGO ISLAND, Newfoundland   MAP 63
FOGO ISLAND INN   ✩✩
210 Main Road   **$275**
Joe Batt's Arm
(709) 701-0764

It's possible to get to Fogo Island, spend a few hours there and get back to Twillingate the same day. But that would be a pity, because Fogo deserves a longer visit. It's just off the northeast shore of Newfoundland. It's windswept and wet and very beautiful. Caribou graze on the uplands in summer, humpback whales migrate along its shores in winter. Zita Cobb, a woman of enormous energy and even more enormous means, is determined to preserve the island through tourism. In 2013 she opened the multi-million-dollar Fogo Island Inn in Joe Batt's Arm, and since then her hotel has become a world-class destination where you're hard pressed to find a room for less then 2000.00 a night. The food is remarkable, the service impeccable. But the dining-room has only as many tables as there are rooms at the inn, and guests have priority. This means you can't get a reservation unless there is a vacancy at the inn, and that isn't common. You aren't allowed to take photographs inside (these people pay for anonymity) and nobody will tell you the dinner menu or the price. (The figure at the top is an educated guess.) What we do know is that Newfoundland native Jonathan Gushue—who had been up in Ontario running Langdon Hall in Cambridge and The Berlin in Kitchener—took over the kitchen at the beginning of 2018. He's a very talented chef, but then Zita Cobb is a very shrewd innkeeper.

Open 5 pm to 9 pm. Licensed. All cards. You must book ahead. &

FOGO ISLAND   **MAP 63**
NICOLE'S CAFE   ☆
159 Main Road   **$125**
Joe Batt's Arm
(709) 658-3663

Not a lot happens on Fogo without connecting to Zita Cobb. Peter and Margaret Decker are lifelong friends of hers, and when she heard that their daughter Nicole wanted to leave her catering job in St. John's and come home to the island, Cobb mobilized her Shorefast Foundation to help. She encouraged Nicole to turn her catering experience into a restaurant of her own, provided the assistance to make it happen, and even sent over her chef consultant Steve Vardy to design the menu, train the kitchen and open the restaurant. It all worked out about as well as everything else Cobb touches, and now if you can't eat at the Inn—and who can?—Nicole's is the go-to place on the island. The café is right on the highway as you come into town, a few hundred yards past the very discreet parking lot of the Fogo Island Inn. Inside is a large, bright room with plank floors, pine ceilings, cheerful orange walls and big picture windows looking out over both arms of Joe Batt's bay. The menu starts with things like cod cakes, mussels and marinated turbot, and goes on to New York steak, chicken breast with partridge-berry chutney, cornmeal-crusted cod, pappardelle with salt beef and risotto with sweet potato and goat cheese. Everything makes the maximum use of local ingredients, from the tomato broth with garden herbs to the feather-light fish and chips. Even a hearty Newfoundland staple like cod au gratin, served in a miniature orange baking dish topped with green onions, becomes an impossibly light and creamy confection. Zita Cobb may have launched the boat, but Nicole Decker is proving she can steer it.

Open Monday to Saturday 10 am to 8 pm from early May until mid-October. Closed on Sunday. Licensed. All cards. Book ahead if you can. &

FREDERICTON, N.B. MAP 64
BREWBAKERS
546 King Street **$150**
(506) 459-0067

It's a good thing Brewbakers has such likeable food and service, because the steep climb to the third-floor diningroom isn't getting any easier. At least on summer weekends there's the added incentive of live jazz on the rooftop patio outside. Stewart Sharp doesn't make a lot of changes to his menu, though the familiar flat-iron steak has now been joined by a Wagyu ribeye (for 95.00). Everyone likes the seafood, particularly the fish cakes and the maple-glazed Atlantic salmon. There's a good selection of local craft beers on tap.

Open Monday 11.30 am to 9 pm, Tuesday to Thursday 11.30 am to 10 pm, Friday 11.30 am to 11 pm, Saturday 5 pm to 11 pm, Sunday 5 pm to 9 pm. Licensed. Amex, Master Card, Visa.

FREDERICTON   MAP 64
THE PALATE
462 Queen Street   **$100**
(506) 450-7911

It's easy to underestimate the Palate—it's a bit too large and a bit too plain. But the truth is, the service has always been efficient and friendly, the prices low, the quality of the ingredients high and the cooking surprising. We've always said they were at their best with soups, and the seafood chowder is crammed with clams, scallops and haddock. But when it comes to braised lamb shank or pulled pork won tons, the results are amazing. The noon-hour specials (8.95 for a sandwich with soup or a salad) are always worthwhile. And the sweets are all made locally and made well—the molten-lava cake, for instance, is known all over Fredericton, though we ourselves prefer the sticky toffee cake. The wine-list has grown in the last year or two—there are now nine good reds and seven whites.

Open Monday 11 am to 3 pm, Tuesday to Friday 11 am to 3 pm, 5 pm to 9 pm, Saturday 10 am to 3 pm, 5 pm to 9 pm. Closed on Sunday. Licensed. All cards. Book ahead. &

FREDERICTON   MAP 64
TERRACE ROOM
Crowne Plaza Hotel   **$130**
659 Queen Street
(506) 451-1804

The Crowne Plaza has a new chef, Matt Mackenzie. He's made a lot of changes, but patrons of the Lord Beaverbrook (as it used to be called) still find the place warm and well served. The menu has been enlarged, but the kitchen still uses local suppliers—including their own rooftop garden, where they grow vegetables and green herbs. The rooftop is also home to a number of beehives, which supply the dining-room with honey. The chef does a lot of his own foraging as well. He now serves a pre-theatre dinner, and people like its vegan chocolate mousse as well as anything else on the menu. The coffee is strong, the wine-list ample but fairly priced.

Open daily 6.30 am to 2 pm, 5 pm to 10 pm. Licensed. All cards.
&

FREDERICTON   MAP 64
WOLASTOQ WHARF   ☆
527 Union Street   **$130**
(506) 449-0100

St. Mary's First Nation have made a remarkable success of Wolastoq Wharf—as, indeed, they seem to have done with most of their businesses. Right now this is the best restaurant in Fredericton, wrong side of the river or not. It's an elegant and spacious room, decorated in shades of black and white, with a wall of water behind the reception desk to greet you at the door. Seafood is the specialty of the house: lobster, scallops, halibut, salmon and several different treatments of haddock. To start there are oysters, mussels, shrimp, calamari and, of course, chowder. You can have a whole lobster or a stuffed lobster for dinner, and lobster rolls for lunch. But most people order the seafood fettuccine or the perfectly cooked risotto of scallops, lobster and shrimp (a formidable dish—all the portions are large and if the kitchen has a fault it's that it leans strongly to cream). From the land there's a cider-glazed pork chop and a striploin steak. The wine-list isn't long, but it's cheap. The presentation is lively, the service friendly and knowledgeable. And there's even off-street parking at the front door.

Open Monday to Friday 11 am to 4 pm (lunch), 4 pm to 9 pm (dinner), Saturday and Sunday 9.30 am to 4 pm, 4 pm to 9 pm. Licensed. All cards. Free parking.

Nobody can buy his way into this guide and nobody can buy his way out.

FREEPORT, N.S.   MAP 65
LAVENA'S CATCH   ★★
15 Highway 217 W   **$80**
(902) 839-2517

Freeport is at the southern end of Digby Neck and to get there from Digby you take a short ferry trip. The place was settled by Loyalists in 1784 and many of the original buildings are still standing. Overhead, during the spring and fall, migrating birds in their thousands travel the Atlantic Flyway. On the Fundy side there are minke and humpback whales, and you can get tickets to see them at Lavena's Catch, which is run by the captain's sister and is the only good place to eat anywhere near. Lavena makes everything from scratch and everything is special. People have loved this place for all of its eighteen years. They go miles out of their way for the view, the down-home friendliness and, above all, the cooking. We've talked about the Digby scallops for years, and we now have no hesitation in saying that the haddock is a wonder. In fact, this may be the best fish soup you've ever tasted. If you don't like seafood, ask instead for the turkey soup or the liver. The vegetables and greens come straight from Lavena's garden. As for Aunt Heather's freshly baked sweets, they're fabulous.
Open Friday and Saturday 4 pm to 9 pm from 1 April until 31 May, daily 11.30 am to 8 pm from 1 June until 15 October, Friday and Saturday 4 pm to 9 pm from 16 October until 30 November. Closed Sunday to Thursday in the spring and fall. Licensed. All cards.

FROBISHER BAY, Nunavut
See IQALUIT.

GALIANO ISLAND, B.C.   (MAP 211)
PILGRIMME   ★★
2806 Montague Road   **$170**
(250) 539-5392

Jesse McCleery may cook only three days a week, but a glance at his menu makes it pretty obvious where he spends the other four. He spends them foraging through local farms, fields and woods—and even along the Galiano shoreline, which provides him with kelp and sea asparagus. The produce he finds all appears on the constantly changing menu chalked up in Pilgrimme's rustic wood dining-room. Most people here eat tapas-style, sharing several plates at a long communal table: plates like grilled wild salmon, confit of duck with chanterelles, potatoes with bacon and charred buttermilk and fermented cabbage with chili and coriander. Pacific octopus comes with chickpea and chorizo, beef-heart tartar with sea-lettuce, Belgian endive with fermented pear and Tiger Blue cheese from Poplar Grove. Needless to say, the wines are all locally grown.

Open Friday to Sunday 5 pm to 10 pm. Closed Monday to Thursday. Licensed. All cards. Book ahead. &

GANDER, Newfoundland   MAP 66
BISTRO ON ROE
110 Roe Avenue   **$125**
(709) 651-4763

Last year we thought the best place to eat in Gander was in Botwood. Bistro on Roe is a lot more convenient. It's a bright little restaurant in a strip mall out near the airport. The menu is more trattoria than bistro, and friendly to vegetarians. It changes regularly, but usually includes things like chicken alfredo, cod puttanesca, lamb shank and butternut-squash ravioli. We particularly like the pan-roasted cod with wonderful mashed potatoes. To start there's a fine seafood chowder of mussels, cod and shrimp. The Caesar salad is properly made with romaine, and the winter salad comes with roasted beets, goat cheese and candied pumpkin seeds. Our favourite sweets are the flourless chocolate cake and the partridgeberry flaky.

Open Monday to Saturday 5 pm to 10 pm. Closed on Sunday. Licensed. Master Card, Visa. &

Our website is at www.oberonpress.ca. Readers wishing to use e-mail should address us at oberon@sympatico.ca.

GASPE, Quebec

MAP 67

LA BRULERIE
101 rue de la Reine
(418) 368-3366

$70

This place is actually called Brûlerie du Café des Artistes
to distinguish it from other Brûlerie bistros. But as it happens this is the only one in the guide. It's always a pleasure
to stop here. The former C.N.R. telegraph office is now a
cosy restaurant that's open winter and summer and has a
chef who keeps the same menu all year. The same shrimps
from Rivière-au-Renard appear in both the salads and the
sandwiches. Home-smoked salmon comes by the
plateful. They make their own sausages, their own pizzas
and their own pasta. The helpings are generous, the prices
low. A cream-of-mushroom soup and pork tourtière
with sweet potatoes is yours for just 13.50. They roast
their own coffee right here and serve it in all sorts of ways.
Refills are free.

Open Monday to Friday 7 am to 10.30 pm, Saturday and
Sunday 8 am to 10.30 pm. Licensed. Master Card, Visa.

GEORGETOWN, P.E.I.

(MAP 37)

CLAMDIGGERS
7 West Street
(902) 652-2466

$135

At first glance, Clamdiggers looks a bit more commercial
than a serious restaurant should. It's a big place, right on
the shore of Cardigan Bay with marvellous sea views,
three dining areas and an 1800-foot deck. But the fact is
that the kitchen *is* serious, and takes nothing for granted.
They buy all their fish every morning and fillet it by
hand. Their steaks are aged for 21 days, and people seem
to like them as much as the lobster. The waiters are both
attentive and knowledgeable. We ourselves like to start
with the so-called Georgetown steamers (soft-shell clams
in white wine) and then go on to the crab-leg lunch
(which offers half a pound of snow-crab legs) or a south-
shore lobster supper with mussels and potato salad. The

batter on the haddock may not be as light as we'd like, but the fish inside is perfectly cooked, and the tartar sauce is a wonder. The restaurant does great salads and several fresh vegetables, but we still can't praise the sweets. Georgetown has the oldest live theatre on the Island and a first-class golf course. It's well worth your time.

Open daily 11.30 am to 4 pm from 1 April to 20 November. Licensed. Amex, Master Card, Visa. Book ahead. &

GIBSONS, B.C. (MAP 209)
CHASTERS
Bonniebrook Lodge
1532 Ocean Beach Esplanade **$130**
Sunshine Coast
604) 886-8956

When Bonniebrook Lodge was sold a few years ago, the new owner wisely kept on the chef at Chasters, which is now the best place to eat on the Sunshine Coast. Eddie Malcomson's menu is brief and consistent, with only a few seasonal variations. Popular starters are the slow-cooked pork belly with celeriac remoulade, the twice-baked crab soufflé, the housemade mushroom ravioli and the panko-crusted seafood cakes with chipotle aioli. To follow we like the roasted pork tenderloin in a cider reduction, the honey-glazed duck and the pricey rack of lamb with a fresh herb and mushroom crust. The three-course table d'hote is an inexpensive way to get a feel for the restaurant, but we don't like its choices as well. The service is always a pleasure, and the wine-list offers a broad selection of the better Okanagan vintages.

Open Thursday to Sunday 5.30 pm to 8.30 pm. Closed Monday to Wednesday. Licensed. Master Card, Visa. Book ahead if you can. &

This is a guide to Canadian restaurants from coast to coast—the first ever published and the only one of its kind on the market today.

GLENVILLE, N.S. (MAP 151)
GLENORA DISTILLERY ☆
13727 Highway 19 **$145 ($350)**
Cape Breton
(800) 839-0491

Glenora produces the only single-malt whisky (called Glen Breton) in North America. There are several vintages: just remember, the older the better. The distillery has nine bedrooms, a pub and a dining-room—with a ceilidh performed by local musicians every noon and every evening. The cooking may not be quite what it used to be, but the seafood chowder is still splendid and so is the boiled lobster. To follow there's a delightful sticky toffee pudding that comes with a welcome shot of Glen Breton. The wine-list is surprising, offering a number of bordeaux, as well as all the usual Scotch single malts.

Open daily 11 am to 3 pm (in the pub), 5 pm to 8.30 pm from 1 May until 24 October. Licensed. Amex, Master Card, Visa. Book ahead. ౬

GODERICH, Ontario **MAP 71**
THYME ON 21 ☆☆
80 Hamilton Street **$150**
(519) 524-4171

Nothing will hurt Thyme on 21 unless Peter and Catherine King lose their long-time chef, Terry Kennedy, which doesn't seem likely. They've been together ever since this old Victorian house was turned into a restaurant. By now Kennedy has developed working relationships with most of the local suppliers, and he has a rare talent for cooking even the simplest dish. There's a different fish special every week, and whether it's perch or pickerel or salmon, you know it'll be correctly cooked. The beef all comes from Huron County, the pork from Metzger, and both beef and pork are always cooked *à point*. Kennedy is really at his best with vegetables and people usually start their meal with a spring-roll. In fact, the vegetable soufflé stuffed with goat-cheese, spinach and red peppers can't be taken off the menu. He makes all his own sweets, and at the moment the best of them is the flourless-chocolate cake with an orange ganache. The wine-list isn't very large, but they have some good things by the glass and one spectacular bottle, Moet et Chandon's Dom Perignon for 260.00.

Open Tuesday to Sunday 11.30 am to 2 pm, 5 pm to 8 pm from the middle of June until Labour Day, Tuesday to Friday 11.30 am to 2 pm, 5 pm to 8 pm, Saturday 5 pm to 8 pm, Sunday 11.30 am to 2 pm (brunch), 5 pm to 8 pm from Labour Day until the middle of June. Closed on Monday. Licensed. Master Card, Visa.

GOLDEN, B.C.   MAP 72
THE CEDAR HOUSE   ☆☆
735 Hefti Road   **$185**
(250) 344-4679

The Cedar House is a slice of paradise on ten acres of secluded mountainside just south of Golden. There are nature trails through the property that show off the unforgettable scenery. Organic gardens grow vegetables and fruits. Inside the dining-room, Brad Unrau keeps a watchful eye on every detail of your evening. The menu offers half-a-dozen starters and half-a-dozen main courses, and you won't go far wrong with any of them. We like to begin with the duck-and-wild-mushroom tart or the baked brie in a wild-berry coulis, and then go on to the braised bison short-ribs with juniper and thyme, the duck confit salad or the wild Arctic char with lemon, ginger and cream. For sweet try the pot de crème or the lemon curd in phyllo pastry. After dinner take a walk to the resort's lookout for a stunning view of the Canadian Rockies. You can even bring your coffee or last glass of wine with you.

Open Wednesday to Sunday 5 pm to 9.30 pm. Closed on Monday and Tuesday. Licensed. All cards. Book ahead if you can. &

Nobody but nobody can buy his way into this guide.

GOLDEN

ELEVEN 22
1122 10 Avenue S
(250) 344-2443

MAP 72
☆
$110

Konan Mar calls this place a restaurant, a grill and liquids. The wine-list, to be sure, is very large and very cheap. So is the menu, which changes all the time. They don't make their own cannelloni any more, but what they do serve is so good that few people seem to have noticed. Their Asian dishes (nasi goreng and pad Thai) are attractive takes on familiar dishes. There's always some fresh fish, but the chef isn't as good with fish as with meat. He's at his best with veal bratwurst, Kassler pork chops and, of course, Black Angus beef with stilton and roasted garlic or smoked paprika butter. Sweets are one of the specialties of the house, and the chocolate truffles are very good too. *Open daily 5 pm to 10 pm from mid-May until mid-October and from mid-November until mid-April. Licensed. Master Card, Visa.* ♿

GRAND MANAN, N.B.

THE INN AT WHALE COVE
26 Whale Cove Cottage Road
North Head
(506) 662-3181

MAP 73
☆☆
$150 ($300)

We were afraid that six fast car ferries a day (in summer— in winter it's four a day) would spoil Grand Manan. We were wrong. They haven't. Laura Buckley still runs Whale Cove year-round, and runs it as well as she ever did. She does admit that local beef, lamb and pork are in short supply, but the salmon farms are flourishing and blueberries and strawberries are still plentiful. The main house in North Head was built in 1816, and Willa Cather bought one of the neighbouring cottages. Laura has now filled the place with old Shaker furniture and lots of books. If you're lucky you can even see whales from the front verandah. As for the menu, it changes every day and concentrates on fresh local seafood, though there's usually some chicken and some lamb. Lobster is still easy to get, and halibut and haddock have come back in a big way. The liquor store has gone private, and so is a lot better than it used to be.

Open Saturday and Sunday 6 pm to 8 pm from Mother's Day until late June, daily 6 pm to 8 pm from late June until mid-October. Closed Monday to Friday in the spring. Licensed. Master Card, Visa. Book ahead.

GRAND MANAN
See also CAMPOBELLO ISLAND.

GRAND PRE, N.S.   (MAP 220)
LE CAVEAU
11611 Highway 1   **$160**
(902) 542-7177

Le Caveau is the restaurant of the Grand Pré vineyard. If you come here on a fine summer day, you can't help but be charmed by what you see. The building is very grand and very beautiful. It overlooks the vineyard from a hilltop site, a short distance from the highway. The wine-list is large and impressive. The dining-room is handsome. Jason Lynch has been in charge of the kitchen for at least ten years. He has a small menu and changes it often. On our last visit we chose the red-deer tartar and the house-smoked salmon. Order game to follow—like the lovely Martock Glen boar porchetta. The kitchen is good with bread too, though they charge 5.00 for it, which seems to us too much.

Open Tuesday to Saturday 5 pm to 9 pm from late April until mid-May, 11.30 am to 2 pm, 5 pm to 9 pm from mid-May until late October, 5 pm to 9 pm from late October until the end of December. Closed on Sunday and Monday. Licensed. All cards. Book ahead if you can. &

The price rating shown opposite the headline of each entry indicates the average cost of dinner for two with a modest wine, tax and tip. The cost of dinner, bed and breakfast (if available) is shown in parentheses.

GRAVENHURST, Ontario   MAP 75
BLUE WILLOW
900 Bay Street   **$90**
(705) 687-2597

The Blue Willow started life as an English tea-shop, but it grew up to become a café and is now the best place to have lunch in Gravenhurst. The menu offers homemade soups, salads that range from a simple Caesar to grilled chicken or grilled scallops and shrimp, sandwiches—we particularly like the bacon and brie—a ploughman's lunch of ham and cheese, chicken pot-pie and Guinness beef stew. There's also a good quiche Lorraine, which comes in individual sizes with salad or soup. To follow there's a wide selection of classic British cakes and pies, as well as some fine gingerbread and even a sticky toffee pudding.
Open Monday to Thursday 11 am to 4 pm, Friday and Saturday 11 am to 8 pm, Sunday 11 am to 3 pm from 1 July until 31 August, Tuesday, to Thursday 11 am to 4 pm, Friday and Saturday 11 am to 8 pm, Sunday 11 am to 3 pm from 1 September until 30 June. Closed on Monday in winter. Licensed. Master Card, Visa. Book ahead if you can. &

GRAVENHURST
See also BRACEBRIDGE.

GUELPH, Ontario   MAP 76
ARTISANALE CAFE   ☆☆
214 Woolwich Street   **$150**
(519) 821-3359

Guelph has fostered several fine restaurants over the years: Bistro Six, La Cucina and most recently the Artisanale Cafe. Artisanale is located in a lovely limestone house in the heart of downtown. It's a simple, elegant space, with harvest tables for large groups. The chef and owner is Yasser Qahawish, who trained at George Brown and ran the kitchen at Osgoode Hall for many years. He cooks in the French country style, offering whatever he can buy fresh, and his dishes are like the cuisine of his boyhood in Kuwait—simple and full of flavour. His appetizers range from an endive-and-beet salad to chicken-liver mousse. The morel salad is simply prepared with arugula and vinaigrette dressing. Main courses run to fish, pasta and steak frites. The steaks may be the best you can get in Guelph. Even the hanger steak has great taste. The sweets are fine, especially the tarte tatin and the warm crêpe with rhubarb and whipped cream. Yasser Qahawish never seems to lose his enthusiasm for promoting good food: there's usually a three-course prix-fixe for about 35.00, as well as a children's menu, half portions for children under twelve, and a family discount between 5 and 6 o'clock.

Open Wednesday to Sunday 11.30 am to 3 pm, 5 pm to 9 pm. Closed on Monday and Tuesday. Licensed. Master Card, Visa. Book ahead if you can. &

GUELPH
See also MORRISTON.

GUYSBOROUGH, N.S.	**MAP 77**
DESBARRES MANOR	☆
90 Church Street	**$175 ($425)**
(902) 533-2099	

Guysborough is still very much as it always was, that is, a stretch of unspoiled country on Highway 16. The lovely DesBarres Manor was built in 1837 for W.F. DesBarres, who was a Supreme Court justice. It's been a hotel since 2003, winning awards of excellence every year. The ten bedrooms are spacious, with large bathrooms and enormous beds. It's a lovely place to stay, especially when there's a chef like Anna in the kitchen. She offers a seasonal four or five-course dinner every night, making full use of her organic garden. In season lobster is the main attraction. When lobster is not in season, there's salmon, haddock and pork tenderloin. For lunch they pack you a gourmet picnic basket. If you come in their off season (between 30 September and 1 May) and give them some notice, they'll take you in and give you dinner.

Open daily 6 pm to 8 pm by appointment only from 1 May until 30 September. Licensed. Master Card, Visa. You must book ahead.

HAIDA GWAII, B.C.   **MAP 78**

Queen Charlotte City (it's really just a village) is a mile or so east of the ferry terminal on Graham Island. We really liked the Purple Onion here, but sadly it has closed. The best choice now is the Queen B at 3208 Wharf Street (telephone (250) 559-4463). It's a funky place that caters to vegans and vegetarians and to anyone who doesn't mind noise. The menu offers such things as fish and vegetables, but little shellfish, because it's too expensive. Dana Adams changes her menu every day and makes everything in her own kitchen. She's good with such things as soups, quiches and pasta and in season she has blackberries, salmon-berries and huckleberries. Wild raspberries grow right next door. They're open Monday to Saturday from 9 am to 5 pm (sometimes earlier) and take all cards. No liquor.

HAIDA GWAII   **MAP 78**
CHARTERS   ☆☆
1650 Delkatla Street   **$100**
Masset
(250) 626-3377

Mike Picher first came to Haida Gwaii as a visiting chef, and liked the islands so much he came back with his partner Kaylene MacGregor to stay. He's a superb cook, so it was good to hear that he has settled at Charters. The restaurant is close to the Masset docks, which supply him with fresh seafood. Try the prawn ravioli or the seafood fettuccine with salmon, prawns and scallops. But the local Richardsons beef is almost as fine, particularly the melt-ingly tender short-ribs. We also like his wild-mushroom soup and his Caesar salad, which comes with applewood bacon and fried parmesan crisps. (He actually candies his own bacon.) Or you can try the butter-poached lobster salad, which comes with an asparagus and goat cheese panna cotta. Everything is beautifully presented, often with some of the micro-greens they grow themselves, and the short wine-list has bottles from all over the world. There aren't many tables, so you should call ahead to get one.

Open Wednesday to Sunday 5 pm to 9 pm from 1 April until 21 December. Closed on Monday and Tuesday. Licensed. Master Card, Visa. Book ahead. &

HAIDA GWAII   **MAP 78**
HAIDA HOUSE   ☆
2087 Beitush Road   **$80 ($250)**
Tlell
(250) 557-4600

Tlell is about 30 minutes from Queen Charlotte City, but if you want to go for dinner be sure to book ahead, because most of the tables at the Haida House are held for people who are staying there. It's a new 34-room lodge on seven acres of land—a beautiful building in a beautiful setting. It's the best place to stay anywhere on the islands, which are about the closest thing this country has to the Galapagos. Recently, the Gwaii Haanas National Park was named the best nature park in North America. Certainly the bird life is spectacular. The chefs prepare aboriginal dishes as well as regular Canadian fare. As for breakfast, it's a feast, offering such things as smoked-salmon omelettes, homemade jam and excellent coffee. Everything is made from scratch and the ingredients are all the real thing.

Open daily 5 pm to 7.30 pm from the beginning of May until the end of September. Licensed. Master Card, Visa. &

HALIFAX, N.S.   **MAP 79**
CHIANTI   ☆☆
1241 Barrington Street   **$150**
(902) 423-7471

Jan Wicha has owned Cafe Chianti for as long as most of us can remember. His Czech-inspired garlic soup is part of our lives. Nowadays, however, he's featuring northern

Italian cuisine, and his executive chef, Tony Vassalo, has worked wonders with the menu. Their calamari are marinated and then fried before being tossed in a spicy pomodoro sauce with olives and chilis. Their minestrone (with Tuscan beans, spinach and garlic) is almost too filling. The pasta is as good as any you'll get in Italy. If you're looking for seafood, order the linguine di pescatore, which is full of shrimps, scallops, mussels and lobster. If you're not, try the lamb on polenta, the breast of duck with mascarpone, dried currants and pine-nuts or the beef tenderloin with celery, sweet potatoes and a brûlée of gorgonzola. Save room, if you can, for a piece of flourless chocolate cake.

Open daily 11.30 am to 2.30 pm, 4.30 pm to 10 pm. Licensed. All cards. &

HALIFAX   **MAP 79**
CHIVES   ★★
1537 Barrington Street   **$160**
(902) 420-9626

Chives was completely remodelled in 2017, and its new space is at once more comfortable and more modern. Craig Flinn has also revamped the menus—which now change every two to three weeks—but the important things, like the restaurant's signature buttermilk biscuits served in a brown paper bag with butter and molasses on the side, the lobster risotto, the Prince Edward Island beef, the maple crème brûlée and, for that matter, Flinn himself, still remain. Among the new dishes we like the duck rillettes with orchard peaches, the dayboat halibut with smoked-pepper ratatouille and the hand-stretched burrata with sautéed shishito peppers. The wines are few and familiar, and the service can be leisurely, but the staff will be happy to sell you one of the chef's cookbooks while you wait.

Open daily 5 pm to 9.30 pm. Licensed. All cards.

If you use an out-of-date edition and find it inaccurate, don't blame us. Buy a new edition.

HALIFAX

ELEMENTS ON HOLLIS

Westin Hotel
1181 Hollis Street
(902) 496-7960

MAP 79

☆

$115

Elements on Hollis is only three minutes away from the Farmers' Market, which is where Raj Gupta gets the fresh, high-quality ingredients that are the hallmark of his cooking. The level of service is extraordinary—one traveller reports that his overcooked lamb was no sooner served than it was taken away and replaced, without him saying a word. The 30.00 Sunday brunch makes a great occasion, with countless choices of seafood, salads and cold cuts, roast beef and turkey carved to order, and a whole separate room full of sweets. There's even a children's table, low to the floor and stacked with hot-dogs, macaroni, hamburgers and do-it-yourself ice-cream sundaes. During the week the à la carte menu offers pork belly, scallops, breast of free-range chicken, hot-and-sour lobster dumplings and a pad thai that is the equal of any in the city. *Open Tuesday to Saturday noon to 2 pm, 5.30 pm to 10 pm, Sunday noon to 2 pm (brunch). Closed on Monday. Licensed. All cards.* &

HALIFAX

EPICURIOUS MORSELS

5529 Young Street
(902) 455-0955

MAP 79

☆☆

$110

Jim Hanusiak, the owner and chef of Epicurious Morsels, is quiet and soft-spoken. Perhaps for that reason, his restaurant—which is one of the best in town—doesn't get talked about as much as it should. He smokes his own salmon and cures his own gravlax, and both are as good as any we've tasted. If you want, you can get them to take home. Everyone likes his gingered salmon in phyllo, the wild-mushroom risotto and the breast of duck with honey and coriander. Finish up with a wedge of shaker lemon pie with slices of fresh lemon across the top. The wines aren't flashy or expensive, but they go well with the food, and have been chosen for exactly that reason.

Open Tuesday to Friday 11.30 am to 2.30 pm, 5.30 pm to 9.30 pm, Saturday 10.30 am to 3 pm (brunch), 5.30 pm to 9.30 pm, Sunday 10.30 am to 3 pm (brunch). Closed on Monday. Licensed. All cards. &

HALIFAX   MAP 79
FREDIE'S FANTASTIC FISH HOUSE
8 Oland Crescent   **$50**
(902) 450-3474

You can eat outside here—though remember, the summer in Halifax is only about three weeks long—but the patio is narrow and cramped. The space inside never used to be much better, but it's recently been expanded and renovated to make more room for the best fish and chips in town. Fredie (or Tammy Frederick) started in a truck parked outside Peggy's Cove, where she developed a huge following. If you come a second time it's likely, no matter how busy they are, that you'll be remembered. The fish is never more than a day old and sometimes it was landed that morning. It's first lightly prepped and then pan-fried to order, a procedure that keeps the flesh moist. They use no salt and no seasoning. Just the fish and the hand-cut fries. They also have pan-fried clams and scallops, but the fish and chips is better. Fredie's offers an authentic Maritime experience. Come and see. It's down a side street in the Bayers Lake Shopping Centre, within sight of the movie theatres.

Open Monday to Wednesday 11 am to 7 pm, Thursday to Saturday 11 am to 7.30 pm. Closed on Sunday. No liquor. Master Card, Visa. &

HALIFAX   MAP 79
THE HIGHWAYMAN
1673 Barrington Street   **$120**
(902) 407-5260

The Highwayman opened only recently, but it already

has a following in Halifax. It's a warm and comfortable place, upscale but still intimate, with an ambitious and creative bar. The kitchen specializes in Spanish-style tapas, and most of the dishes are quite small. It's a place for parties of friends, for sampling and sharing. It seats only forty people, but reservations are usually not necessary.

Open Tuesday to Thursday 4 pm to midnight, Friday and Saturday 2 pm to midnight, Sunday 4 pm to midnight. Closed on Monday. Licensed. Master Card, Visa. &

HALIFAX
MAP 79

THE KITCHEN TABLE
2157 Gottingen Street
(902) 446-8222

★★★

$160

The Kitchen Table is tucked away in the back of Ratinaud's French delicatessen in the North End. Ratinaud's is by far the best deli in the city, and the same can probably be said of the restaurant, though very few people are so far aware of it. Which is perhaps just as well, since the room seats only twenty people—fourteen at a shared table and six at the kitchen counter. Dinners are eight courses long, and last more than three hours. No-one knows what will be served, but no-one has ever minded. The food is that good. We can't tell you what to expect since four of the eight dishes change every week, but everything Frederic Tandy touches—duck, lamb, oysters, scallops, crab—is marvelous.

Open daily at 7 pm. Licensed. All cards. Book ahead.

HALIFAX
MAP 79

DA MAURIZIO
Brewery Market
1496 Lower Water Street
(902) 423-0859

★★

$190

Some restaurants are good because they never change, and Da Maurizio is one of them. And this in spite of the fact that Maurizio Bertossi sold the place several years ago to his executive chef, Andrew King. The change was seamless, perhaps because King had been at the restaurant by then for almost twenty years. The place has been redecorated, but they're still making butternut-squash soup, pumpkin risotto, eggplant, gnocchi, scallops, pork belly, squid, linguine, lamb, chicken and veal—the list is endless. Armando Mantolino has been the pastry chef for the last sixteen years, and his lemon mascarpone pudding and chocolate hazelnut mousse are both lovely. The wine-list is extensive, and some of the Italians are first-class bargains.

Open Monday to Friday 11.30 am to 2 pm, 5 pm to 10 pm, Saturday 5 pm to 10 pm. Closed on Sunday. Licensed. All cards. Book ahead. &

HALIFAX	**MAP 79**
STORIES	☆☆
The Halliburton Inn	**$150**
5184 Morris Street	
(902) 444-4400	

As they like to say themselves, Stories is the best-kept secret in town. At least the lack of crowds keeps the noise level down—this is one of the very few Halifax restaurants where it is possible to have a quiet conversation. The menu, always small, has become smaller: there are now only five appetizers, five main courses and five sweets. Everything is impeccably prepared and faultlessly presented. Our favourite main course is still the roasted breast of duck with bourbon mashed sweet potato. Almost as fine is the breast of guinea hen with smoked cheddar mash. The cooking is always accomplished, and there's no shortage of excellent wines in the cellar.

Open daily in summer 5 pm to 9 pm. Closed on Monday in winter. Licensed. Amex, Master Card, Visa. Book ahead if you can. &

This symbol means that the restaurant is rated a good buy. This & means that there is wheelchair access to both the tables and the washrooms.

109

TAKO SUSHI   ☆
480 Parkland Drive   **$80**
(902) 405-8855

Tako is by far the best sushi bar in Halifax. Kevin Chen has
been a sushi chef for almost twenty years. He makes all the
usual noodle dishes, but it's with sushi that he's made his
name. The best of his rolls is the Venus Roll, with its tuna,
butterfish, hamachi and tobiko all wrapped in a thin sheet
of cucumber. But we also like the St. Benedict's Roll,
named for St. Benedict's church nearby, whose priest first
told us about this restaurant. The Fuji San and Ginja rolls
are almost as good. You can start your meal, if you like,
with a sushi pizza, stuffed with avocado, white tuna and
flying-fish roe. Tako is near Bedford, fifteen minutes by
car from downtown Halifax. It looks like nothing
outside, but it has sushi like you never had it before.
*Open Monday to Saturday 11 am to 10 pm, Sunday noon to 10
pm. Licensed. All cards.* &

TAREK'S   ☞❒
3045 Robie Street   **$50**
(902) 454-8723

Tarek's has hardly changed at all in the fifteen years it's
been here. Tarek himself is still at the door to greet you
with a small bowl of hot soup—a welcome touch in cold
weather. He likes to quote his personal slogan, "Fresh
thinking, healthy eating," which is as true today as it ever
was. There's nothing fancy about Tarek's, but everything
is good, very good. An Egyptian visitor told us there was
nothing to match it west of Cairo. (Though Tarek is actually Syrian.) The menu has expanded in the past year to
include a well-received curried ginger chicken and a half-
and-half beef and chicken shawarma. If you want a good
deal, ask for a couple of chicken skewers—the first one
costs 15.00 but the second is only 2.00 more, which is
pretty hard to beat.

Open Monday to Saturday 11.30 am to 7.30 pm. Closed on Sunday. No liquor, no cards. No reservations. ♿

HALIFAX **MAP 79**
2 DOORS DOWN
1533 Barrington Street **$100**
(902) 422-4224

Since this place is two doors down from Chives, it's called 2 Doors Down. Craig Flinn says: "it's about the food I love to eat—simple, well-prepared, unpretentious." The menu is eclectic and eccentric: calamari with red-dragon sauce, smoked pork chops with fried mac'n'cheese and pumpkin pickle, braised shortribs with mashed potatoes. Many people come for the hand-ground burgers—the cheeseburger has been on the menu since the restaurant opened in 2013. Sweets include salted-caramel cheesecake, sticky toffee pudding and a gluten-free ice-cream sandwich with a warm chocolate cappuccino ganache. The wine-list is small, but there are plenty of beers. While you wait for a table you can make yourself comfortable with a drink and a snack in the adjoining Bar & Bites (formerly Temple Bar).
Open daily 11 am to 10 pm. Licensed. All cards. No reservations.

HALIFAX
See also CHESTER.

HAMILTON, Ontario **MAP 80**
ABERDEEN TAVERN
432 Aberdeen Avenue **$120**
(905) 523-7707

The Aberdeen has been successful since the day it opened. They like to begin with a spinach-and-strawberry salad, which is a lot better than it sounds, or yellowfin tuna tartar with feta cheese and fresh basil; we ourselves prefer the chilled pea soup. There's also a devastatingly rich short-rib poutine, served in a cast-iron skillet. Main courses include braised beef, roasted duck breast, steelhead trout and a superb sweet-pea risotto with sea scallops, lemon ricotta, pancetta and aged balsamic vinegar. There's a separate vegetarian menu: tacos with brussels sprouts, butternut squash ravioli and coconut curry with broccoli and fried chickpeas. Best of the sweets is the sour-cherry crumble with vanilla ice-cream.

Open Monday to Thursday 11.30 am to 4 pm, 5 pm to 10 pm, Friday 11.30 am to 4 pm, 5 pm to 10.30 pm, Saturday 10 am to 3 pm (brunch), 5 pm to 10.30 pm, Sunday 10 am to 3 pm (brunch). Licensed. Master Card, Visa. Book ahead.

HAMILTON
BRUX HOUSE
137 Locke Street S
(905) 527-2789

MAP 80
☆☆
$185

The Brux House is owned by Fraser Macfarlane and Georgina Mitropoulos, like Quatrefoil in Dundas (see above). It's been open for only a couple of years, and last year the menu was overhauled and made lighter and more appealing. They offer a large selection of craft beers as well as wine—in fact they have a beer flight, which is a novel idea. Their most interesting appetizer is a jerk-marinated dish of squid with green mango, pickled chili and a purée of scallions. The kale salad is an unusual dish; it comes with goat cheese, pumpkin seeds, sweet potato and dried currants in a pomegranate vinaigrette. More remarkable than either is their roasted cauliflower in an emulsion of brown butter with almonds, dried fruit and green herbs. The main courses are almost as striking. If you feel like going vegetarian, try the rice, bean and walnut burger with avocado, tomato and pickled jalapenos. There are, however, only two sweets, one of which, the bee-sting cake with burnt-honey ice cream, is delightful. The other is not.

Open Tuesday to Saturday noon to 10 pm. Closed on Sunday and Monday. Licensed. Amex, Master Card, Visa.

Every restaurant in this guide has been personally tested.

LA CANTINA
60 Walnut Street S **$75/$125**
(905) 521-8989

La Spiga Pizzeria, the informal kitchen at La Cantina, has a wood-burning pizza oven and a bar. They make fifteen varieties of thin-crust pizzas, and we can recommend them all. The most likeable are the Margherita (made with mozzarella and bocconcini, fresh basil and sliced roma tomatoes), the Vegetariana and the San Marco (made with chicken, capers, hot and sweet peppers, red onions and mozzarella). They also do some pasta, including a fine whole-wheat spaghetti ortolano and a spaghetti con polpette, which is made with veal meatballs—essentially comfort food, but beautifully done. Vicolo 54, the formal dining-room, is grander and more ambitious than La Spiga. They have no fewer than ten pasta dishes. We like the jumbo shells, filled with crab, shrimps, scallops, lobster and cheese. The best dish on the menu is, however, the porcini risotto with crimini mushrooms, drizzled tartufo oil and shaved parmesan cheese—a rich but wonderful creation. The sweets are of little interest, but the wine-cellar is splendid.
Open Tuesday to Thursday 11.30 am to 2.30 pm, 4 pm to 10 pm, Friday 11.30 am to 2.30 pm, 4 pm to 11 pm, Saturday 4 pm to 11 pm. Closed on Sunday and Monday. Licensed. Amex, Master Card, Visa.

EARTH-TO-TABLE BREAD BAR ☆
258 Locke Street S **$90**
(905) 522-2999

Earth to Table is an artisanal bakery by day and a restaurant for lunch and dinner. There are always lineups at the door—a second location recently opened in Guelph (105 Gordon Street, telephone (519) 767-2999). Best of the daily soups is probably the parsnip and apple, but if that isn't offered there's nothing wrong with the others: tomato and basil, celeriac and garlic, carrot and ginger. Or you can share a plate of calamari with chorizo, basil, chili peppers and lemon aioli. To follow there are burgers (one meat, one quinoa), mac and cheese and a fried chicken sandwich, but what those lineups at the door are really waiting for is pizza. We like the Mexican Street Corn with mozzarella, white sauce, jalapeno, cilantro, chili powder and lime aioli. Almost as good is the roasted mushroom with garlic, kale, mozzarella and thyme. If you have room for anything more after that, there's a fine caramel apple pie.

Open daily 11 am to 4.30 pm, 5 pm to 10 pm. Licensed. Master Card, Visa. &

HAMILTON   MAP 80
THE FRENCH
37 King William Street   **$120**
(905) 528-3737

The French opened in Hamilton only recently, but it's already one of the hottest places in town. Start with the housemade sourdough bread, which is almost worth the 6.00 they charge for it. Then there are two excellent appetizers: the grilled calamari with capers and tomatoes in brown butter and the lamb meatballs with mint, tomato and yogurt. Some of the main courses, like the trout amandine and the quiche de jour, are a little too familiar, though we like the ricotta gnocchi and the lamb burger with harissa aioli. To follow try the lemon tart with blueberries, and after that—if you're not the one driving—a café l'Orange, filled with cognac, Grand Marnier and whipped cream.

Open Monday to Friday 11.30 am to 3 pm, 5 pm to 10.30 pm, Saturday 10 am to 3 pm (brunch), 5 pm to 10.30 pm, Sunday 10 am to 3 pm (brunch), 5 pm to 9 pm. Licensed. Master Card, Visa. Book ahead.

HAMILTON
See also ANCASTER, BURLINGTON, DUNDAS.

HEDLEY, B.C. (MAP 161)

THE HITCHING POST
916 Scott Avenue **$65**
(250) 292-8413

The Hitching Post has always offered good food at very
reasonable prices. It looks as rustic outside as you'd expect
in this old mining town, but the room inside is bright and
warm with well-finished wooden floors. This was one of
the first permanent structures built in Hedley. Originally
a department store, it was turned into a restaurant in the
late nineteen-seventies. There's a surprising number of
vegetarian choices, particularly at lunch: a vegetarian
focaccia sandwich with swiss cheese, a veggie burger
made with black beans and a primo pasta with onions,
garlic and sun-dried tomatoes. At night it's all about comfort food: pork chop with homemade baked beans, a
slow-roasted stack of beef brisket, corn-crusted coho
salmon, barbecued chicken and even a New York steak
Madagascar with brandy and green peppercorns. Almost
all of these cost less than 20.00, which is amazing value.
To follow there's crème brûlée and a strawberry cheesecake. The wines all come from Similkameen or Okanagan
wineries.
Open Wednesday to Sunday 11 am to 8 pm. Closed on Monday
and Tuesday. Licensed. All cards.

HOPE, B.C. MAP 82

OWL STREET CAFE
19855 Owl Street **$60**
(604) 869-3181

Things don't change much at the Owl Street Cafe,
because the owners are pretty happy with everything the
way it is. Sometimes the Cafe gets too crowded, but
usually you don't have to wait long, considering that
everything is cooked to order from scratch. They're no
distance at all from Exit 168 on the Trans Canada; look
for a raw-pine A-frame—it was made from trees killed by
beetles in Manning Park. The inside walls are decorated

with hundreds of owls donated by visitors and friends. You order your meal at the counter and they deliver it to your table, which you get to share with other guests. They have coin-operated washing-machines where you can take care of your laundry while you eat your soup and sandwich. There's a good chicken club, but the smoked-meat is even better.

Open Tuesday to Saturday 8.30 am to 11 am (breakfast), 11 am to 4 pm (lunch). Closed on Sunday and Monday. Licensed. Master Card, Visa. &

ILE D'ORLEANS, Quebec (MAP 158)
CASSIS MONNA & FILLES
1225 chemin Royal   **$95**
Saint-Pierre
(418) 828-2525

Cassis Monna has 40 acres of land on the north shore of the island, across from the Montmorency Falls and not far from the bridge to the mainland. It's a family business and there have been five generations since Louis Monna's time. The family long ago discovered that the island is rich in black currants (which don't mind hard winters), and they now sell 40,000 bottles of black-currant wine every year. The present generation (Catherine and Anne) have a small terraced restaurant where they serve nothing but dishes made with cassis—chicken popcorn with cassis honey, foie gras mousse and pulled pork with housemade fries. They also have a dairy bar with nineteen varieties of ice cream, all remarkable. One night a passing driver found that all they had left in the larder for his dinner was bread and cheese, foie gras and sausage—all made with cassis. He loved it. The restaurant is attached to the winery, where you can book a tour of the estate.

Open Monday to Thursday 11 am to 7 pm, Friday to Sunday 11 am to 9 pm from 1 July until 31 August, Saturday and Sunday only from 1 September to mid-October. Licensed. Master Card, Visa. Book ahead.

Nobody but nobody can buy his way into this guide.

ILES DE LA MADELEINE, Quebec
See MAGDALEN ISLANDS.

INGONISH BEACH, N.S. MAP 84
THE PURPLE THISTLE ☆☆
Keltic Lodge **$165**
383 Middlehead Peninsula
(902) 285-2880

It must be 40 years since we came around a curve on the
Cabot Trail and got our first glimpse of the Keltic Lodge,
high on its sea-girt peninsula. But the memory has lasted.
Even when we failed to admire the cooking at the Lodge,
we never missed an opportunity to walk to the end of the
peninsula to enjoy the view. Others were quicker to
praise the Highland Links golf course, which is one of
Stanley Thompson's finest achievements. A couple of
years ago for the first time they hired a chef who came
from Cape Breton. Daryl MacDonnell has given new life
to a kitchen that had begun to need it. Most people come
here for the South Bay lobster, their signature dish. Ask
for an appetizer portion, which is half the size of the main
dish. People also admire the greens with local honey
vinaigrette, the oysters from Mabou, the line-caught halibut and the grass-fed tenderloin. The kitchen gets better
every year, and it now has an excellent wine-list and
perfect service as well. Don't miss the fiddlers in the bar.
They're good.
Open daily 6 pm to 9 pm from 12 May until 23 October.
Licensed. All cards. ♿

IQALUIT, Nunavut MAP 85
THE GRANITE ROOM ☆
Discovery Lodge **$205**
1056 Mivvik Street
(867) 979-4433

The Granite Room in the Discovery Lodge was our first
choice in Iqaluit for several years. Then we switched to
what is now called the Frob in the Frobisher Inn. Both

117

are expensive in an expensive town. But it's worth remembering that Iqaluit is on the Great Circle Route from the West Coast of Canada to Europe. Planes stop there, so you can always count on a supply of fresh beef and lamb and fresh greens, regardless of the weather. You can also count on halibut and Arctic char from Pangnirtung. The Frob offers an amazing Sunday brunch for about 40.00. They also have a crêpe station where they make particularly good waffles. But many of their other meals are marred by poor service. The Granite Room, on the other hand, seems to have no problems with service and has a beautiful setting to boot. Dinner entrées start at 50.00, but people say that its cooking is the equal of most farther south. If you can make lunch the main meal of the day, you can hope for a bill in the twenties or thirties.

Open daily 11.45 am to 2 pm, 6 pm to 9 pm. Licensed. All cards. Book ahead. &

IVY LEA, Ontario   (MAP 90)
THE IVY
61 Shipman's Lane   **$145**
Lansdowne
(613) 659-2486

The Ivy, just off the Thousand Islands Parkway near Brockville, has been beautifully restored, as have the grounds and the marina. Robert Gobbo, the chef, has a shorter menu this year, but he uses the small-plate format to make every order look its best. Dishes are seldom simple. The Ivy salad, for instance, comes with greens, candied walnuts, whisky-flavoured sous-vide pears and blue-cheese snow; Pacific halibut comes with a stew of lobster curry with coconut and lime crème fraîche. Even the shrimp cocktail is dressed with homemade tomato jam. They always try to use locally-sourced produce, right down to the beef and the duck. The kitchen makes a fine sticky toffee pudding and has a large wine-list and a number of craft beers.

Open daily 5 pm to 9 pm from Easter until Mother's Day, daily

11.30 am to 9 pm from Mother's Day until Labour Day, daily 5 pm to 9 pm from Labour Day until Thanksgiving. Licensed. Amex, Master Card, Visa. Book ahead if you can. &

JASPER, Alberta   MAP 87

The Raven at 504 Patricia Street (telephone (780) 852-5151) is a cozy spot with a small but varied menu that is kind to vegetarians and vegans. People come for the Moroccan chickpea-and-kale strudel as much as the seafood pot, the schnitzels and the lamb. It's open daily from 5.30 pm to 10 pm, is licensed and takes Master Card and Visa. Syrahs down the road at 606 Patricia Street (telephone (780) 852-4559) is a more upmarket venue with significantly higher prices, but their three-course table d'hote for 29.95 is a splendid bargain. The service is quick and friendly, the presentation polished. Don't miss the duck confit. Syrahs is open daily from 5.30 pm to 9 pm, is licensed and takes all cards. And finally, 620 Connaught Drive opposite the Via station is home to two very different restaurants. Fiddle River upstairs (telephone (780) 852-3032) is where Jasper goes for seafood. It's quiet and candlelit at night, and by day has a fine view of the mountains. The helpings are enormous. The chowder and the house fettuccine are both chock-full of seafood, and none of it is overcooked. If you'd rather have meat, there are schnitzels and duck. It's open daily from 5 pm to 9.30 pm, is licensed and takes all cards. Downstairs on the lower level is Downstream (telephone (780) 852-9449) a stylish room that has become very popular with the late-night set. There's a good selection of Canadian beers to go with their baby back ribs, and the poutine has real cheese curds. Downstream is open daily from 5 pm to 1 am, is licensed and takes Master Card and Visa.

KAMLOOPS, B.C.   MAP 88
ACCOLADES   ☆
Thompson Rivers University   **$175**
900 McGill Road
(250) 828-5354

Accolades is a training kitchen. Under the supervision of chef-instructor Ron Rosentreter, the students prepare a limited but well-designed menu of three courses. And he must be teaching them something, because the dining-room invariably sells out. A meal might start with pan-seared Atlantic scallops with dry miso and red chili foam or roasted pork belly glazed with maple mustard. Following a housemade entre-course of sorbet, there are things like Cornish hen, rib-eye steak, lamb two ways and roasted halibut with lobster sauce and side-stripe prawns. Sadly the sweet trolley has gone, replaced by four choices, usually sticky toffee pudding, lemon tart, chocolate sponge cake and crème brûlée. The wine-list is modest, but so are its markups. The prix-fixe is now 50.00 plus wine, tax and tip.

Open daily 11.30 am to 3 pm, 5.30 pm to 9 pm. Licensed. All cards. You must book ahead. ⅙

KAMLOOPS   **MAP 88**
BROWNSTONE   ☆
118 Victoria Street   **$130**
(250) 851-9939

Brownstone languished for a few years while the owners, chef Dale Decaire and his wife Connie, considered selling it, but now they seem to have thrown themselves back into the fray. The brownstone the restaurant occupies, an old Bank of Commerce building in downtown Kamloops, was built in 1904 and provides a beautiful setting for Dale Decaire's seasonal regional cuisine. His mussels come from Salt Spring Island and are served in a tequila-chipotle cream sauce; his Kamloops rainbow trout is dressed with a herb aioli; his Pacific cod comes in a Thai green curry. There's also chicken Marbella, braised with olives, capers and fruit, Brome Lake duck, pork cheeks with sourdough gremolata and even a bacon-wrapped elk meatloaf with wild mushrooms in brandy and peppercorn-potato mash. The wine-list is mostly Okanagan, but if you'd like something else you can bring it in for a 25.00 corkage fee.

Open daily 5 pm to 9 pm. Licensed. Master Card, Visa. Book ahead if you can. ⅙

HELLO TOAST
428 Victoria Street   **$45**
(250) 372-9322

This is a great place to bring the kids for breakfast or brunch. The walls are decorated with family photos and the waitresses all wear pyjamas. There are soups (barley, split pea and Thai curry), salads, rice bowls, club sandwiches, burritos and paninis, but what you really come to Hello Toast for is eggs. Lots of eggs. The eggs benedict are famous, particularly the version made with pulled pork, though the Montreal smoked meat option comes a close second. Then there are the omelettes, lots of omelettes. And the scrambled eggs, with chorizo, mushrooms, cheddar, spinach and bacon. Everything is served with perfectly crisp home-fried potatoes.
Open Monday to Saturday 7.30 am to 3 pm, Sunday 8 am to 3 pm. Licensed. All cards. No reservations. &

KAMLOOPS   **MAP 88**
THE NOBLE PIG
650 Victoria Street   **$100**
(778) 471-5999

The Noble Pig is a vast room filled with TV screens that feels more like a sports bar than a gastropub. But it has a long and ambitious menu, and the kitchen keeps things surprisingly consistent. The brewmaster's plate features pork and duck rillettes, salami and artisan cheeses. There are several variations on the comforting theme of mac'n'cheese—with pulled pork, with caramelized onion and green peas, even with portobello mushrooms and truffle oil. There's a pair of pizzas, a Carnivore and a Herbivore, but we find the flatbread topped with golden beets, roasted squash, peppers, onions, arugula pesto, goat cheese and parmesan more interesting, as well as quite a bit cheaper. There are even several poutines—try the beef with peppercorns. More conventional choices include roasted lamb chops for a very reasonable 15.00, beef stroganoff, chicken korma and tuna dashi. And the beer is great.

Open Monday to Wednesday 11.30 am to 11 pm, Thursday to Saturday 11.30 am to midnight, Sunday 3 pm to 10 pm. Licensed. All cards. &

KAMLOOPS   MAP 88
TERRA
326 Victoria Street   **$120**
(250) 374-2913

Terra isn't cheap, but it's worth every penny. David and Andrea Tombs change their menu every month according to what's available in season, and the kitchen works closely with local farmers and artisans who supply it with exceptional produce. Each monthly menu offers to start your meal with "a soup made daily with ugly vegetables and love." Or you can try the charcuterie plate, the crisp pork belly or the scallops with roasted cauliflower and fresh grapes. There is always some BC fish—sablefish or lingcod perhaps—but Kamloops is ranching country, and that means beef, lamb and bison. Hand-cut pappardelle is topped with slow-braised bison ragu; angus flat-iron steak is rubbed with coffee and spice and served in a cherry jus. For sweet try the so-called "fire and ice": molten chocolate cake with semifreddo and banana brûlée.

Open Monday to Saturday 5 pm to 9 pm. Closed on Sunday. Licensed. All cards. Book ahead if you can. &

KELOWNA, B.C.   MAP 89
BLARNEY STONE
Inn at Big White   **$90**
5340 Big White Road
(250) 491-2009

Big White, an hour from Kelowna in the Monashee Mountains, is Canada's second-largest ski resort. The Blarney Stone is open only in winter, but they have outstanding pub food. You can start your morning with the "nearly all-

day Irish breakfast"—eggs, bacon, sausages, baked beans, mushrooms, tomatoes and potatoes—or settle for the all-you-can-eat continental buffet. For lunch and dinner there are Yorkshire puddings filled with beef, pork or mush-rooms, mussels in Guinness, garlic and onion and slow-braised lamb stew made with Irish ale. Not to mention fish and chips, barbecued spareribs, shepherd's pie, steak-and-ale pie and a skirt steak sandwich. Best of the sweets is the banoffee pie. There's an outstanding collection of Irish beers, both on tap and by the bottle, as well as a number of Okanagan wines. The service is friendly and the view of the mountains from the patio is spectacular.
Open daily 8 am to midnight from 21 November until 15 April. Licensed. All cards. Book ahead. &

KELOWNA   **MAP 89**
BOUCHONS
1180 Sunset Drive: Unit 105   **$145**
(250) 763-6595

Bouchons is more traditional than either Raudz or the Waterfront and its menu is larger. In fact, it's too large. They offer crab and scallop ravioli, baked pear with roquefort, lingcod with a sweet-pepper coulis, bouilla-baisse and a cassoulet Toulouse-style. There are almost as many mains, among them scallops en croûte, rabbit, lamb provençale and tenderloin of beef. The best of the sweets, we think, is the iced Okanagan lavender soufflé. They have a three-course table d'hôte, featuring escargots de bourgogne, breast of duck with raspberry vinegar and tarte tatin made with pears. The wine-list is big and quite ambitious.
Open daily 5.30 pm to 10.30 pm. Licensed. Amex, Master Card, Visa. &

This is a guide to Canadian restaurants from coast to coast—the first ever published and the only one of its kind on the market today. Every restaurant in the guide has been personally tested. Our reporters are not allowed to identify themselves or to accept free meals.

KELOWNA

MAP 89

FIXX CAFE AND PASTA BAR
3275 Lakeshore Road
(256) 861-3499

$125

Fixx is a fine new place to eat in Kelowna, owned and operated by Lisa Cham. It's pretty hard to find in its suburban mall, but they have a lovely garden patio that's an island of calm in the concrete jungle. There are only fifteen seats and often it's hard to get a table for lunch. But when you do, ask for some of their famous pasta—the classic putanesca or the linguine bolognese with its tangy chorizo and tomato sauce. We recommend all the penne dishes, including the breast of chicken with asparagus, mushrooms and gorgonzola, as well as the Usual Suspects, a rich and hearty combination of beef tenderloin, wild mushrooms, spinach, chili, garlic, olive oil and white wine. Their beef tenderloin, lamb and Pacific salmon are all locally sourced and perfectly cooked. The ice cream is as good as any we remember, and the service easily matches the food and wine. For a modest corkage fee, you can, if you like, bring your own wine.

Open Tuesday to Friday 11 am to 3 pm, 5 pm to 9 pm, Saturday 5 pm to 9 pm. Closed on Sunday and Monday. Licensed. Master Card, Visa. Book ahead.

KELOWNA

MAP 89

OLD VINES
Quail's Gate Winery
3303 Boucherie Road
(800) 420-9463

☆☆
$150

Old Vines was recently named one of Canada's top hundred restaurants, and it's easy to see why. The location is exquisite and the food is superb. Roger Sleiman's ingredients come from local farms, his own kitchen garden and regional waters. Sadly, the afternoon tapas list has gone, but many of its choices, like the albacore tuna tartine, the truffle and parmesan fries and the arancini with garlic aioli, can still be found elsewhere on the menu. At lunch there's trout, chicken, beef brisket, a lamb burger and duck fettucine. In the evening there's Arctic char with sidestripe prawns and leek fondue, lamb shank with harissa and couscous, roast pork with cabbage and blue cheese and (for 48.00) a premium 30-day dry-aged Cache Creek ribeye steak, with black-garlic potato pavé, cipollini onions and bone marrow. The sweets are equally rich and complex: we prefer the vanilla bean panna cotta and the broken lemon tart filled with lemon curd. Needless to say, a glass of Old Vines icewine would go well with either one.

Open Monday to Saturday 11.30 am to 2.30 pm, 5 pm to 9 pm, Sunday 10.30 am to 2.30 pm (brunch), 5 pm to 9 pm. Licensed. Amex, Master Card, Visa. &

KELOWNA   **MAP 89**
RAUDZ   ☆
1560 Water Street   **$160**
(250) 868-8805

Rod Butters may have taken over Terrafina in Oliver, but he's still to be found here in Kelowna, at RauDZ. His menu hasn't changed much, except for the prices, but the bright modern room with the open kitchen at the back still attracts long lineups (there are no reservations). People keep coming back for things like the famous crab cappuccino, the venison carpaccio, the wild boar meatballs, and the plums wrapped in bacon. Main courses include a fine Arctic char crusted with oats, bison shortrib with sumac and a range of excellent steaks. Butters also has a nice line in reimagined comfort foods, like fish and chips, poutine and cheeseburgers. Try one and see what he makes of it, starting with the ketchup made out of blackberries. There's a dessert tasting menu of four or five choices, or you can settle for everybody's favourite, the double-chocolate mashed-potato brioche with raspberry sorbet and warm chocolate sauce. The wine-list is impressive and expensive, but all the vintages—not surprisingly, Butters is obsessively locavore—are from the Okanagan.

Open daily 5 pm to 10 pm (later on weekends). Licensed. Amex, Master Card, Visa. No reservations. &

KELOWNA   **MAP 89**
THE TERRACE   ☆☆
Mission Hill Winery   **$160**
1730 Mission Hill Road
(250) 768-6467

There are three good reasons to stop at the Terrace at Mission Hill: the wines, the food and the views. Every one of the 60 arbour-covered seats has a view of the valley below, and Matthew Batey makes sure that the food doesn't come second. Chilled vichyssoise is served with chamomile-cured salmon, smoked egg yolk and rye crostini, octopus is served with a pea-shoot fritter, yogurt and mint, torchon of foie gras with rhubarb jam and merlot lees. Main courses include Haida Gwaii halibut with linguine and green peas, pan-seared char with pineapple weed and wild cress soup, organic chicken breast with crackling focaccia, pancetta and spinach. Note that the kitchen closes early, before it gets dark. If you want to eat late, come for lunch.

Open daily noon to 7 pm from mid-May until mid-September. Licensed. All cards. &

KELOWNA   **MAP 89**
THE WATERFRONT   ☆
1180 Sunset Drive: Unit 104   **$145**
(250) 979-1222

Waterfront was enlarged a couple of years ago, and a lot of its charm got lost. But Mark Filatow has kept his small menu essentially unchanged. He's still concentrating on such things as braised veal cheeks, ravioli carbonara and sweetbreads with handmade pappardelle. He also makes excellent squid chorizo, octopus with rosemary and ricotta cavatelli with grana padano and brown butter. And he still has his ambitious wine-list and his fine

espresso. For seven years in a row, Waterfront has been called the best restaurant in the Okanagan by *Vancouver Magazine*.
Open daily 5 pm to 10 pm (later on weekends). Licensed. Amex, Master Card, Visa. Book ahead. &

KELOWNA
See also OKANAGAN CENTRE.

KINGSTON, Ontario   *MAP 90*

Woodenheads at 192 Ontario Street (telephone (613) 549-1812) has the best thin-crust pizzas in town, though it can be noisy and crowded. If you don't like any of the 40 combinations on offer you can build your own, or choose instead from the menu of tapas, salads and paninis. There are even a few larger plates. They also have wine and several draft beers. Olivea at 39 Brock Street (telephone (613) 547-5483) offers Italian food Canadian-style, mainly pastas and risottos, plus some traditional antipasti and salads and usually three or four main courses and sweets. The Red House at 369 King Street E (telephone (613) 767-2558) is really a pub, with some of the best fries in Kingston, as well as a menu of soups, sandwiches and some well-cooked and innovative main courses like local cotechino sausages with red wine and lentils. Windmills (telephone (613) 544-3948) has been at 184 Princess Street for at least 25 years. It's open all day and offers an eclectic mix of Italian, Thai, Cajun and African food. Their best dishes are the slow-roasted leg of lamb and the Thai black cod. Their sweets are good and they have some first-class draft beers. There are a great number of sushi restaurants in Kingston, most of them run by Koreans. The best is probably Ta-Ke at 120 Princess Street (telephone (613) 544-1376). They have a wide range of soba and udon dishes, as well as sushi, tempura, teriyaki and a number of Korean specialties. Sapporo beer is on tap. Delightfully Different at 197 Wellington Street (telephone (613) 766-5966) has reopened and offers many leaf teas (in your choice of pot) with excellent housemade pastries, soups and sandwiches.

We accept no advertisements. We accept no payment for listings. We depend entirely on you.

KINGSTON MAP 90
AQUATERRA ☆
Delta Waterfront Hotel **$135**
1 Johnson Street
(613) 549-6243

AquaTerra may not be quite what it was in its heyday, but
its kitchen is still one of the best in Kingston. And you can
eat here for surprisingly little: the three-course table
d'hôte costs only 45.00. For that you get a choice of four
appetizers, four main courses and a sweet. Different and
carefully chosen vegetables come with each course.
Dinner may start with something like pan-seared scallops
or a plate of excellent charcuterie, and go on to lobster
with asparagus or rack of lamb from Australia with
turnips and a carrot purée. Lunch is simpler, featuring
soup, salad, pasta and steak frites. The wine-list is mainly
from Niagara, and most of the wines are VsA. Bottles
start at less than 30.00, which is hard to beat. There's also
a short list of dessert wines and a number of single-malt
whiskies.
Open Monday to Saturday 11 am to 11 pm, Sunday 11 am to 10
pm. Licensed. All cards. ⌖

KINGSTON MAP 90
BAYVIEW FARM ☆☆
4085 Bath Road **$195**
(613) 389-4419

We've been following Clark Day around town for a long
time now—from the River Mill to Clark's by the Bay to
Clark's on King to AquaTerra. When he left AquaTerra a
few years ago, we thought he had hung up his hat and laid
the legend to rest. But retirement didn't appeal, and
before long he'd decided to open Bayview Farm in his
family homestead on Collins Bay. The original nine-
teenth-century stone house was bought by Clark Day's
grandparents, and it is where he still lives today. Day likes
to say you can't make a silk purse out of a sow's ear, and
while this adage may have put Wagyu beef (at 110.00) on

his menu, it has also led him to continually search for the best possible ingredients from a large network of local farmers and producers. The menu typically offers six appetizers, six main courses and three sweets. We like the elm-smoked Arctic char mousseline, the maple duck brest with garam masala in a coconut broth and the lamb rack crusted with mint and mustard. The wine list is extensive, the service—often by members of the family—is exemplary and Clark himself will be there cooking for you or talking to you, or both.

Open Tuesday to Saturday 5 pm to 9 pm. Closed on Sunday and Monday. Licensed. Master Card, Visa. Book ahead. ᕕ

KINGSTON   MAP 90
CASA
35 Brock Street   **$175**
(613) 542-0870

There are other Italian restaurants in Kingston, but Casa (formerly Casa Domenico) is by far the most sophisticated and probably the most expensive. Of course they have pasta, but they're more interested in the traditional dishes of northern Italy. That means starting with something like chickpea and roasted garlic soup or perhaps gamberoni (shrimps, capers and garlic with a spicy olive-oil sauce) or one of the ten or twelve salads (our favourite is the pear with gorgonzola and spiced cashews). Then there are fourteen or so pastas, all served in main-course sizes. But don't miss the roast chicken with prosciutto and lemon sage or the veal marsala with rosemary potatoes—an exceptional dish. There's also an admirable plate of Atlantic salmon with black pepper, fennel and pancetta. The extensive wine-list covers most of the better Italians.

Open Monday to Thursday 11.30 am to 10.30 pm, Friday 11.30 am to 11.30 pm, Saturday noon to 11.30 pm, Sunday noon to 10 pm. Licensed. All cards.

This is a guide to Canadian restaurants from coast to coast—the first ever published and the only one of its kind on the market today.

KINGSTON   **MAP 90**
CHEZ PIGGY   ☆
68 (rear) Princess Street   **$160**
(613) 549-7673

Chez Piggy is Kingston's favourite restaurant. It's now 38 years old, and has long been a fixture, with a large and loyal clientele, friendly staff and a cozy ambience. The menu changes all the time, but there's always a club sandwich on the list. It's the best in town. Apart from soup, there are a number of old familiars to start with, like mussels piri-piri and shrimps with garlic. Lunch always has some pasta, two or three salads, a couple of burgers and an array of sandwiches made with good housemade bread. Dinner might start with lemon-and-pepper duck wings, duck confit or lamb three ways (ribs, confit and sausage). The sweets are all made in-house, and the wine-list has a little of everything, modestly priced. On Sundays there's a brunch, and in the evenings, a traditional roast.
Open Monday to Saturday 11.30 am to midnight, Sunday 10 am to midnight. Licensed. All cards. ♿

KINGSTON   **MAP 90**
CHIEN NOIR   ☆
69 Brock Street   **$160**
(613) 549-5635

Chien Noir considers itself a French bistro, and indeed it compares favourably with many of its kind in Paris. They expect you to start lunch or dinner with a salad (the niçoise, say, with seared tuna) or perhaps with a sharing plate (something like mussels with potatoes and chorizo or sautéed mushrooms with pecorino and a poached egg). For your main course there's a choice of bouillabaisse, chicken chasseur with mushrooms and the inevitable steak frites. The club sandwich is especially likeable. The wine-list is comprehensive, and there are nine craft beers on draft, including one or two that are brewed specially for the restaurant.
Open Monday to Saturday 11.30 am to 2.30 pm, 5 pm to 11 pm,

Sunday 10 am to 3.30 pm (brunch) 5 pm to 9.30 pm. Licensed. All cards. Book ahead.

KINGSTON   **MAP 90**
THE CURRY ORIGINAL
253A Ontario Street   **$70**
(613) 531-9376

The Curry Original is still about the best Indian (or Bangladeshi) restaurant in Kingston, or so we think. The place was opened by Ali and Weais Afzal more than twenty years ago and they're still in charge of the front of the house. They have all the traditional dishes—curries, kormas, vindaloos, dhansaks, bhoonas, biryanis and tandooris. Everything is fresh and carefully prepared, but, sad to say, the menu almost never changes. It's best to start with an onion bhaji, a samosa or daal, then go on to tandoori chicken (cooked in the traditional clay oven) or chicken tikka or one of the special dishes like kashmiri chicken, with peanuts, sultanas, coconut and homemade yogurt. Then try the barfi, which is homemade cottage cheese with coconut and pistachio nuts. On weekdays they offer a string of lunch dishes, all priced at less than 10.00. The wine-list majors in wines from Prince Edward County and draft beers from India.
Open Tuesday to Saturday 11.30 am to 2 pm, 5 pm to 9.30 pm, Sunday 5 pm to 9.30 pm. Closed on Monday. Licensed. All cards. &

KINGSTON   **MAP 90**
DAYS ON FRONT
730 Front Road   **$150**
(613) 766-9000

Days on Front is in an unprepossessing strip mall a long way from the centre of town, but it may be worth the trip to sample a locally-sourced menu supervised by Matthew Day. The chef is Jay Legere, who has worked in several of the restaurants recommended in this guide. It's a good idea to start with a beet salad or seared scallops in a spinach

131

purée, followed by breast of duck in a cranberry risotto. There are only a few sweets, the best of which is probably the banana bread pudding. On the wine-list they have (they claim) 40 wines that cost less than 40.00 a bottle. Book ahead unless you come late.

Open Monday to Thursday 11.30 am to 10 pm, Friday and Saturday 11.30 am to midnight. Closed on Sunday. Licensed. All cards. &

KINGSTON   **MAP 90**
THE RIVER MILL
2 Cataraqui Street   **$175**
(613) 549-5759

The River Mill tends to be overlooked by visitors because it's outside the city centre, but it has a beautiful setting. The dining-room opens onto the Cataraqui River, and they have plenty of free parking. There are a number of attractive appetisers, like scallops with smoked pork belly and braised oxtail with snails and mushrooms. The main courses are more traditional: pan-seared salmon with chorizo, rack of lamb with pistachio and breast of duck with lentils and ginger. The sweets change every day, two or three beers are always on tap and there's a large wine-list. At lunch there are salads and sandwiches together with smaller plates of some of the dinner choices.

Open Monday to Friday 11 am to 2.30 pm, 5 pm to 11 pm, Saturday 5 pm to 11 pm. Closed on Sunday. Licensed. All cards. Free parking.

KINGSTON   **MAP 90**
THE RUSTIC SPUD
175 Bagot Street   **$100**
(613) 544-6969

The Rustic Spud appears to be doing very well in a location that failed in the past as a greasy spoon, corner grocery, pizza joint and deli. Father and son Scott and Joel Latimore are in charge of the front of the house and the kitchen respectively, and between them they seem to

132

have got things just right. The bar offers a good selection of craft beers, and the restaurant at the back of the house has a small and attractive menu, along with some of the best pizzas in town. Start with the fried oysters with blood-orange aioli or a plate of ponados (spiral potatoes salted and spiced), and go on to something like the blackened chicken supreme, with spinach, goat cheese, potato cake and caramelized onion sauce. Or try one of the pizzas—you can build your own from a choice of four sauces, six cheeses, eight meats and fourteen different toppings.

Open Monday to Wednesday 11 am to 9 pm, Thursday to Saturday 11 am to 10 pm, Sunday 11 am to 9 pm. Licensed. All cards.

KINGSTON
See also IVY LEA.

KINGSVILLE, Ontario   **(MAP 218)**
METTAWAS STATION
169 Lansdowne Avenue   **$140**
(519) 733-2459

Kingsville is the southernmost town in Canada, the home of the Jack Miner bird sanctuary and a gateway to Point Pelee National Park. More than a hundred years ago, Hiram Walker commissioned a noted architect to design the Kingsville railway station. In 2008 Janet and Anthony Del Broca took it over to open Mettawas. Del Broca's likeable cooking is at its best with pasta, but visitors also speak highly of the Sicilian arancini and the rack of lamb. In summer they add local perch and pickerel. There's a good tiramisu and most of the wines are from Niagara.

Open Tuesday to Friday 11.30 am to 9 pm, Saturday and Sunday noon to 9 pm. Closed on Monday. Licensed. Master Card, Visa. ♿

Where an entry is printed in italics this indicates that the restaurant has been listed only because it serves the best food in its area or because it hasn't yet been adequately tested.

KITCHENER, Ontario MAP 93
THE BERLIN ☆
45 King Street W **$180**
(519) 208-8555

Jonathan Gushue has sold his stake in the Berlin to take
over the kitchen at the Fogo Island Inn (see above). It
remains to be seen how his replacement, Benjamin Lillico,
will measure up, but first indications are promising. Like
Gushue, Lillico is a graduate of Langdon Hall over in
Cambridge, and their standards are notoriously high. His
menu is short and changes every month. Much of it is
cooked over the open flames of a coal-fired grill—you can
sit by the open kitchen and watch. Appetisers range from
Ontario lamb tartar to seared foie gras and a chilled bay-
scallop crudo with orange, fennel and bacon crumble.
Main courses include an exceptional duo of pork—
braised neck and a crispy confit of pork belly—and a
moist and flaky Arctic char with artichoke and lentils.
Among the sweets we like the chocolate mousse cake with
salted caramel ice-cream. The wine-list is extensive, but
for a restaurant that advertises "true Canadian cuisine"
seems very short on Canadian vintages.
Open Tuesday to Saturday 5 pm to 10 pm, Sunday 11 am to 2
pm. Closed on Monday. Licensed. Master Card, Visa.

KITCHENER MAP 93
THE FORK AND CORK
1458 Weber Street E **$120**
(519) 208-0606

Kitchener seems to have finally discovered the Fork and
Cork. Every Friday and Saturday evening the place is
jammed, even though it's almost as big as an aircraft
hangar. What people are coming for is upscale comfort
food, everything from burgers and pizzas to sea bass with
roasted shrimp. The soups can be bland, and we usually
have one of the starters instead, like double-stuffed ravioli
or smoked duck salad with watermelon radish and swiss
cheese. To follow there's Ontario duck, chicken breast

wrapped in prosciutto and beef shoulder hunter style, which means grilled with bacon, mushrooms and shallots, and served with kale and a celeriac purée. Some evenings they offer a four-course prix-fixe which is a buy at 50.00 a head. There are a number of craft beers on tap and a long wine-list.

Open Monday to Thursday 11.30 am to 10 pm, Friday and Saturday 11.30 am to 11 pm, Sunday 10 am to 10 pm. Licensed. Master Card, Visa. Book ahead. &

KITCHENER (MAP 93)
TWH SOCIAL
Walper Hotel **$110**
1 King Street W
(519) 745-8478

TWH Social is tucked away under the Walper Hotel (hence the initials), and can be hard to see from the street. The restaurant is long and dark, dominated by a bar that seems to go on forever. Its menu is upscale gastropub, ranging from burgers (try the Moroccan lamb burger) to more elaborate dishes like rogan josh, Thai chicken and grilled salmon. The soups are all good, particularly the chicken, and the grilled octopus with charred tomato is about as good as octopus gets. Everyone likes the ricotta gnocchi, which is lightly pan-fried in chicken broth. Other favourites are the cured salmon with lemon curd, the steak frites and the osso buco with polenta. Nearly all the wines are available by the glass, and there's a fine list of craft beers—we particularly like the Blanche de Chambly from Unibroue.

Open Monday to Thursday 11 am to 11 pm, Friday 11 am to midnight, Saturday 4 pm to midnight. Closed on Sunday. Licensed. Amex, Master Card, Visa. &

KITCHENER
See also WATERLOO.

Our website is at www.oberonpress.ca. Readers wishing to use e-mail should address us at oberon@sympatico.ca.

LAHAVE, N.S. (MAP 100)
LAHAVE BAKERY
3421 Highway 331 **$35**
(902) 688-2908

The LaHave Bakery has stirred fond memories for 30 years and more. With its tin ceilings, old tables and chairs and period photographs, it'll remind you of another day. There are Molly bars, date squares, hearty soups, loaded pizzas, haddock burgers, bagels stuffed with smoked salmon and paninis and wraps of all kinds. They have everything, and everything is good. Of course they bake bread, a number of varieties—orange and raisin, barley and many others. And in 2016 they cleaned out the adjoining boat-repair shed and opened a magnificent bookshop. There's a piano with an invitation to "play a few tunes." Tea is served every day at three o'clock. Don't miss LaHave on any account.
Open daily 8.30 am to 6.30 pm in summer, 9 am to 5 pm in winter. No liquor. Master Card, Visa.

LAKE LOUISE, Alberta MAP 95
THE POST HOTEL ★★★
200 Pipestone Road **$325 ($750)**
(800) 661-1586

When we first came to Lake Louise, the Château was the obvious place to stay, and the lake looked just like the postcards. But for many years now we've been recommending that you backtrack from the lake to stay instead at the Post Hotel, one of the few remaining mountain lodges. The Post is still built from its original hewn logs and every room is complete with a wood-burning fireplace. George and André Schwarz bought the place in 1978, when it was little more than a ruin, and 40 years later it is magnificent. Hans Sauter, their chef, has a fabulous menu that runs to six courses in the grand manner, featuring things like bison and caribou, and the award-winning wine-cellar holds more than 25,000 bottles. It has the best burgundies in Canada, and holdings of old

136

barolos and super-Tuscans that beggar belief.
Open daily 11.30 am to 2 pm, 5 pm to 9 pm. Licensed. All cards.
Book ahead. &

LAKE LOUISE
See also FIELD.

LANTZVILLE, B.C. (MAP 121)
RISO FOODS
Lantzville Plaza **$120**
7217 Lantzville Road
(250) 390-0777

Sarah Wallbank is the driving force behind Riso in
Lantzville, which is a small hamlet just north of
Nanaimo. She went to Naples and worked in a Michelin-
rated restaurant with three generations of chefs, and she
learned. Her menu is short and the big draw is the pizza,
which is almost as good as our benchmark at 900 Degrees
down in Langford. Try the calabrese sausage, topped with
chili, fennel, mozzarella and sundried tomatoes. The best
of the mains are the braised lamb shanks and the pan-
roasted halibut. Riso also serves an exceptional brunch:
eggs with a bufala meatball in a tomato and cheese sauce,
eggs Florentine with grapefruit hollandaise, creamed
wild mushrooms on house-baked bread, and even a
calzone stuffed with two poached eggs, calabrese sausage,
spinach, mushrooms and cheese. A glass of prosecco to go
with your eggs is 10.00, mimosa a dollar more.
*Open Wednesday to Saturday 2 pm to 10 pm, Sunday 10 am to 9
pm. Closed on Monday and Tuesday. Licensed. All cards. Book
ahead.* &

LETHBRIDGE, Alberta MAP 97
MIRO
212 5 Street S **$130**
(403) 394-1961

Miro Kyjak trained in Europe and ran a successful restaurant in Calgary before he moved to Lethbridge. He

learned everything from his father, who told him that simplicity is the mark of perfection. He makes everything from scratch, and that means the bread, the soups and the sweets. His wine-list has won an award of excellence from the Wine Spectator for ten straight years. Fresh fish is available every day and pasta is always on the menu, along with such dishes as wild-boar meatballs in tomato sauce. The pavlova is the best of the sweets—don't miss it if it's there to be had.

Open Tuesday and Wednesday 5 pm to 9 pm, Thursday 11.30 am to 1.30 pm, 5 pm to 9 pm, Friday 11.30 am to 1.30 pm, 5 pm to 10 pm, Saturday 5 pm to 10 pm. Closed on Sunday and Monday. Licensed. All cards. &

LONDON, Ontario   MAP 98
DAVID'S
432 Richmond Street   **$135**
(519) 667-0535

David Chapman ran a seafood bistro for many years before he opened this place, and he's always been at his best with fish. Bay scallops have never been our favourite ingredient, but he does wonders with them here; his sauce is remarkable. He's also good with pan-roasted lake trout, pan-roasted sea-bass and pan-roasted skate, something that's seldom seen in Canadian restaurants. The obligatory filet mignon is on the dinner menu, where there's also duck confit, veal cheeks and osso buco with bone marrow and corn risotto. The vegetables are plain, but at the end of the meal there's sticky toffee pudding— and a very good one at that. He has a fixed-price menu that changes every day and a special *du jour* at noon. David's is not expensive, and his *prix-fixe* costs only 26.00 for two courses and 30.00 for three. There's a short but sensibly-priced wine-list.

Open Monday and Tuesday 5 pm to 10 pm, Wednesday to Friday 11.30 am to 2.30 pm, 5 pm to 10 pm, Saturday and Sunday 5 pm to 10 pm. Licensed. Master Card, Visa.

Every restaurant in this guide has been personally tested.

LORNEVILLE, N.S.   MAP 99
AMHERST SHORE COUNTRY INN   ☆
5091 Highway 366   **$160 ($325)**
(800) 661-2724

Rob Laceby inherited his mother's boundless enthusiasm for cooking along with her kitchen. He and his wife Mary are a great comfort to travellers along this lovely stretch of the Northumberland Strait. Their huge garden may be bigger than ever, now that they have found a keen young gardener to help with the weeding of the herbs and vegetables, and it supplies most of the restaurant's needs. The handsome dining-room looks out across the gardens to the sea. Rob doesn't stick to familiar recipes: his cream of onion soup comes with roasted red peppers, his baked haddock with dill, his maple-brined pork tenderloin with blueberries. The angel pie with meringue and lemon curd is the most popular sweeet. And they always have Benjamin Bridge Nova 7 in the cellar.

Open daily at 7.30 pm by appointment only from early May until late October, Friday and Saturday at 7.30 pm by appointment only from late October until early May. Closed Sunday to Thursday in winter. Licensed. Master Card, Visa. ♿

LUNENBURG, N.S.   MAP 100
FLEUR DE SEL   ☆☆☆
53 Montague Street   **$200**
(902) 640-2121

Fleur de Sel has exquisite food, perfect service and a calm, seductive ambience. The menu changes frequently, but butter-poached lobster is always on offer, and rightly so. Adams and Knickle scallops are usually featured as well— lightly cooked and beautifully tender. Martin Ruiz-Salvador emphasizes local organic produce: the beef comes from P.E.I. and the pork from the Annapolis Valley. One of our most memorable meals was eaten here, when we were offered a bluefin tuna just caught offshore with rod and reel. It was amazing.

Open Wednesday to Sunday 5 pm to 9 pm from mid–April until late October. Closed on Monday and Tuesday. Licensed. All cards. Book ahead. ♿

LUNENBURG   MAP 100
LINCOLN STREET FOOD
200 Lincoln Street   **$100**
(902) 640-3002

This small restaurant has quickly established itself as an important element in Lunenburg's restaurant scene. The menu changes often, focusing on fresh local produce and vegetarian dishes. There's a three-course *prix-fixe* for 45.00, but the specials are always interesting—halibut, for instance, with knockweed pesto, or lamb shanks or housemade gnocchi with roasted tomato and lobster sauce. This is not where you should go for a quiet, romantic meal—the room is always crowded and noisy— but it is a place for fun and good food.
Open Wednesday to Saturday 5 pm to 9 pm from 1 May until 31 December. Closed Sunday to Tuesday. Licensed. All cards.

LUNENBURG   MAP 100
SALT-SHAKER DELI
124 Montague Street   **$95**
(902) 640-3434

The Salt-Shaker just keeps getting better and busier. As almost the only restaurant in Lunenburg that's open in winter it's close to the hearts of local residents, and in summer it's packed with tourists looking for its famous seafood chowder (which has won all sorts of awards). The service is fast and friendly, and there's always something new to try: bahn mi burgers, gnocchi with local bacon, roasted brussels sprouts with sherry and tarragon. Old favourites like the lobster rolls, the mussels Portuguese-style, the shredded-pork tacos and the thin-crust pizzas (fourteen varieties of them) are always available. There's a brunch on the weekend with, as always, vegan and gluten-free choices.
Open daily 11 am to 9 pm from early May until mid-October,

Monday to Thursday 11 am to 8 pm, Friday and Saturday 11 am to 9 pm, Sunday 11 am to 8 pm from mid-October until early May. Licensed. All cards. No reservations. ♿

LUNENBURG   MAP 100
SOUTH SHORE FISH SHACK   ☞📱
108 Montague Street   **$85**
(902) 634-3232

The Fish Shack has the freshest and best fish and chips on the South Shore. When they run out, someone hurries off to get more—five minutes away. You place your order at the bar, and are given a plastic lobster that will light up and buzz when it's ready. Pick up your tray and take it to a table on the deck overlooking the harbour. Fish and chips are the best seller, but they also have a superb lobster roll, scallops, clams and whole steamed lobsters. In 2016 Martin and Sylvie Ruiz-Salvador expanded into the Half Shell Oyster Bar next door. It's the only place in town that's open after 9 o'clock. They offer six varieties of oyster as well as small plates of pan-fried sardines, Adams and Knickle scallops, excellent crab rolls and even a few vegetarian dishes like green-olive soup. Everything is perfect.

Open daily noon to 8 pm from late May until early October. The Oyster Bar is open noon to 10 pm in June and September, noon to midnight in July and August. Licensed. No cards.

LUNENBURG
See also LaHave, Mahone Bay, Martin's Brook, West Dublin.

MAGDALEN ISLANDS, Quebec   MAP 101

There are sixteen islands in the 60-mile arc of the Magdalens. All but Entry Island are linked by sand dunes, and route 199 runs the whole length of the archipelago. More than half of the total population live on Ile Cap-aux-Meules. The next largest is Ile Havre-Aubert, which is at the southern end of the chain. Everywhere there's fine hiking, swimming and sailboarding. The

Madelon Bakery at 355 chemin Petitpas on Cap-aux-Meules (telephone (418) 986-3409) has been here since 1964. It has a scattering of tables, inside and out, and offers a wealth of baked goods. We've also had good reports of the salmon pies, the Greek salads and the cold cuts. Big sandwiches are made to order, and if you're looking for a packed lunch, this is a good place to get it— they're open daily from 6 am to 9 pm. The Magdalens are known for their soft raw-milk cheese, which is like reblochon and is produced by the indigenous breed of cattle known as Canadienne. Gérémie Arsenault first came here in 1998 and fell in love with the raw-milk cream he saw everywhere. He returned with 60 head of cattle and is now turning out 25,000 wheels of cheese a year. He likes to say that the sea winds add a touch of salt to his recipe. You can buy some at the Fromagerie du Pied de Vent on Ile Havre-aux-Maisons (telephone (418) 969-9292). The ferry from Souris in Prince Edward Island takes five hours, but you can also get here by plane. Too few people come to the Magdalens, which is a shame.

MAGDALEN ISLANDS   **MAP 101**
BISTRO DU HAVRE
Auberge Havre-sur-Mer   **$90 ($250)**
1197 chemin de Bassin
Ile Havre-Aubert
(418) 937-5675

The Bistro du Havre has only just opened, but you should know about it because it's rather good and certainly cheap. Dinners start with smoked salmon or a seafood casserole, followed by cod and chips or lamb or tenderloin of beef, and finish with crème brûlée. And the inn is a lovely place to stay, with brightly-coloured rooms facing the beach and the open sea.
Open Monday and Tuesday 8 am to 11.30 am, Wednesday to Sunday 8 am to 11.30 am, 5 pm to 9 pm from 1 June to 30 September. Master Card, Visa.

If you wish to improve the guide send us information about restaurants we have missed. Our mailing address is Oberon Press, 145 Spruce Street: Suite 205, Ottawa, Ontario K1R 6P1.

MAGDALEN ISLANDS

MAP 101

CAFE DE LA GRAVE

969 route 199   **$90**

La Grave

Ile Havre-Aubert

(418) 937-5765

The Café de la Grave is still flourishing, despite its recent change of owners. It's always had a lively atmosphere and a lot of music—Sonia Painchaud, the original owner, was a talented musician, and the group of islanders who bought the place from her are determined to keep up the tradition. It's right next to the theatre, where a number of old fishing boats have been turned into restaurants and boutiques. The chef keeps his menu small and simple—fishcake, fish pot-pie, tourtière, sandwiches and cakes. Seal, a staple of the Magdalens, appears regularly in a poutine. The dining room is small, but it's well appointed and comfortable and the meals are always attractively presented. They have a few wines and a good selection of local beers.

Open Monday to Saturday 9 am to 11 pm, Sunday 10 am to 10 pm (brunch) from 1 May until 15 October. Licensed. Master Card, Visa.

MAGDALEN ISLANDS

MAP 101

QUAI 360   ☆☆

360 chemin de Quai   **$140**

Cap-aux-Meules

Ile Cap-aux-Meules

(418) 986-7680

We certainly didn't expect Taka in Etang du Nord to close just after we gave it three stars. But luckily we have a strong replacement right in Cap-aux-Meules, close to the harbour. Quai 360 may be upmarket, but it has a pleasantly laid-back atmosphere and friendly service. And the cooking is very good indeed. The scallops are perfectly underdone, whether alone with mushrooms or paired with crab in a creamy risotto. If you want meat, try the lamb ribs. For sweet, you can always count on raisin poutine, a traditional Magdalen Islands take on bread pudding. There's a splendid choice of open wines—you can talk about them with the owner, who is also the sommelier.

Open Wednesday to Friday 11.30 am to 2 pm, 5 pm to 9 pm, Saturday 5 pm to 9 pm. Closed Sunday to Tuesday. Licensed. Master Card, Visa.

MAGDALEN ISLANDS   MAP 101
LA MOULIERE
Hôtel Vieux Couvent   **$150 ($300)**
292 route 199
Ile Havre-aux-Maisons
(418) 969-2233

This old convent has always been one of the most attractive places to stay in the Magdalens. The bedrooms have been charmingly restored and the many-windowed sea-views are spectacular. For years Evangeline Gaudet was one of the best-known chefs in the Islands. When she and her husband retired and hired Denis Landry from New Brunswick as a partner, he renovated the dining-room and put in a bigger bar. But some things will never change. This has always been a gay and lively place, and it still is. Mussels are cultivated in a lagoon nearby, and cod, clams, scallops, halibut, herring, mackerel, shrimps and lobster are all available. Some people don't like the halibut, but lamb shanks and ribs have found new admirers. They still sell their raspberry vinaigrette by the bottle, and the house wheat beer is always on tap.

Open daily 5 pm to 9 pm from 1 April until 15 June, daily 11 am to 2 pm, 5 pm to 9 pm from 16 June until 18 September, daily 5 pm to 9 pm from 19 September until 1 January. Licensed. Master Card, Visa.

The price rating shown opposite the headline of each entry indicates the average cost of dinner for two with a modest wine, tax and tip. The cost of dinner, bed and breakfast (if available) is shown in parentheses.

MAGDALEN ISLANDS

LA TABLE DES ROY
1188 route 199
Etang du Nord
Ile Cap-aux-Meules
(418) 986-3004

MAP 101
★★★
$250

MAP 101
★★★
$250

Johanne Vigneau has been the leading chef in the Magdalen Islands for 40 years, and she's still as much in love
with the Islands and their produce as ever. Her restaurant,
La Table des Roy, has always made much use of local
resources. It was never cheap; a five-course seafood
dinner now costs 96.00 a head. For that you get sea snails,
sushi-style scallops, halibut, crab salad or lobster. The
lobster comes in a hot broth with cayenne and saffron.
Presentation is always remarkable. Our sweet of choice is
the sponge-cake with cheese and strawberry ice. There
are now 200 wines in the cellar, many of them organic.
Open Tuesday to Saturday 6 pm to 9 pm by appointment only
from the middle of June until late September. Closed on Sunday
and Monday. Licensed. Amex, Master Card, Visa. Book ahead.

MAHONE BAY, N.S.

THE BARN
458 Main Street
(902) 531-2499

(MAP 100)
$65

This restored barn next to Suttles and Seawinds has been
busy since the day it opened in 2017. It has a lot of rustic
charm, with comfortable sofas and chairs, and old road
signs hanging on the barnboard walls. They serve
excellent cappuccinos, lattes, hot chocolates and teas
together with pastries from La Vendéenne over in Block-
house, and a limited light lunch of soup, sandwiches and
salad, supplied by Mateus and Rebecca's (see both below).
The Barn is at once cozy and hip, and has quickly become
the town's meeting place.
Open daily 8 am to 6 pm. No liquor. Master Card, Visa.

Nobody but nobody can buy his way into this guide.

MAHONE BAY (MAP 100)
MATEUS ☆
533 Main Street **$140**
(902) 531-3711

Mateus is a happy place, with live music, affordable prices
and creative cooking. The menu emphasizes local seafood:
the Thai curry mussels are everyone's favourite, but we also
like the shrimp-and-scallop succotash with fresh beans,
corn and bacon, the halibut, the haddock and the lobster.
Meats usually include rack of lamb, duck and a meltingly
tender beef tenderloin. There are always gluten-free, vegan
and vegetarian options. The sweets are decadent, and on
Monday nights wine by the glass is only 5.00.
*Open daily 11.30 am to 9 pm (closed on Tuesday and Wednesday
in winter). Licensed. Master Card, Visa. Book ahead.* ♿

MAHONE BAY (MAP 100)
REBECCA'S
249 Edgewater Street **$95**
(902) 531-3313

Rebecca's has moved from Main Street to Edgewater
Street, just where you enter the town from Highway
103. Its big, wide windows take full advantage of the
postcard view of the three churches. Home-cooked
meals are served for brunch, lunch and dinner, and they
have regular music nights once a week. Brunch features
fishcakes with hollandaise sauce, baked beans, a fried
egg and fruit. For more important meals they have a
double-smoked beef burger with caramelized onions,
whipped potatoes and fresh vegetables and pulled lamb
on a goat-cheese risotto with tzatziki and market vegetables. For vegetarians there's a spicy pasta of peanuts
and spaghetti squash. Everything is carefully prepared
and beautifully presented. The service is fast and
friendly.
*Open Tuesday to Saturday noon to 8 pm, Sunday 11 am to 3 pm.
Closed on Monday. Licensed. Master Card, Visa. Book ahead if
you can.*

LA MALBAIE, Quebec   **MAP 103**
CHEZ TRUCHON   ✩ ✩
1065 rue Richelieu   **$180 ($295)**
Pointe-au-Pic
(888) 662-4622

We all thought Dominique Truchon was a permanent fixture in the kitchen at the Auberge des Peupliers in Cap à l'Aigle, where he first made his name. Three or four years ago, however, he and his wife, Annie, opened their own restaurant in a handsome old house in Pointe-au-Pic. Here they created a discreetly formal dining-room, eight luxurious bedrooms and a beautiful heated terrace. The service is impeccable (in both languages) and you can taste the freshness of the food with every bite. It didn't take Chez Truchon long to gain pride of place in an area crammed with outstanding restaurants. The chef aims to showcase the local terroir (Charlevoix lamb, for instance) with a sprinkling of international specialties. Most of his best dishes are basically simple—tartine of venison, veal shanks, magret of duck, Arctic char. Ask for the pudding au chomeur with maple cream (better still, check it's on the menu when you book). There aren't many open wines, but all the bottles are imported directly from the vineyard. You must book ahead (the last time we checked, they were taking reservations three months in advance). *Open daily 5.30 pm to 9 pm. Licensed. Amex, Master Card, Visa. Book ahead.*

LA MALBAIE
See also CAP A L'AIGLE.

MANITOULIN ISLAND, Ontario   **MAP 104**
GARDEN SHED   ☞
231 Sideroad 10   **$20**
Tehkummah
(705) 859-2393

If you visit Manitoulin Island in 2018, don't miss the Garden Shed, because it's not likely to open next year. You'll find it in the middle of J.D.'s Garden Centre, a plant nursery that's fascinating in itself. The Garden Shed is small, quiet and extremely cheap. There's no written menu; the waiter will tell you what they have that day. Breakfast costs 2.95 for eggs and bacon, toast and perogies. Many people, however, prefer the vegetarian "breakfast in a bowl." Try it and see. Lunch brings soup or salad, a grilled sandwich or a deep-pan quiche. The place will remind you of the early, innocent days of Garden's Gate. It's friendly and wholly unexpected.

Open daily 9 am to 3 pm from 1 May until 31 July, daily 9 am to 2 pm from 1 until 31 August. Licensed for beer and wine only. Master Card, Visa.

MANITOULIN ISLAND   MAP 104
GARDEN'S GATE   ☆
Highway 542   **$105**
Tehkummah
(705) 859-2088

Everybody loves the garden here. The house may be quaint and the food may be comforting, but the moment you open the gate is always pure joy. The garden is thick with bird feeders, and hummingbirds are everywhere. And the exotic flowers and plants share the land with an assortment of vegetables, so what appears on your plate is always perfectly fresh. Rose Diebolt makes everything from scratch to her own recipes. She breads and pan-fries her whitefish instead of cooking it on a grill, and most of her customers like it that way. There's a new abattoir down the street, which means that local lamb is on the menu again. Longtime suppliers bring her blueberries, strawberries and raspberries. Salads don't really interest her, but sweets do. She makes about ten a day—lemon tart, pecan pie, carrot cake and key-lime pie—and people say they're about the best they've tasted. Rose and her husband John search every year for new Niagara wines and local craft beers, and both are surprisingly good.

Open Tuesday to Sunday noon to 8 pm from 1 May until 30 June, daily noon to 8 pm from 1 July until 31 August, Tuesday to

148

Sunday noon to 8 pm from 1 September until 31 October. Closed on Monday in the spring and fall. Licensed. Master Card, Visa. Book ahead if you can. &

MARKHAM, Ontario   (MAP 204)
FOLCO'S   ☆
42 Main Street N   **$135**
(905) 472-6336

Folco's has been around for a while and it just keeps on getting better and better. Some years ago the chef-owner turned his back on the rat-race in Toronto and went to Italy to study cooking. He eventually opened Folco's, where he now makes all the pasta on site. He likes to change his menu often, but regulars have been slow to trade in their pasta fagioli for squash and blood-orange soup, however well it's made. He makes everything to order and often flies in ingredients from Italy. Diners speak highly of the fish and the chicken; we ourselves always seem to order ravioli, which is beautifully made here. The breads are baked in-house and the salads are all good. We also like the torta di nona, which is a lemon sponge-cake layered with mascarpone cheese.

Open Monday to Friday 11.30 am to 3 pm, 5 pm to 10 pm, Saturday 5 pm to 10 pm, Sunday 4.30 pm to 10 pm. Licensed. Master Card, Visa. Book ahead if you can.

MARKHAM   (MAP 204)
INSPIRE
144 Main Street N   **$130**
(905) 554-2889

Inspire is probably the most popular restaurant in Markham. It serves Asian fusion food. The menu is seasonal, and changes nearly every day. We recommend the fried chicken with waffles, the duck-confit taco or one of the burgers for lunch; for dinner try the udon carbonara covered in Italian sausage, braised beef and mushrooms with a quail egg on top. If the restaurant is crowded, the service can be slow. Bottled wines are pretty scarce—

order a beer or wine by the glass.

Open Tuesday and Wednesday 11.30 am to 3 pm, 6 pm to 10 pm, Thursday to Saturday 11.30 am to 3 pm, 6 pm to 11 pm, Sunday 11.30 am to 3 pm, 6 pm to 10 pm. Closed on Monday. Licensed. All cards. Book ahead. &

MARTIN'S BROOK, N.S. (MAP 100)
OLD BLACK FOREST CAFE
10117 Highway 3 **$80**
(902) 634-3600

Thomas and Barbara Heimert have been running this small, popular restaurant since 1998. The welcome is friendly, the portions are large and the food is wonderfully authentic. There are a number of schnitzels, sauerbraten, maultaschen (our favourite, topped with onions and gravy), spaetzle, goulash soup and even—if you want to switch sides—fish and chips. Their Black Forest cake is baked on the premises, as are the excellent strudels and cakes. In summer, if you can find a seat, you can eat outside on the deck.

Open Tuesday to Sunday 11.30 am to 9 pm from mid-April until mid-December. Closed on Monday. Licensed. Master Card, Visa. Book ahead if you can.

MASSEY, Ontario MAP 110
DRAGONFLY
205 Imperial Street **$60**
(705) 865-3456

This stretch of Highway 17 has almost nowhere to eat except the Dragonfly. No wonder the place is packed. It has a large (too large) menu of international dishes, but burgers (especially the ones topped with goat cheese) are the big sellers. People also eat a lot of the pasta, usually with shrimp or with chicken. The Dragonfly's fries are handcut to order, and they take the trouble to serve fresh green vegetables as well. Don't ask about their liquor license, it's been a never-ending struggle. For the moment, the best you can do is sit out on the patio with a glass of de-alcoholized beer. Nothing costs very much, and the service is patient and friendly.

Open Tuesday to Sunday 11 am to 9 pm. Closed on Monday. No liquor. Master Card, Visa. Book ahead if you can. ♿

MATTAWA, Ontario · MAP 111
MYRT'S 🖢☝
610 McConnell Street · **$40**
(705) 744-2274

Mattawa is a friendly place and even in a dine-and-dash place like Myrt's the waiters quickly make you feel like a local. Scott Edworth serves comfort food and serves it fast all day long. He never lets you down; in fact, you'd have to go a long way to find a better cheeseburger with bacon or a better butter tart. He makes all his own soups, all his own pies and all his own pizzas. He makes all his own fish and chips too, using nothing but the freshest haddock. He grinds all his own beef for the hamburgers. And he puts on a hot special every day at noon. Bikers on the Temiskaming Loop are told to stop here, and everyone else should do the same.

Open daily 6 am to 8.30 pm. Licensed. Master Card, Visa. ♿

MEDICINE HAT, Alberta · MAP 112
THAI ORCHID ROOM
36 Strachan Court SE · **$95**
(403) 580-8210

Sounantha and Ken Boss migrated to Vancouver 38 years ago, and before long moved on to Medicine Hat. In all that time they've never wavered in their allegiance to Thai cooking. Their menu now is almost too long—they have ten vegetarian entrées in all. But everything is very fresh and very authentic. Start with the hot-and-sour soup or the fisherman's soup and go on to the yellow curry with chicken and coconut rice or the peanut curry (or the green curry or the red curry). They're all great. There's always chicken satay, spring asparagus with garlic and mussels with spicy black beans. Everybody asks for the white-chocolate crème brûlée at the end of the meal. There aren't many wines, but there are some interesting loose teas.

Open Tuesday to Thursday 11 am to 9 pm, Friday 11 am to 10 pm, Saturday 4.30 pm to 10 pm, Sunday noon to 9 pm. Closed on Monday. Licensed. Amex, Master Card, Visa. &

MIDDLE WEST PUBNICO, N.S. (MAP 223)
RED CAP ☆
1034 Highway 335 **$95**
(902) 762-2112

The Red Cap has been in business for 70 years and it's changed hands only once in all that time. You'll find the village on the South Shore, about 30 miles east of Yarmouth, which makes it a two-hours' drive from the Digby ferry. The Pubnicos still have an active fishing fleet; in fact the dollar value of their catch is the highest east of Montreal. The kitchen has every kind of fish and shellfish at its disposal, and the fish on offer is always stunningly fresh. Nearly every ingredient they use is local. They grow their own herbs and buy their vegetables from local farmers. Everything is made from scratch—the sauces, the stocks, the soups and even the onion rings. Most of the wines come from Grand Pré or Peller, but if you like you can bring your own bottle. There's no corkage fee.

Open Monday to Saturday 11 am to 8 pm, Sunday 10 am to 7 pm. Licensed. Amex, Master Card, Visa. &

MONCTON, N.B. MAP 115
THE WINDJAMMER ☆
Hôtel Delta Beauséjour **$200**
750 rue Principale
(506) 854-4344

The Windjammer is formal, dark, well served and extremely expensive. The tasting menu of five courses runs to 78.00, and on the regular à la carte bison costs 65.00, Wagyu beef 99.00. They have Beau Soleil oysters, pan-seared foie gras with rhubarb and fig chutney, snails in garlic butter, a shrimp-and-scallop stir-fry, rack of lamb, fresh Atlantic salmon, Fundy lobster and a variety of steaks, but actually you may do better with the tasting menu. Many of the wines are sold in six-ounce and nine-ounce carafes, but on the whole it's a good list, featuring wines from Oyster Bay, Kim Crawford, Liberty School and Peter Lehmann. Valet parking is free.

Open Monday to Saturday 5.30 pm to 10 pm. Closed on Sunday. Licensed. All cards. Valet parking. Book ahead if you can.

MONTAGUE, P.E.I. (MAP 37)

WINDOWS ON THE WATER ☆
106 Sackville Street **$100**
(902) 838-2080

Lillian Dingwell's lovely old house on the Montague River speaks of serenity, of a time when things didn't change twice every second. Her cooking is old-fashioned, but everything she makes is perfectly fresh. Customers will tell you that she should win an award for her seafood chowder. If you think her beef expensive, ask instead for the pan-seared haddock or the grilled salmon with maple syrup. We like the blue mussels in a white-wine mirepoix and usually order them, because they're about the best thing the Island has to offer. Lillian has no difficulty in buying fresh produce or anything else she needs. The sweets she makes herself, and they're famous, especially the bread pudding with brown-sugar sauce. The wine-list continues to improve and she also has several local beers on hand. In summer you can sit outside on the wrap-around deck and enjoy the view.

Open daily 11.30 am to 4 pm (lunch), 4 pm to 9.00 pm (dinner) from 1 June until 30 September. Licensed. All cards. Book ahead if you can. ⓑ

We accept no advertisements. We accept no payment for listings. We depend entirely on you. Recommend the book to your friends.

MONTREAL, Quebec   **MAP 117**
BOUILLON BILK   ★★★
1595 boulevard St.-Laurent   **$200**
(514) 845-1595

The food here is fabulous, the service friendly and efficient. The menu changes with the seasons and all the ingredients are locally sourced. Start with carpaccio of fluke (a kind of flounder). The fish is pressed flat, cut into a disk and topped with sea-urchin, shiitake mushrooms, sugar-snap peas and sesame crisps. The pasta is all perfectly al dente—try the cappelletti cups, stuffed with seasoned ground pork and served in a wine broth with tomatoes and clams. There's also a fine dish of venison with black-trumpet mushrooms, onions and grapes, guinea fowl with hedgehog mushrooms, dates and endive and even eel sweetbreads with oyster mushrooms and leeks. The wine-list offers an exceptional number of New York vintages, which is rare in this country. Dinner is expensive, but lunch is just as good—come then unless money is no object. Bouillon Bilk is worth your time— the menu is highly unusual and the cooking is remarkable.

Open Monday to Friday 11.30 am to 3 pm, 5.30 pm to 11 pm, Saturday 5.30 pm to 11 pm. Closed on Sunday. Licensed. Amex, Master Card, Visa. Book ahead.

MONTREAL   **MAP 117**
MAISON BOULUD   ★★
Ritz-Carlton Hotel   **$225**
1228 Sherbrooke Street W
(514) 842-4224

Daniel Boulud has not been entirely fortunate in his Canadian restaurants. But Montreal and the Ritz-Carlton have proved to be perfect hosts to his concept, and to the chef, Riccardo Bertorelli, that he chose to make it happen. The ground-floor dining-room is very grand, but it's also peaceful and seductive. The best tables face a large open fireplace. In summer you can sit on the garden terrace, though you'll have to book well in advance. We've never been able to resist the breakfast buffet, which is open from 7 to 10.30 every morning. Among other things, it offers housemade granola, farm yogurt, Quebec cheese, smoked salmon, scrambled eggs, bacon and sausages, all for 42.00. Later in the day, you should look at the six-course tasting menu—the chef spent years developing it. The cooking is always light-hearted and delicate—try the scallops and sweetbreads. The sweets are excellent, particularly the apple pudding with caramel and sea-buckthorn. The wine list is of course stunning (and expensive).

Open daily 7 am to 10.30 pm. Licensed. Amex, Master Card, Visa. Book ahead. &

MONTREAL **MAP 117**
LA CHRONIQUE ☆☆
104 avenue Laurier o **$200**
(514) 271-3095

La Chronique's new premises have a bright, contemporary kitchen, and Marc de Canck is cooking there in a bright and contemporary style. He starts with veal carpaccio, red-tuna tataki and (admittedly expensive) duck foie gras. To follow there's Gaspé halibut with black chanterelles and a curl of prosciutto or roasted venison with turnips and Brussels sprouts. They do a first-class job with seafood—scallops, sea-bass and bream. The housemade sorbets are all attractive, and so is the orange baba. The sommelier favours Blue Mountain, but the riesling from Niagara is a much better buy. Lunch is just as good as dinner, and the Scottish gravlax is beyond compare.

Open Monday and Tuesday 6 pm to 9 pm, Wednesday to Friday 11.45 am to 1.45 pm, 6 pm to 9 pm, Saturday and Sunday 6 pm to 9 pm. Licensed. All cards. Book ahead if you can.

The map number assigned to each city, town or village gives the location of the centre on one or more of the maps at the start of the book.

MONTREAL   **MAP 117**

LE CLUB CHASSE ET PECHE   ☆☆☆

423 rue St.-Claude   **$200**

(514) 861-1112

This is an amazing restaurant—we've said it before and we say it again. It may be expensive, but it's one of the top five restaurants in Montreal and one of the top dozen in Canada. Normally it's open only in the evening, but in the two weeks before Christmas they also serve lunch. If you can book a table then it's a fine opportunity to enjoy great cooking at bargain prices. Their risotto, stuffed with suckling pig and shavings of foie gras, has been on the menu since the restaurant opened, and it's easy to see why. They like to call the surf and turf their signature dish. It comes with a small portion of lobster and kobe-beef hanger steak—60.00 but worth it. There's also wild boar, magret of duck with sunchokes and wildflower honey, pheasant and salmon, all rather cheaper. The magret of duck tastes even better than it looks, and that's saying a lot. Masami Waki is the pastry chef and he's one of a kind. Try his bombe of chocolate ice cream and caramel pie.

Open Tuesday to Saturday 6 pm to 10.30 pm. Closed on Sunday and Monday. Licensed. Amex, Master Card, Visa. Book ahead.
♿

MONTREAL   **MAP 117**

LES COUDES SUR LA TABLE   ☞

2275 rue Ste.-Catherine e   **$95**

(514) 521-0036

Elbows on the Table may be down in the east end, but what they save in rent they pass on to their customers. The lunch menu offers three courses for 16.00—with main dishes like bavette de boeuf with frites (this is the most popular choice and usually sells out), acini di pepe (tiny grains of pasta in a sauce of cream, mushroom, spinach and sage) and salmon tartar with avocado, mango and cilantro, followed by sweets like tarte au citron and chocolate crémeux. At night prices inch up a bit and the food gets more complex: milk-fed calf's liver with Morteau sausages and spaetzle, scallops with boudin noir, seared sweetbreads with chorizo and shallots and roast venison with braised endives and barley risotto. The kitchen makes few mistakes, the service is polished and there's a fine list of European and North American wines at reasonable prices both by the bottle and by the glass.

Open Tuesday and Wednesday 11.30 am to 2 pm, Thursday and Friday 11.30 am to 2 pm, 5.30 pm to 10 pm, Saturday 5.30 pm to 10 pm. Closed on Sunday and Monday. Licensed. All cards. Book ahead if you can. &

MONTREAL   MAP 117
DAMAS
1201 avenue Van Horne   **$120**
(514) 439-5435

Damas is Syrian, combining Middle Eastern cooking with sophisticated presentation and the best of every sort of ingredient. They opened in 2011, but moved only recently to Van Horne after a fire. The new place will remind you of One Thousand and One Nights. The fattet makdous—three eggplants stuffed with ground lamb in tomato sauce—is a popular favourite, as is the knafeh to follow, filled with cheese and topped with pistachios and syrup. There's also a six-course tasting menu at 95.00 a head, featuring dips, pita, fattoush salad, beef and lamb tartar, grilled octopus, grilled shrimp and chicken kebab. Or you can save 20.00 by having one course less. The well chosen wines come from Greece and western Europe.

Open Tuesday to Thursday 5 pm to 10 pm, Friday 5 pm to 11 pm, Saturday 4 pm to 11 pm, Sunday 4 pm to 10 pm. Closed on Monday. Licensed. All cards. You must book ahead. &

MONTREAL   MAP 117
DOMINION SQUARE TAVERN
1243 Metcalfe Street   **$185**
(514) 564-5056

This fine old building was restored by the chef Eric

Dupuis and his partner Alexandre Baldwin to look much as it did when it was built in 1927. Once the tavern was up and running they started work on the building next door at 1237 Metcalfe Street, and it opened as the Balsam Inn (telephone (514) 507-9207). English-style pub food is a new departure for Dupuis, but he offers things like bangers and mash, Welsh rarebit, Cornish game hen and braised beef in a rich dark gravy, alongside pâté de campagne, house-made charcuterie and, best of all, a gorgeous dish of bone marrow. Dominion Square is always packed, and everyone seems to have a good time. The Balsam Inn used to be quieter and cheaper, but success has reached there too and now it's only cheaper. It serves small plates for sharing, because that's what the chef likes to cook and what the mostly young crowd like to eat. Don't miss the flatbread, which is at its best with local goat-cheese. After 9 o'clock there's a *menu du jour* every night of the week. Both restaurants are known for their cocktails, but in spite of that children are welcome. *Dominion Square is open Monday to Friday 11.30 am to midnight, Saturday and Sunday 4.30 pm to midnight. The Balsam Inn is open Tuesday to Saturday 11.30 am to 11 pm, and closed on Sunday and Monday. Both are licensed and take all cards.*

MONTREAL   **MAP 117**
ESTIATORIO MILOS   ☆☆
5357 avenue du Parc   **$125**
(514) 272-3522

The creator and owner of Estiatorio Milos, Costas Spiliadas, is a master of quality control. That's why this is still the best Greek restaurant in Montreal. It's a big place, operating on three levels, with white plaster, marble and cloth hangings—and the most elegant washrooms in the city. Fresh fish is flown in from the Mediterranean every day, and laid out on ice in the open kitchen. It can get expensive in the evening, but lunch—which might offer organic lentil soup, smoked salmon and herring with Santorini capers—is much more affordable. The dinner menu is at its best with seafood: char-grilled octopus and beautifully tender calamari, Atlantic halibut, sea-bream, swordfish and a warm lobster salad with Metaxa brandy. Sister restaurants have now opened in Athens, New York, Las Vegas, Miami and London, but this is where it all began, and it's still the one to match.

Open Monday to Wednesday 2 pm to 3 pm, 5.30 pm to 11 pm, Thursday and Friday 2 pm to 3 pm, 5.30 pm to midnight, Saturday 5.30 pm to midnight. Closed on Sunday. All cards. Book ahead. ♿

MONTREAL   **MAP 117**
L'EXPRESS   ☆
3927 rue St.-Denis   **$130**
(514) 845-5333

The menu at the Express has hardly changed since the restaurant opened in 1980. People come for the pâté, the foie gras, the bouillabaisse, the steak frites and the steak tartar. But there are other things: leeks vinaigrette, a lush and lovely fish soup, warm goat-cheese salad, veal kidneys, Toulouse sausage, octopus salad and roasted bone marrow. Sweets include caramelized apple tart, maple profiteroles and a blueberry and apple crumble. The wine-list is one of the best in Montreal—there are no fewer than 11,000 bottles in the cellar. And after midnight, l'Express is the only game in town.

Open Monday to Friday 8 am to 3 am, Saturday 10 am to 3 am, Sunday 10 am to 2 am. Licensed. All cards. Book ahead. ♿

MONTREAL   **MAP 117**
LE FANTOME   ☆
1832 rue William   **$175**
(514) 846-1832

The dining area looks small and unassuming, but the cooking here is exceptional, the service all it should be, the prices moderate. The chef, Jason Morris, is a master of his craft, but he's not above making gluten-free food (or even vegetarian food) if you ask for it. Instead of an à la carte, Morris offers two *menus de dégustation* (one large, one small). The large menu starts with an amuse bouche of chicken livers with blackberries and goes on to a beautiful beet-and-nut salad with crème fraîche, beef and red-pepper stir-fry, poached salmon with lemon purée and a popcorn risotto. Two sweets come with the dinner—raspberry sorbet and poached pear with whipped mascarpone cheese. The smaller menu features pasta—the gnocchi with asparagus can be especially recommended. The menus change every week, but one item often recurs—a peanut-butter sandwich with fig jam and foie gras. It's delicious but very expensive. The helpings can be small, and the dining-room noisy.

Open Tuesday to Saturday 6 pm to 11 pm. Closed on Sunday and Monday. Licensed. Amex, Master Card, Visa. Book ahead.

MONTREAL	**MAP 117**
LES 400 COUPS	★★
400 rue Notre-Dame e	**$145**
(514) 985-0400	

Guillaume Cantin has now been replaced in the kitchen by Jonathan Rassi, but the ingredients are still fresh and local and the cooking as imaginative as ever. The restaurant is particularly friendly to vegetarians: try the stuffed parsnips, the cauliflower with oats and birch, the chanterelles with kale and blue cheese, the terrine de noix and the chicory and sunchoke salad. The seafood is equally memorable: eel with horseradish, sea-bream with plums, cucumber and juniper berries and Arctic char with sea-buckthorn and black radish. To follow there's lemon cream with Thai basil, apple sable breton and chocolate cake with concord grape sorbet.

Open Tuesday to Saturday 5.30 pm to 10 pm. Closed on Sunday and Monday. Licensed. All cards. You must book ahead. &

This is a guide to Canadian restaurants from coast to coast—the first ever published and the only one of its kind on the market today. Every restaurant in the guide has been personally tested. Our reporters are not allowed to identify themselves or to accept free meals.

MONTREAL   **MAP 117**
FOXY   ☆
1638 rue Notre-Dame o   **$130**
(514) 925-7007

Eric Girard and Dyan Solomon, who are Foxy's owners,
learned their trade at Olive et Gourmando (see below),
which they have run together for nearly twenty years.
(Foxy is the name of their dog, Olive and Gourmando
are their cats.) Olive et Gourmando has never served
dinner, but Foxy serves nothing else. It was designed by
the legendary Zebulon Perron, and features a lot of
wood and a number of pictures of Foxy. Everything is
cooked on the charcoal grill or in the wood-fired oven.
The menu starts with charred flatbreads and goes on to
grilled meat or fish paired with an abundance of local
produce. Look for the baked feta with grapes, cherry
tomatoes, currants and garlic, or the winter coleslaw,
made with burnt cauliflower and brussels sprouts. From
the oven and grill the best things are the roasted coquelet
with avocado and green onions, the grilled sea-bass with
aioli and celery, the baked gnocchi with ricotta and the
charred baby back ribs. There's a long wine-list and
some surprising cocktails.
Open daily 5.30 pm to 11 pm. Licensed. All cards. Book ahead.
&

MONTREAL   **MAP 117**
HOOGAN AND BEAUFORT
4095 rue Molson   **$130**
(514) 903-1233

Hoogan and Beaufort were the names of the two men
who owned this building before it became a factory
making tanks and trains during World War II. The tall
windows and towering ceilings have been retained
from those days, along with a lot of exposed heating
and electrical systems. Lunch is always a good buy here
since nothing costs more than 20.00, even though they
offer such appetizers as half a quail, ragoût of venison

and octopus carpaccio, and mains like Quebec lamb and magret of duck. In the evening they add venison tartar, crispy sweetbreads, short-ribs, Cornish hens and a striploin of beef with shimeji mushrooms and anchovy butter. The wine list emphasizes private imports and natural vintages—a lot of unusual names—as well as a good selection of local and imported beers.

Open Tuesday 5.30 pm to 10.30 pm, Wednesday to Friday 11.30 am to 1.30 pm, 5.30 pm to 10.30 pm, Saturday 5.30 pm to 10.30 pm, Sunday 10.30 am to 2.30 pm (brunch). Closed on Monday. Licensed. All cards. ♿

MONTREAL	MAP 117
HVOR	☆
1414 rue Notre-Dame o	**$250**
(514) 937-2001	

The food at Hvor—which means *where* in Danish—changes weekly. But there's no menu: a succession of small plates, all novel and well conceived, will be put in front of you, and you won't know until then what you're having. What you see is what you get. Everything is local, and much of it comes from the restaurant's terrace garden, which grows more than 2,000 species of vegetables, fruits, spices, herbs and flowers—even beehives. The meals are eclectic: we recently started with a sweet-potato tartelette, went on to brochette de canard, pizza au za'atar, carpaccio of lamb, fish soup, okonomiyaki with truffles, scallops and sweetbreads, and wound it all up with a plate of mignardises. The chef recently spent a year in Japan, and the influences at Hvor are global. Prices are high: think of it as going to a theatre—or an opera.

Open Wednesday to Sunday 6 pm to 10.30 pm. Closed on Monday and Tuesday. Licensed. All cards. Book ahead. ♿

☞ This symbol means that the restaurant is rated a good buy. This ♿ means that there is wheelchair access to both the tables and the washrooms.

MONTREAL   MAP 117
IKANOS
112 McGill Street   **$160**
(514) 842-0867

Ikanos is situated in the heart of old Montreal. It's chic,
modern and friendly. The chef and owner, Constant
Mentzas, is interested in contemporary Mediterranean
cuisine. This usually means tapas inspired by Greek cooking—meat, fish and seafood slowly grilled over an open
fire, along with seasonal vegetables prepared with care
and finesse. Ikanos has the only Spanish-made wood-
burning Josper oven in the province, and it makes a difference. Their zucchini is out of this world, and so are the
fried squid, the grilled shrimp and the sea-bream. In the
evening scallops are served with celeriac, apricots and
capers, lamb is braised with pomegranates and guinea
fowl is wrapped in vine leaves and served with cilantro.
There's also sea-bass, red snapper and a rib-eye steak.
Lunch is about things like salmon sashimi with pomegranate, orange and fennel, or guinea fowl with cherry,
beets, yogurt and coriander. For brunch you can have
shakshuka shrimps served with anchovy and garlic rapini.
The service is impeccable, as are a number of the Greek
wines.
*Open Monday to Wednesday 11.30 am to 2.30 pm, 5.30 pm to
10.30 pm, Thursday and Friday 11.30 am to 2.30 pm, 5.30 pm
to midnight, Saturday 5.30 pm to midnight, Sunday 10 am to
3.30 pm, 5.30 pm to 10.30 pm. Licensed. All cards. Book
ahead.*

MONTREAL   MAP 117
JOE BEEF   ☆
2491 rue Notre-Dame o   **$175**
(514) 935-6504

David McMillan likes to say about his restaurant: "I
would never eat here—it's too crowded." And it is.
Recently we were told that a table for two would not be

available for six months. There's no printed menu—the ever-changing dishes are scrawled (in French only) on dimly-lit chalkboards that everyone finds hard to read. And of course it's much too loud. Fortunately the food is very good. You might be offered zucchini blossoms stuffed with smoked meat, veal tongue with black truffles, sea urchin with jalapeno aioli or headcheese croquettes. (Joe Beef is not for the faint of heart.) Pastas include foie gras ravioli in duck broth and lobster spaghetti. The deboned quail is stuffed with ricotta, wrapped in pork, and served in a lobster broth, the veal sweetbreads are covered with braised antelope and mushroom gravy, the veal shoulder comes with a bone-marrow risotto. You might even be offered a horse ribeye steak. This is not a place for nuance; its effects are big and bold and full of noise and drama.

Open Tuesday to Saturday 6 pm to 10 pm. Closed on Sunday and Monday. Licensed. Master Card, Visa. You must book ahead. ♿

MONTREAL MAP 117
LEMEAC ☆
1045 avenue Laurier o **$175**
(514) 270-0999

Leméac's menu is big and familiar. Customers tend to know what they're getting. Maxim Vadnais and Olivier Belzile offer classic bistro fare served by professionals. You can start, if you like, with oysters or a fish soup with croutons and rouille, and go on to braised short-ribs, confit of duck, beef or salmon tartar, Icelandic wild cod and pan-seared veal chop. For vegetarians there's a salad of panko-crusted goat-cheese, apple and walnuts, mushroom ravioli and a risotto of wild mushrooms and asparagus. The smoked salmon comes from their own smokehouse. Pain perdu is their signature sweet, served with caramel and maple syrup and dulce de leche ice cream. The wine-list offers almost 500 vintages by the bottle, and a number of those by the glass. Leméac is expensive, but at noon the table d'hôte starts at 19.00, and

there's a late-night prix-fixe for 28.00 after 10 pm.
Open Monday to Friday noon to midnight, Saturday and Sunday 10 am to 3 pm (brunch), 6 pm to midnight. Licensed. All cards. Book ahead. &

MONTREAL   MAP 117
THE LIVERPOOL HOUSE   ☆
250 rue Notre-Dame o   **$170**
(514) 313-6049

This was the second restaurant opened on the block by the Joe Beef group, and in no time it became as crowded and noisy as Joe Beef itself. (Though they do still answer their telephone, which is more than you can say for Joe Beef). The big helpings and the chalkboards are the same, and the menu is broadly similar, though much of the seafood here is raw. Lobster spaghetti is the most expensive dish on offer. The oysters come from both the East Coast and the West. Everything appears to be casually prepared, but actually the kitchen cooks in high style, and everything has a lot of flavour. David McMillan will tell you he has the most sophisticated customers in North America; that they actually eat sweetbreads, tripe, cheeks, heart, ears and tails. As for the wine-list, it covers one whole wall.
Open Tuesday to Saturday 5 pm to 10 pm. Closed on Sunday and Monday. Licensed. Master Card, Visa. You must book ahead. &

MONTREAL   MAP 117
MAISON PUBLIQUE   ☆☆
4720 rue Marquette   **$135**
(514) 507-0555

The Maison Publique looks and feels like a British gastropub. And that's not suprising, because the owner, Derek Dammann, used to work for Jamie Oliver in London at the original Fifteen restaurant. Oliver ended up lending Dammann the money to start this restaurant on his own. Try the maiale tonnato, a pork charcuterie slathered with Dijon mayonnaise and topped with shaved parmesan, or the thinly sliced beef heart in romesco sauce. Everything on the menu is strictly Canadian and as locally sourced as possible. The helpings are generous, even the rabbit and sweetbreads. Dammann is at his best with seafood—sockeye salmon, crab tart or baked oysters in beer and béchamel sauce. You need to book ahead for the popular brunch, which offers housemade boudin, Welsh rarebit and pancakes with hot peppers and bacon. The blackboard offers a number of unusual Canadian wines.

Open Wednesday to Friday 6 pm to midnight, Saturday and Sunday 10.30 pm to 2 pm (brunch), 6 pm to midnight. Closed on Monday and Tuesday. Licensed. All cards. Book ahead. ♿

MONTREAL   MAP 117
MERCURI
645 rue Wellington   **$175**
(514) 394-3444

Mercuri is located in a converted warehouse in the heart of the Old Port. It has two kitchens and two menus, one available at lunch and one at dinner. The *menu midi* starts with beef tartar, gravlax and grilled shrimp with green onions, and goes on to chicken piri-piri and poisson du marché. Dinner is more ambitious. There's a raw bar to begin with (tuna sashimi and beef tartar), followed by octopus with red chili, ravioli, venison, striploin, baby back ribs, tuna with artichokes and market fish, together with your choice of beef or turkey from the fire-pit. The noise level in Mercuri has been measured at 75 decibels, so be warned.

Open Tuesday to Friday 11.30 am to 2.30 pm, 6 pm to 10.30 pm, Saturday 6 pm to 11 pm. Closed on Sunday and Monday. Licensed. All cards. ♿

MONTREAL   MAP 117
MIRCHI
365 place d' Youville   **$80**
(514) 282-0123

Mirchi is by far the best value for money that we know of in town. The restaurant is in fact a pure delight. It occupies an historic building in Old Montreal, and the cuisine is East Indian. To start, ask for the chana bhoona (chickpeas cooked in a soft spice curry and served with mint sauce). Or there's chicken tikka or prawn poori— they're all good. Main courses include vegetable bhajis, lamb Mirchi—which is tossed with garlic and fresh crushed ginger and served with tomato and coriander—a fish tikka and king-prawn phatia (a sweet-and-sour Persian curry with coconut). The chai is made from scratch, or there's Indian beer. Everything is beautifully presented and served.

Open Monday to Friday 11 am to 2 pm, 5 pm to 10.30 pm, Saturday and Sunday 5 pm to 10.30 pm. Licensed for beer and wine only. Visa. Book ahead if you can.

MONTREAL   **MAP 117**
MONTREAL PLAZA
6230 rue St.-Hubert   **$250**
(514) 903-6230

Montreal Plaza was proclaimed one of Canada's best new restaurants in 2015 and now, only two years later, its chefs (formerly at Toqué) have attracted the attention of the *New York Times*. It's located in the St.-Hubert plaza, in a space designed by the restaurant architect Zébulon Perron, who has made a warm, elegant place to enjoy fine food. The best way to go is the tasting menu for 80.00 a head. This starts with venison or salmon tartar, followed by whelks in garlic butter, Arctic char with sea-urchin cream, radish cannelloni with bologna and peanut sauce and sliced deer heart and calamari served with red cabbage, red onion, popcorn and hay. For sweet there's a glacé aux pommes—layers of frozen apple and cake sliced very thinly and served to resemble a flower. There are a number of wines for less than 40.00 and many more for less than 60.00. They also have some great craft beers, all either locally brewed or imported from Vermont.

Open daily 5 pm to 11 pm. Licensed. All cards. Book ahead. &

Nobody but nobody can buy his way into this guide.

MONTREAL   **MAP 117**
LE MOUSSO   ☆☆
1023 rue Ontario e   **$295**
(438) 384-7410

Le Mousso is like a Michelin two-star restaurant in France, but without the pomp and circumstance. The building is very old and once housed a printing shop. Everything has been designed for the eye as much as the palate. There's no à la carte: the eleven-course tasting menu starts with oysters in a Wagyu-beef mignonette, and goes on to foie gras with maple sugar and roast potatoes on a bed of burning hay. A wonderful sea-urchin tart with herbs and dried flowers comes next, then calamari in squid ink, sturgeon caviar, crab salad with green strawberries, sous-vide chicken with black truffles and lamb with wild peppers. The two sweets—buttermilk ice cream in a strawberry coulis and chamomile popsicle with crumbled maple sugar on top—are equally exotic. If it weren't for the rap music on the soundtrack this would be the ultimate restaurant.

Open Wednesday to Saturday 6 pm to 10 pm. Closed on Monday, Tuesday and Sunday. Licensed. All cards. You must book ahead.

MONTREAL   **MAP 117**
OLIVE ET GOURMANDO   🖐
351 rue St.-Paul o   **$60**
(514) 350-1083

This has been Montreal's favourite place to start the day for almost twenty years. For breakfast there are croissants, brioches, an oeuf coquette—a sort of shakshouka with chorizo and avocado—and poached egg paninis. The most intriguing of the lunch sandwiches is the Pomme, a panini filled with bacon, walnut butter, cheddar and sliced apples. There are also cajun and Cuban sandwiches, a tartine and a number of huge salads. Get there as early as you can, because the lineups at the door only get longer.

Open daily 9 am to 5 pm. Licensed for beer and wine only. All cards. No reservations. ♿

MONTREAL   MAP 117
O'THYM   ☆
1112 boulevard de Maisonneuve e   **$85**
(514) 525-3443

There are a lot of B.Y.O.B. restaurants in Montreal these days. How they survive without liquor revenue is anyone's guess, but apparently they do. One of the best is O'Thym. It's located just five minutes from the Métro, and there's no corkage fee. The menu, which changes constantly, is written up on a gigantic chalkboard. Each night there's a different tartar or tataki. Pan-seared foie gras is often on the menu, and they always do a good job with fish. Try the cod if it's available, or the scallops. For sweet there's blueberry-bread pudding and a chocolate ganache. The popular weekend brunch features a Wellington croissant, which is made with Wagyu beef and chorizo.
Open Monday 6 pm to 11 pm, Tuesday to Friday 11.30 am to 2.30 pm, 6 pm to 11 pm, Saturday and Sunday 10 am to 2 pm (brunch), 6 pm to 11 pm. B.Y.O.B. All cards. Book ahead. ♿

MONTREAL   MAP 117
PARK   ☆
378 Victoria Avenue   **$275**
(514) 750-7534

Park serves some of the best (and most expensive) sushi in Montreal. It's a favourite with the Montreal Canadiens who, win or lose, are extremely well paid and can afford it. Antonio Park, the owner and chef, has lived in Paraguay, Argentina, Brazil, Japan, the USA and Canada, and his food is predictably eclectic. There's sashimi, maki and nigiri (on gold-medal koshihikari short-grain rice). Park makes his own soya sauce, rice vinegar and shark-skin-grated fresh wasabi, and ferments his own kinchi. There's a range of salads, and hot dishes such as Argentinian empanadas and a classic Korean bibimbap. As always, the best way to cover it all is to choose the omekase dinner: five courses for 95.00 or six for 115.00. Or you can come for lunch and have some miso soup and a bento box for a fraction of that.

Open Monday to Thursday 11.30 am to 2.30 pm, 5.30 pm to 10 pm, Friday and Saturday 11.30 am to 2.30 pm, 5.30 pm to 11 pm. Closed on Sunday. Licensed. All cards. Book ahead. ♿

MONTREAL   **MAP 117**
TOQUE!   ★★★
900 place Jean-Paul-Riopelle   **$225**
(514) 499-2084

Normand Laprise and Christine Lamarche still live in a world of surprises, most of which are to be found among their appetizers and amuse bouches. The most remarkable of these is the sea-urchin, adorned with oysters, ginger, soy, daikon and cucumber. (There are also scallops with sumac and gin and carpaccio of venison with sea snails.) It's a good idea to ask for two appetizers and pass on the main courses, which, apart from the rack of sucking pig, are more pedestrian. The wine-list too is full of surprises. There are only half a dozen Canadian wines, but at the other end of the list there's a grand-cru Saint-Emilion and a Mouton-Rothschild for 2000.00 a bottle. For ordinary people there's a sauvignon blanc from Naramata for 81.00 and a chardonnay from the Beamsville Bench for 103.00. But Toque! is not really meant for ordinary people. It's for people who are able and willing to pay for amazing delicacies presented in the most elegant surroundings.

Open Tuesday to Friday 11.30 am to 1.45 pm, 5.30 pm to 10 pm, Saturday 5.30 pm to 10.30 pm. Closed on Sunday and Monday. Licensed. Amex, Master Card, Visa. Book ahead. ♿

MONTREAL   **MAP 117**
VIN PAPILLON   ★
2519 rue Notre-Dame o   **$140**

The Papillon takes no reservations; as a matter of fact it doesn't even have a telephone. There's no printed menu and the daily offerings are written up on a chalkboard. But they have a loyal following (the place was completely full on a recent cold, wet Saturday afternoon). Some of the dishes come from Joe Beef down the street, but they're mostly centred around vegetables. They usually offer chanterelle-and-porcini-mushroom crostinis, charred brussels sprouts and a cheese soufflé made with spinach. The swimming scallops come from B.C., not the East Coast. They smoke their own ham, which they serve with white cheddar from P.E.I. People come back and back for the roasted whole cauliflower and the wonderful herring. They buy most of their wines from small, organic producers and sell them quite cheaply. Helpings are small, tapas-style, so it's a good idea to bring some friends and sample as many dishes as you can.

Open Tuesday to Saturday 3 pm to midnight. Closed on Sunday and Monday. Licensed. Master Card, Visa. No reservations. &

MONT TREMBLANT, Quebec   **MAP 118**
LE CHEVAL DE JADE   ✫✫✫
688 rue de St.-Jovite   **$200**
St.-Jovite
(819) 425-5233

Mont Tremblant's most famous restaurant began as a farmhouse in St.-Jovite. Olivier Tali and Frédérique Pironneau put all they had into transforming it. Tali is the only Canadian winner of the Ordre des Canardières, which came to him for his caneton à la Rouennaise, the signature dish of the Tour d'Argent in Paris. This means pressed duck flambéed with cognac and finished with foie-gras butter. It costs 104.00 for two, and must be ordered a day ahead (and not at all on weekends). A grande cuisine version with fresh truffles, Hennessy XO cognac and slices of seared duck foie gras costs 175.00. Tali aims to have the freshest and best fish anywhere in the Laurentians and he probably does. His bouillabaisse menu at 55.95 starts with a green-lentil-and-octopus salad and goes on to a Mediterranean bouillabaisse stuffed with seafood. The discovery menu has nine courses for 91.00

(143.00 with wine pairings) and includes breast of duck with truffles and scallops with their coral. The regular à la carte is of course simpler and cheaper, but it does offer feuilleté of snails, foie gras de canard and fish soup, followed by casserole of squid, braised lamb shank and red-deer steak. They buy all their supplies locally and we especially admire their truffled duck and their red deer. The presentation is always beautiful, and the wine-list is splendid.

Open Tuesday to Saturday 5 pm to 10 pm. Closed on Sunday and Monday. Licensed. Amex, Master Card, Visa. Book ahead. &

MONT TREMBLANT   MAP 118
MILLE PATES
780 rue de St.-Jovite   **$95**
St.-Jovite
(819) 717-3830

Mille Pâtes is a small boutique that sells pasta. It's becoming a compulsory stop for many people on their way to the mountain. And what's not to like? It's homey, it's Italian and its pasta is wonderfully fresh. The menu keeps growing, and the rich and flavourful spaghetti bolognese has now been joined by things like shredded duck tartar on linguine and pulled pork on columbine. The soups, the salads and the sweets all come from the kitchen.

Open Monday and Tuesday 10.30 am to 6 pm, Wednesday to Sunday 10.30 am to 10 pm. Licensed. Master Card, Visa.

MORRISTON, Ontario   (MAP 76)
ENVER'S   ☆
42 Queen Street   **$150**
(519) 821-2852

We've been writing about Enver's for many years now. Enver Bismallah established the restaurant in 1982. He didn't do much to modernize the old grey-brick storefront, but he made the place famous. In 2000 he sold it to Terri Manolis, and vanished. Manolis has kept the faith with the help of a number of chefs, always using top-quality produce. She now has her own garden, where she grows heirloom tomatoes and greens of all sorts. There's a new bar and dining-room and a splendid new patio. The current chef, John Harcourt, still makes many of the old dishes, notably the rack of lamb, the pâté of chicken liver and foie gras and an asparagus soup that has many admirers. He's also added several of his own dishes, among them a fine savoury cheesecake, great fresh mussels and wonderful steaks. The wine-list is simply amazing, and the service is perfect.

Open Tuesday to Friday 11.30 am to 2 pm, 5 pm to 8.30 pm, Saturday 5 pm to 8.30 pm. Closed on Sunday and Monday. Licensed. Amex, Master Card, Visa. Book ahead if you can. &

MURRAY HARBOUR, P.E.I. (MAP 37)
NO. 5 ☆☆
5 Church Street **$80**
(902) 962-3668

No. 5 was opened in 2015 in a deconsecrated church by Wade Little, a New Zealander. The building has become a big part of the restaurant's appeal—diners take tours of its features—and No. 5 is extremely popular. The kitchen concentrates on what Wade Little likes to call clean food, which means made in the kitchen with no additives or preservatives. Until mid-afternoon he features sandwiches, soups and salads. He makes his own bread and uses it for all his sandwiches. The menu changes annually, and the corn chowder you loved last year may no longer be available. But there will always be burgers, and there will always be fries, which you can have plain, salted or spiced. Evening meals are more substantial, featuring barbecued chicken with walnut mustard and a number of specials. The soups and sweets are all wonderful. The service is very attentive. This is slow cooking at its best.

Open Wednesday to Saturday 11 am to 8 pm, Sunday 11.30 am to 6 pm. Closed on Monday and Tuesday. No liquor. No reservations. Master Card, Visa.

NANAIMO, B.C.   MAP 121
LE CAFE FRANCAIS
153 Commercial Street   **$120**
(250) 716-7866

Over the last few years, the Café Français has become one
of the best places to eat in Nanaimo. People like the traditional bistro fare in this homey, well worn restaurant
that's as short on decor as it is long on great food at reasonable prices. The place is run by Gilles Le Patezour and his
two sons, who wait on tables with professional ease. You
start with a rich onion soup or with snails. After that, they
do a great job with crêpes, both savoury and sweet. The
best of the savoury crêpes are the chicken in white wine
and the seafood in cream, followed closely by the duck
and the beef. Cuisine minceur has no place here; the
sauces are all traditionally rich and thick. Look for the
salmon, the halibut and the sea-bass on the daily menu,
though we also like the lamb shanks and steaks. The wines
aren't cheap, but you can bring your own bottle and pay
only a few dollars for corkage. Le Café Français offers
great value for money.
Open Tuesday to Saturday 5 pm to 9.30 pm. Closed on Sunday
and Monday. Licensed and bring your own bottle. All cards.

NANAIMO   MAP 121
CHRISTINA'S ON THE LAKE   ☆☆
2367 Arbot Road   **$150**
(250) 753-2866

Long a favourite of ours with its attractive lakeside
setting, the Bistro at Westwood Lake got a new name in
2016 when Christina Paterson, the former sous-chef,
bought the restaurant. She had already served a three-year
apprenticeship at the Hastings House on Salt Spring
Island, and brought several dishes with her from there.
Lunch is a comfortable meal with moderate prices. Dungeness crab-cake, saltspring mussels and ground-beef patties can all be had without breaking the bank. In the
evening, you might begin with Belgian endive or parsnip-

and-apple soup, and go on to a number of mains all priced below 30.00: lingcod, stuffed breast of chicken or spring salmon with a wild-mushroom risotto. Christina is nimble with pastry—try her chocolate-truffle tart with chantilly cream or her lemon semi-freddo with a meringue and raspberry purée.

Open Wednesday to Saturday 11.30 am to 2.30 pm, 5 pm to 8.30 pm. Closed on Monday, Tuesday and Sunday. Licensed. All cards. &

NANAIMO   MAP 121
CROW AND GATE PUB
2313 Yellow Point Road   **$90**
(250) 722-3731

At the Crow & Gate you go up to the bar, order what you want—soups, chowders, hot pies, sandwiches—and pay up front before the meal is brought to your table. If you're wise, you'll ask for smoked-salmon chowder and the leek-and-Stilton quiche. In winter, go for the oyster stew, which you can eat right in front of the fireplace. For sweet share a rich bread pudding with brandy. Dinner specials start at 5 o'clock and locals flock here early on the best nights, which are Thursdays for bouillabaisse, Fridays for roast lamb with rosemary and Saturdays for roast beef and Yorkshire pudding.

Open daily 11 am to 11 pm. Licensed. All cards. No reservations. &

NANAIMO   MAP 121
THE HILLTOP   ☆
5281 Rutherford Road: Unit 102   **$140**
(250) 585-5337

The Hilltop started as a deli, but since 2013 Ryan Zuvich has been creating remarkable meals at this 25-seat restaurant that looks more like a home than a business. There's no view, hilltop or not—it's only the food that matters. You begin with an endive or beet salad, or perhaps with saltspring mussels or seared albacore tuna, and go on to roast pork with rosemary, Arctic char with a sweet-pepper piperade or roasted cod with chorizo and clams. Finish with a piece of lemon olive-oil cake or a warm beignet. You can bring your own bottle if you pay 20.00 for corkage.

Open Monday and Thursday to Sunday 5 pm to 10 pm. Closed on Tuesday and Wednesday. Licensed. All cards. ♿

NANAIMO   MAP 121
THE NEST
77 Skinner Street   **$100**
(250) 591-2721

Its move to Skinner Street seems to have given the Nest renewed vitality, with an expanded menu and longer hours. Jen Ash and Nic Braun make extensive use of local organic ingredients in their cooking. Their food is mainly French and Italian, with Asian touches here and there. You can have roast beef and Yorkshire pudding if you like, or smoked prawns with paprika and garlic. They're good with pasta, especially potato gnocchi tossed in pesto. The wild coho salmon makes a pleasant dish, though we prefer the braised lamb shank. Others have admired the free-range breast of chicken stuffed with brie from Qualicum Beach, and the duck glazed with soy and ginger. There's a nice selection of B.C. wines costing less than 30.00 a bottle.

Open Tuesday to Friday 11.30 am to midnight, Saturday and Sunday 5 pm to midnight. Closed on Monday. Licensed. All cards. ♿

NANAIMO   MAP 121
NORI
6750 N Island Highway   **$80**
(250) 751-3377

Nori is a sushi bar with a Korean accent. It's located in a Costco mall, which brings them a lot of business—along with plentiful parking. The menu is extensive and the best way to get to know the place is to order one of the

Omakase dinners, which might feature salmon, scallops, prawns, eel and tuna. There are a number of excellent appetizers, including breaded octopus, crab croquettes, oysters and agedashi tofu. We like the beef tataki with ginger ponzu and if you enjoy ramen, try it with pork-belly and miso. You won't go wrong if you focus instead on sashimi, some of which—hamachi for instance—is familiar, but which also includes local spot prawns, wild salmon, pickled Norwegian mackerel and geoduck clam. Nori isn't particularly cheap, but like its next-door neigh-bour, it's good value for the money.

Open Wednesday and Thursday 11.30 am to 2.30 pm, 5 pm to 9.30 pm, Friday and Saturday 11.30 am to 2.30 pm, 5 pm to 10 pm, Sunday noon to 2.30 pm, 5 to 9.30 pm. Closed on Monday and Tuesday. Licensed. Master Card, Visa. &

NANAIMO   **MAP 121**
2 CHEFS AFFAIR
123B Commercial Street   **$35**
(250) 591-4656

This is still the best place in Nanaimo for breakfast. The highlight is Love at First Bite, which means French toast made with egg bread flavoured with pumpkin, cinnamon and vanilla bean. They also have a breakfast frittata with onion, ham, sausage and house-made tomato ketchup. At noon, go for the French-onion tart or the fish three ways—or perhaps the Lover's Quarrel, which is mush-room ravioli with rustic tomato sauce. Nothing ever changes at the Affair, and that may be a problem. Some people think the spark of romance is fading, that it's becoming tired and familiar. We'll keep you posted.

Open Monday to Friday 8 am to 4.30 pm, Saturday and Sunday 8 am to 3 pm. No liquor. All cards.

NANAIMO
See also CEDAR, LANTZVILLE.

Our website is at www.oberonpress.ca. Readers wishing to use e-mail should address us at oberon@sympatico.ca.

We're sorry to say goodbye to the All Seasons Café—we've been together for many years. Nowadays people seem to prefer The Library in the boutique Hume Hotel at 422 Vernon Street (telephone (250) 352-5331). It has a large and familiar menu, well prepared year in and year out, waiters who have been there forever and live jazz every night. And it keeps long hours, Monday to Thursday 11 am to 11 pm, Friday and Saturday 11 am to midnight, Sunday 5 pm to 10 pm. It has a license, takes Master Card and Visa and has wheelchair access. But the Kootenay Tamil Kitchen at 318 Anderson Street (telephone (778) 463-1008) is a hard alternative to resist. It serves south-Indian cuisine, and the chef gives everything he prepares its own distinctive flavour, from the simple dosas to the lamb and coriander curry. It's early days for the Kootenay Tamil, and the prices are still low and the service faultless. Grab it while you can. They're open Tuesday to Sunday 8 am to 2.30 pm, 4.30 pm to 9.30 pm, closed on Monday, take Master Card and Visa and are wheelchair accessible.

NEW GLASGOW, N.S.   MAP 123
THE BISTRO   ☆☆
216 Archimedes Street   **$125**
(902) 752-4988

The Bistro opened in 2002. Since then Heather Poulin and Rob Vinton have run the place as a relaxed but upscale restaurant, something New Glasgow badly needed. They're also strong supporters of the local arts community, whose work regularly hangs on the restaurant walls. Receptions are held for every opening, which makes the Bistro a special place. The menu itself is quite short. It may start with a warm chicken salad on a bed of romaine, and continue with one or two of Rob's specialties— salmon perhaps, with prawns stuffed with baby bok choy, spinach and whipped potatoes spiced with horseradish sauce. The best of the sweets is probably the chocolate peanut-butter cup (it's not a cup) on graham crackers with sprinkled peanuts. The wine-list is large and changes every month to match each new menu.

Open Tuesday to Saturday 5 pm to 9 pm. Closed on Sunday and Monday. Licensed. All cards. Book ahead.

NEW GLASGOW   MAP 123
THE DOCK
130 George Street   **$90**
(902)752-0884

The Dock is a traditional Irish pub that's been looking after New Glasgow for more than twenty years. Their all-day menu tries to have something for everyone: dips, soups, sandwiches, salads, pasta, seafood and daily specials. There are vegetarian and gluten-free options and even a kid's menu. Fish and chips is the most popular dish, along with the seafood chowder with Irish soda bread. There's also charcuterie, tacos (fish or chicken) and lamb shanks. The superb pan-fried haddock is coated with parmesan and panko, and the Asian chicken salad comes with walnuts, sprouts and Thai dressing. The place gets crowded on weekends, particularly on the last Sunday of every month, when the Dock Gang perform traditional music.

Open Monday to Saturday 11.30 am to 9 pm. Closed on Sunday (open for live music from 2 pm to 5 pm on the last Sunday of the month). Licensed. Amex, Master Card, Visa. &

NEW GLASGOW   MAP 123
WEST SIDE BISTRO
142 Stellarton Road   **$75**
(902) 755-9378

Phil Castle prepares everything here in an open kitchen, while his wife Darlene runs the front of the house. Together they have put together an extensive menu: three salads, three stir-fry bowls, three versions of penne pasta, three main courses, three daily specials. Try one of the specials—salmon fish-cakes perhaps, or chicken pot-pie. The open-face chicken sandwich comes heaped on a baguette with mushrooms and mangos. The apple-cranberry bread pudding comes in a large helping with hot rum sauce. There are usually one or two cheesecakes—we like the chocolate butterscotch—and in season blueberry pie. To drink there are only a few wines and beers.

Open Tuesday to Friday 11.30 am to 2 pm, 5 pm to 8 pm, Saturday 5 pm to 8 pm. Closed on Sunday and Monday. Licensed. Visa.

NEW GLASGOW
See also PICTOU, STELLARTON.

NEW GLASGOW, P.E.I.   (MAP 37)
OLDE GLASGOW MILL   ☆
5592 Highway 13   **$100**
(902) 964-3313

Emily Wells was the chef at the Dunes in Brackley Beach (see above) for many years before she left to open her own restaurant. This is it. Her cooking at the Olde Glasgow Mill is wonderful, perhaps even better than it used to be in Brackley Beach. The ribs are amazing and the haddock and the halibut are both beautifully cooked. The vegetables are all fresh and imaginative. And there's a takeout counter where you can buy baked goods and salads of all sorts.

Open daily 11.30 am to 4 pm, 5 pm to 9.30 pm from mid-May until mid-October. Licensed. Master Card, Visa. Book ahead if you can.

NIAGARA-ON-THE-LAKE, Ontario   MAP 125
HOBNOB   ☆
The Charles Inn   **$160**
209 Queen Street
(866) 556-8883

The Charles Inn is a beautifully restored manor house with twelve comfortable bedrooms. The dining-room, which is known as Hobnob, is now in the hands of Adam Rapsey, but the cooking is still as good as any in town. The place settings are formal, the service is discreet and the noise levels pleasantly muted. The menu may be familiar, but there are nice touches, like the lump-crab croquettes that come with the beef tenderloin. The salmon and the Muscovy duck are both old favourites. All the wines are from Niagara, and most of them are quite reasonably priced.

Open Monday to Thursday 5 pm to 8 pm, Friday 11 am to 9 pm, Saturday and Sunday 8 am to 10 am (brunch), 11 am to 9 pm. Licensed. All cards. Book ahead if you can. ✦

NIAGARA-ON-THE-LAKE   MAP 125

RAVINE VINEYARD

1366 York Road   **$110**
St. David's
(905) 262-8463

Ravine Vineyard has been in the same family since 1867. In the early days it operated as a winery with a tasting bar. Now there's a wide-windowed dining-room overlooking the vineyards, and they give you a free pass to the winery with your lunch. The menu is the same for lunch and dinner. It's short, but changes frequently. Very few winery restaurants bake their own bread, raise their own pigs and grow their own organic vegetables. Even the gravlax salmon is house-cured. The kitchen also makes its own sweets, which are mostly old-fashioned and fruity. The wines from the vineyards outside are modestly priced at about 45.00 a bottle or 10.00 a glass.

Open daily 11 am to 3 pm, 5 pm to 9 pm. Licensed. Master Card, Visa. ✦

NIAGARA-ON-THE-LAKE   MAP 125

TREADWELL   ☆

114 Queen Street   **$160**
(905) 934-9797

Stephen Treadwell has years of experience in running a good kitchen, and it shows. The prices aren't low, but why would they be? He is determined to have the best ingredients: the beef, lamb and pork come from

Cumbrae, the mushrooms from Marc Eber, the cheese from Monforte Dairy. His son James is now the sommelier, and together they've built a fascinating list from small local wineries. Recent menus have featured harissa-spiced squash soup, ricotta agnolotti with parsnip velouté, sous-vide Muscovy duck breast, seared Ontario rainbow trout with mussels and Cumbrae pork loin marinated with citrus and chili. Stephen Treadwell has been obsessed with farm-to-table cuisine since long before it became a cliché. The room is bright and cheerful, the service friendly and efficient.

Open Monday to Thursday 11.30 am to 2.30 pm, 5 pm to 9 pm, Friday and Saturday 11.30 am to 2.30 pm, 5 pm to 10 pm, Sunday 11.30 am to 2.30 pm, 5 pm to 9 pm. Licensed. All cards. Book ahead. &

NORRIS POINT, Newfoundland   MAP 126
THE BLACK SPRUCE
Neddies Harbour Inn   **$160 ($385)**
7 Beach Road
(709) 458-3089

With its views over Bonne Bay and the mountains beyond, Neddies Harbour Inn is easily the loveliest place to stay in Gros Morne. And now that Justin Thyme down the road and Java Jack's over in Rocky Harbour have both closed, the Black Spruce restaurant is almost the only place to eat well in the area. Jason Lynch has his hands full these days at the Caveau in Grand Pré (see above), but he spent a lot of time here in Norris Point getting the Black Spruce up and running, and is still listed as their primary chef. It's mainly a consulting role though, and the heavy lifting in the kitchen is done now by the staff he trained and left behind, headed by Joy Newman. On the whole they're making a very able job of it, even if a bit short on brio and way too long on cream (avoid the chowder and the seafood crespelle). All the ingredients are fresh and locally sourced— try the daily market fish. There's also a fine beef striploin and paupiettes of Newfoundland pork with a herb risotto. To follow we can never say no to the figgy duff. The dining-room is as attractive as the rest of the hotel—high ceilings, long windows, pastel yellows and pale woods—a world away from the wilderness outside.

Open Tuesday to Sunday 5 pm to 9 pm from mid May until mid-October. Closed on Monday. Licensed. All cards. &

NORTHEAST MARGAREE, N.S.　　(MAP 151)
THE DANCING GOAT　　　　　　　　　☜
6289 Cabot Trail　　　　　　　　　　**$45**
Cape Breton
(902) 248-2727

The Dancing Goat is a real find. It's always full, though they've moved and have new owners. The kitchen staff hasn't changed and they still have no table service. You go up to the counter, choose what you want from the blackboard and take a number to your table. Every day they have two homemade soups—curried chicken, perhaps, or parsnip with apple. There's always a quiche and there are also a number of sandwiches, all made on thick, home-baked bread with crusts on. There's usually chicken with almonds and (our favourite) bacon with avocado. There's espresso and caffe latte to go with your sandwich and they're both good. You can take the oatcakes and the maple shortbread home with you if you like. There may be no liquor here, but there's just about everything else.

Open Monday to Wednesday 7.30 am to 5 pm, Thursday and Friday 7.30 am to 8 pm, Saturday 7.30 am to 5 pm, Sunday 8 am to 5 pm. No liquor. Master Card, Visa. &

NORTH SYDNEY, N.S.　　　　　(MAP 196)
THE BLACK SPOON　　　　　　　　　☆
320 Commercial Street　　　　　　　　**$75**
Cape Breton
(902) 241-3300

The Black Spoon is a fetching little place that's been making customers happy for many years now. It should be better known, considering that it's only a short hop from the Newfoundland ferry. They serve lunch on weekdays—soup, half a sandwich and a salad for 10.00. If the soup is roasted red pepper, ask no questions, just order a bowl. The chef is fond of mango and maple with his seafood—he even offers a fish sandwich with mango—but we've heard no complaints about his beef Wellington, breast of chicken with pecans or lightly spiced Moroccan haddock. His lobster pot-pie has generous pieces of lobster, scallops and mussels. The Cajun seafood pasta has mussels, shrimp, scallops and lobster on a bed of farfalle. The tables may be crowded, but the helpings are big and the service efficient. The beer is local and very good.

Open Monday to Saturday 11 am to 9 pm. Closed on Sunday. Licensed. Amex, Master Card, Visa.

OKANAGAN CENTRE, B.C.   (MAP 89)
GRAPEVINE
Gray Monk Estate Winery   **$140**
1055 Camp Road
(250) 766-3405

Here it's hard to choose between the venison meatloaf in a reduction of red wine with house-made pear chutney and the Fraser Valley duck confit with cranberry-onion marmalade and homemade spaetzle. Don't hesitate. Despite appearances, the venison meatloaf is much the better of the two. The sweets are all lovely, especially the cheesecake topped with fresh seasonal fruit. Grapevine is still run by Willi Franz and René Haudenschild, and they're as good as ever.

Open daily 11.30 am to 4 pm, 5 pm to 9 pm from 1 April until 31 October. Licensed. Master Card, Visa. ♿

OLIVER, B.C.   (MAP 140)
MIRADORO   ☆
Tinhorn Creek Vineyard   **$140**
32830 Tinhorn Creek Road
(250) 498-3742

Miradoro is owned jointly by Tinhorn Creek Vineyard and Manuel Ferreira of Le Gavroche in Vancouver. The stylish dining-room overlooks many of the South Okanagan producers that supply the kitchen. Jeff Van Geest's cooking is rustic and straightforward, and the menu is largely Mediterranean, circling through Italy, Portugal and Spain. Albondigas or beef-and-pork meatballs come in a robust tomato-and-parmesan sauce, spaghetti bolognese is made with venison and cheese, fregola is served in a carbonara of mushrooms, pepper and egg. Go on to the Arctic char with sweet-pea-and-clam ragu, ricotta gnudi and black trumpet mushrooms, or the lamb shank braised in ras al hanout and yogurt. Our pick of the sweets is the lemon cream with summer fruit preserves, but there's also a plum-and-walnut frangipani tart, pears poached in red wine and an espresso tiramisu. The three-course tasting menu is a buy at 55.00.

Open daily 11.30 am to 3 pm, 5.30 pm to 9 pm. Licensed. All cards. &

OLIVER   **(MAP 140)**
TERRAFINA BY RAUDZ   ☆
Hester Creek Estate Winery   **$140**
Road 8
(250) 498-2229

This award-winning restaurant has been taken over by Rod Butters, the owner of RauDZ in Kelowna. Terrafina will continue to serve many of the Tuscan dishes it's become known for, but those have been supplemented by new creations from Butters. The revamped menu he has worked out with chef Jenna Pillon has a familiar feel. Lunch offers wild-boar meatballs, wagyu-beef carpaccio with chipotle aioli, pork belly carbonara with garlic and tomato linguine with smoked fish and green onion pesto. All of these dishes reappear in the evening at dinner, together with Arctic char, lamb shanks and a flat-iron steak. The winery has always been an attractive place: the dining-room is surrounded by old brick, wooden pillars and wrought iron fixtures, and the patio outside offers a fine view of one of BC;'s oldest vineyards. If you would like to enjoy a glass or two of one of the Hester Creek

wines with your meal, there's no need to drive: a shuttle-bus runs regularly between Osoyoos and the restaurent.
Open Monday to Saturday 11.30 am to 9 pm, Sunday 10 am to 3 pm. Licensed. Master Card, Visa. &

ORANGEVILLE, Ontario   MAP 132
THE BLUEBIRD
100 Broadway   **$85**
(519) 941-3101

It's been twenty years since we first wrote about the Blue-bird. After that it established something of a reputation as a takeout. But the one-time café with hard chairs and arborite tables has now given way to a small high-end din-ing-room. The new space is comfortable and attractive, and it's become very popular. The cooking is basically Italian, and people think highly of the veal and the thin-crust pizzas. Our favourite is the pasta with seafood. The sweets are as remarkable as they ever were, and the wine-list, which is small and well chosen, is as reasonably priced as the food.
Open Tuesday 4 pm to 9 pm, Wednesday to Saturday 11 am to 9 pm. Closed on Sunday and Monday. Licensed. All cards. &

ORANGEVILLE   MAP 132
FORAGE
163 1 Street   **$125**
Credit Creek Plaza
(519) 942-3388

Restaurant One 99 never reopened and has been replaced at 199 Broadway by Rustik. Rustik is attractive, with good service and good cooking, but Forage is now our first choice in Orangeville. Matthew Jamieson and his wife, Wendy, have great experience. Their menu is neither short nor simple, but they do offer a number of dinner specials, such as mushroom ravioli with rosé sauce, Arctic char with lemon and lime and braised lamb shanks. On the regular menu, we still order the seafood stew, because the kitchen is at its best with fish. The sweets are a treat, we think, especially the flourless-chocolate cake. Everything is properly plated and the prices are fair. All the wines are sold by the glass as well as the bottle and there are six craft beers as well as a decent selection of wines.

Open Monday to Saturday 11 am to 9 pm. Closed on Sunday. Licensed. Amex, Master Card, Visa. Book ahead if you can. &

ORILLIA, Ontario   **MAP 133**
WEBERS   ☞
8844 Highway 11 N   **$25**
(705) 325-3696

Webers opened in 1963. After all these years, there's still a feeling of excitement about the place. Rock music is playing loudly on the soundtrack. Nobody waits too long, nobody is disappointed. Children play, lovers touch, tired drivers sit down, at peace, under a tree, somebody goes to the bathroom. Everyone is happy. Webers now has countless flavours of Kawartha ice cream, and if you want a real old-fashioned milkshake you can get it at the ice-cream counter. Each week in summer they process and sell more than three tons of ground beef—at least 50 tons a summer. Their fries all come from potatoes grown, cut and packed in Prince Edward Island. Teenagers take your order, make change and see that you get what you want within minutes, no matter how long the lineup may be. There's free parking for hundreds of cars on both sides of the highway, with an overhead walkway that connects the southbound lot to the restaurant. Webers bought the walkway from the CN Tower and it's the only privately owned bridge over a highway in the province of Ontario.

Open daily 10.30 am to 7 pm from mid-March until the end of December (later on weekends). No liquor, no cards. &

Where an entry is printed in italics this indicates that the restaurant has been listed only because it serves the best food in its area or because it hasn't yet been adequately tested.

OSHAWA, Ontario   **MAP 134**
CYRUS
563 Ritson Road S   **$30**
(905) 448-0892

The Gallery restaurant is long gone. The best place to eat in Oshawa now is Cyrus, just off the 401. Cyrus, as its name implies, is Persian, which means that they cook halal. They buy the best ingredients on the market and cook them to order. Their signature dish is chicken shawarma, which is slow-cooked on a spit and marinated in any number of spices. It's a remarkable dish, but you should also know about the falafel, the lamb kebabs and the tzatziki.

Open Tuesday to Friday 11 am to 8 pm, Saturday noon to 9 pm. Closed on Sunday and Monday. No liquor. Master Card, Visa. Book ahead if you can.

OTTAWA, Ontario   **MAP 135**

A number of stylish new restaurants have opened in Ottawa recently, some with familiar names, some with familiar locations. Oz Kafe at 10 York Street (telephone (613) 234-0907) used to be a fixture at the south end of Elgin Street, then disappeared for a few years before reopening in 2017 in one of the heritage courtyards behind Sussex Drive. The new location—in an old stone house in the court behind Restaurant Eighteen—is one of the most attractive in Ottawa, but it's hard to find, particularly since the restaurant has almost no signage. Best of the main courses are the Nagano pork chop and the charred eggplant; best of the starters is the smoked rare beef. There's also an extensive choice of local cheeses and charcuterie, and even for the Market it's open incredibly late—daily 5 pm to 2 am (with a reduced late-night menu). Licensed, Master Card, Visa. North & Navy at 226 Nepean Street (telephone (613) 232-6289) had large shoes to fill when they moved into the charming brick house occupied for more than ten years by Beckta Dining and Wine, but so far they're managing just fine. Even Steve Beckta still eats there. The northern Italian menu is centred on Venice, which for most of us means cicheti (Venetian tapas) and fegato. Both are well inter-

preted, particularly the rich and tangy liver-and-onions. *Adam Vettorel* used to cook at Domus and Supply and Demand, and he knows what he's doing. Open Monday to Saturday 5 pm to 10 pm, Sunday 4.30 pm to 9 pm. Licensed. All cards. **Erling's Variety** at 225 Strathcona Avenue (telephone (613) 231-8484), off Bank just north of the Glebe, is named after the owner's grandfather's grocery store. It's seen a number of chefs come and go, but *Liam Vainola* has managed throughout to keep up the quality and diversity of his creative small plates—at last count there were fourteen on offer. There's a heavy emphasis on vegetables: try the mushrooms with smoked cheddar and potato polenta or the beets and carrots with feta. Even better are the scallops with celeriac, tabouleh and cauliflower fritter. Open Tuesday to Friday 11.30 am to 2 pm, 5 pm to 10 pm, Saturday 5 pm to 10 pm, Sunday 10 am to 2 pm. Closed on Monday. Licensed, all cards. **Wandee Thai** at 40 Beech Street (telephone (613) 237-1641) down in Little Italy is very much the personal creation of *Nittaya Lynch*, who can be found there every day with one or two helpers rapidly tossing and serving some of the best Thai food in Ottawa. (Wandee was the name of her teacher at cooking school in Thailand.) It's a tiny place with only twelve seats and no license—most of their business is take-out or delivery (through an efficient online ordering system). We usually sit down and have the tom kha soup followed by the penang curry or the red curry with pineapple and shrimp, but everyone likes everything Nittaya cooks. Open Monday to Friday 11 am to 2 pm, 4 pm to 9 pm, Saturday 4 pm to 9 pm. Closed on Sunday. No liquor, Master Card, Visa. **Pure Kitchen** opened their first vegetarian restaurant at 357 Richmond Road in Westboro (telephone (613) 680 5500) and their second soon after at 340 Elgin Street in Centretown (telephone (613 233 7873). Both locations have become something of a phenomenon in Ottawa, serving together more than 1000 meals a day. The original restaurant was inspired by Westboro's Pure Yoga, and both kitchens have a similar focus on good physical and mental health. They sell a lot of cleansing juices with names like Revive, Surge, Electrify and Shine. But they also sell a lot of really delicious smoothies, and the meal plates are not just for vegetarians (which is how they sell 1000 of them a day). The most popular choices are the Radical cauliflower wings, the Fantastic peanut bowl and the Liberty cauliflower wrap (the restaurant goes through hundreds of cases of cauliflowers). There are burgers made with mushrooms and walnuts—try the Royale with cheese, and of course you can get fries with that. There's even poutine with mushroom gravy. An attractive lounge named Charlotte recently opened upstairs on Elgin Street, with a long bar and a number of comfortable seating areas offering inventive drinks and food from the kitchen downstairs. Open Monday to Wednesday 8 am to 9 pm (to 10 pm Wednesday on Elgin), Thursday to Friday 8 am to 10 pm, Saturday 9 am to 10 pm, Sunday 9 am to 9 pm. Licensed. All cards.

OTTAWA   MAP 135
ALLIUM
87 Holland Avenue   **$150**
(613) 792-1313

Ottawa has grown fond of Allium. Arup Jana has been running this remarkably consistent restaurant on the edge of Hintonburg for fourteen years now, and you always know what to expect. Part of his secret is keeping the menus small—there are only four or five choices for each course, and several of those never change. Lunch will always offer steak frites with smoked chili aioli and the house burger with chipotle. Dinners will always start with balsamic mushrooms on toast. The four main courses at night will be steak, fowl, fish and vegetable. And no-one is ever going to let Jana stop making his banoffee pie. Everything is as faultlessly executed as it is familiar. Which brings us to Monday nights. This is when the kitchen has fun. More than ten years ago, long before anyone else in town had heard of them, Jana turned his Monday menu into a long list of small plates. There are usually fifteen or sixteen choices, and you'll want to try them all: roasted duck breast, tuna crudo, beef tataki, grilled lamb chops, curried cauliflower fries, papaya salad, rabbit stew, crispy calamari, buttermilk-fried chicken. But you'll have to book ahead, Mondays at Allium are the worst-kept secret in town.
Open Monday 5.30 pm to 9.30 pm, Tuesday to Thursday 11.30

am to 2 pm, 5.30 pm to 9 pm, Friday 11.30 am to 2 pm, 5.30 pm to 10 pm, Saturday 5.30 pm to 10 pm. Closed on Sunday. Licensed. All cards.

OTTAWA   MAP 135
ATELIER   ☆
540 Rochester Street   **$325**
(613) 321 3537

From Tuesday to Saturday Mark Lepine is serving a twelve-course fixed-price menu of what he calls new Canadian food. His restaurant is at 540 Rochester Street; remember the number, because there's no other way of recognizing the place. The meal starts with a Chopin Waltz—coy names are part of the procedure—followed by a Shrimp Ring, Connect the Dots, You're Being Mighty Selfish, Winter Explosion and so on. The names become tiresome after a while. Each dish has a familiar ingredient (lingcod or shrimp, perhaps) attended by a variety of small tidbits (rutabaga or saffron, say). If you've come to celebrate a birthday or some other special occasion, they'll offer you a piece of cake in liquid nitrogen. Such a meal is expensive—dinner for two costs about 325.00 with a glass of wine. Is it worth it? That's for you to decide.

Open Tuesday to Saturday 5 pm to 10 pm. Closed on Sunday and Monday. Licensed. All cards. You must book ahead.

OTTAWA   MAP 135
BAR LAUREL
1087 Wellington Street W   **$120**
(613) 695-5559

It's hard not to see Bar Laurel as a business decision. Spanish tapas-style restaurants in Toronto like Bar Raval and Bar Isabel are all the rage right now, and it must have seemed to owner Jon Svazas (of Fauna fame—whose family, for what it's worth, come from Lithuania rather than Spain) that the time was ripe to bring some pinchos (or pintxos as he calls them—the menu is resolutely authentic) to Ottawa. He seems to have been right. The restaurant—in the heart of perennially about-to-be-fashionable Hintonburg—is doing almost as well as the mother ship over on Bank Street, which is saying a great deal. One of the reasons Svazas took over the lease of George Monsour's old Back Lane Cafe was the kitchen's two woodburning ovens, to which he has added three Japanese charcoal grills. Almost everything on your plate will pass through one of them. Among the pintxos we like the shrimp, the chorizo, the sobrasada and the tuna; among the snacks and conservas the patatas bravas and the sardines. There are a couple of large sharing plates as well—we've had both good and bad luck with the half and whole chicken, and the dry-aged ribeye is probably a better bet (as it should be for $70). Since this is as much a bar as a restaurant, there is also of course a dynamic wine list, featuring a great many choices by the glass.

Open Monday to Saturday 5.30 pm to midnight. Closed on Sunday. Licensed. Master Card, Visa.

OTTAWA   **MAP 135**
BECKTA   ☆
150 Elgin Street   **$210**
(613) 238-7063

At the end of 2014, Steve Beckta moved his very successful business way upmarket, out of its cosy brick cottage on Nepean Street and into the grandiose Grant House at the corner of Elgin and Gloucester, a landmark heritage mansion that had been undeservedly occupied for many years by Friday's Roast Beef House. Beckta spent a fortune renovating the building, which has now been preserved half-in and half-out of a modern office atrium. He wanted to return it to the grace and dignity of its days as a private home (James Grant was the Surgeon-General of Canada), and its fifty years as the University Club of Ottawa. Keeping the kitchen up to these surroundings was a challenge, and at first there were a few missteps. But everything seems now to be running smoothly. The restaurant is unapologetically high-end:

the dining-room menu is a three-course prix-fixe at 74.00 (there is also a five-course tasting menu at 105.00 per person for the whole table, with optional wine pairings at 52.00 more). If this is too rich for your blood, you can come at lunch or eat in the wine bar. The selections keep changing, but usually include sous-vide octopus, a mousse of foie gras, fresh oysters, Angus striploin, lobster tails and magret of duck. The sweets are elaborate and memorable, and the wine-list is of course enormous.

Open Monday to Friday 11.30 am to 2 pm, 5.30 pm to 10 pm, Saturday and Sunday 5.30 pm to 10 pm. The wine-bar is open from 11.30 am Monday to Friday and from 5 pm Saturday and Sunday. Licensed. All cards. Book ahead. &

OTTAWA   **MAP 135**
CARBEN
1100 Wellington Street W   **$145**
(613) 792-4000

Carben is a relatively new restaurant in Hintonburg, just west of the city centre. It's named for its two founders, Kevin Benes and his wife, Caroline Ngo. Together they've built a short but interesting menu and an inexpensive wine-list. The menu starts with beet salad and runs through pork belly, wood-ear mushrooms, steak tartar and beef cheeks to Arctic char, duck, beef and rump of lamb. Nothing is what you would expect. Wood-ear mushrooms, for instance, come with turmeric aioli and a miso glaze, beef cheeks with pickled cauliflower and wasabi, steak tartar with kimchee and taro-root crisps, scallops in a purée of edamame. Originality is simply an element (an important element) of Kevin Benes' style. The same is true of his choice of wines—there are no clichés on the list.

Open Monday to Friday 5.30 pm to 10 pm, Saturday and Sunday 10.30 am to 2 pm (brunch), 5.30 pm to 10 pm. Licensed. Master Card, Visa.

If you use an out-of-date edition and find it inaccurate, don't blame us. Buy a new edition.

COCONUT LAGOON
853 St. Laurent Boulevard   **$90**
(613) 742-4444

Celebrity Indian chefs are as rare in Canada as Vikram Vij. But nobody told Joe Thottungal. First he won the Gold Medal Plates competition in Ottawa in 2016. That vaulted him into the Canadian Culinary Championships in Kelowna in February of 2017, and nothing daunted, he walked away with the silver medal there, just behind Jinhee Lee of Calgary's Foreign Concept (see above). In both competitions, Thottungal's winning dish was halibut poached in spiced oil, with fish curry crumbs, woodland mushroom aviyal and a lentil emulsion. Definitely not your usual Indian takeout, but the Coconut Lagoon, Thottungal's restaurant in Ottawa East, is not your usual Indian restaurant. Like the rest of us he has to live, and you can find butter chicken and samosas and gulab jamon on the menu—and they're better than anywhere else in town. But you come to the Coconut Lagoon for the things you can't get anywhere else, which means dishes from Thottungal's home state of Kerala in southwest India. Coconut is a big part of Keralan cuisine—hence the restaurant's name—as are tamarind, mangos and limes: try the Naddan chicken or the shrimp mango moilee. We also like the pepper lamb, the mushroom curry and the Nilgiri chicken. To start there's aloo tikki, tandoori lamb chops, shrimp Kakkan and (best of all) ginger soya scallops. And if you're curious about those fish curry crumbs on Thottungal's prize-winning halibut, he made them by dehydrating a traditional fish curry in the oven for twelve hours. He says it was "a little bit hard."

Open Monday to Thursday 11 am to 2 pm, 5 pm to 9 pm, Friday and Saturday 11 am to 2 pm, 5 pm to 9.30 pm, Sunday 11 am to 2 pm, 5 pm to 9 pm. Licensed. Amex, Master Card, Visa.

Every restaurant in this guide has been personally tested. Our reporters are not allowed to identify themselves or to accept free meals.

OTTAWA

MAP 135

DATSUN
380 Elgin Street
(613) 422-2800

☆
$125

Datsun has a good location at the foot of Elgin Street, right next door to El Camino, Matthew Carmichael's popular Mexican taco bar. It has a well-appointed interior, with bar stools that look like gigantic springs. It has an interesting menu, good presentation and good Asian cooking. Almost everything is hot and spicy. Start with spicy chicken wings, Japanese eggplant or tuna tartar furikake, wasabi and nori. If you can afford it, ask for the tuna sashimi with pickled ginger and yuzu ponzu. The most exciting of the big dishes is the green curry of pink shrimps and seared scallops. You can drink either sake or a craft beer. There are several of these, but we like Beau's best, which goes nicely with the deep-fried ice cream.

Open Monday to Saturday 5.30 pm to 11 pm. Closed on Sunday. Licensed. Master Card, Visa. Book ahead. &

OTTAWA

MAP 135

EIGHTEEN
18 York Street
(613) 244-1188

$185

Founded at the beginning of this century, Restaurant Eighteen has become the grandfather of Ottawa restaurants—older even than Beckta, Allium, Whalesbone and the Wellington Gastropub. Its premises in a grand old limestone house on York Street in the Byward Market are expensive and its menu is relentlessly high-end, but year after year it is still a force to be reckoned with. Ottawa is filled with chefs who used to cook here: people like Chris Deraiche (see Wellington Gastropub below), Matthew Carmichael (see Datsun above and Riviera below) and Walid El-Tawel (see Fairouz below). And for this we all owe a debt to Eighteen's unfailingly high standards. The current chef, David Godsoe, used to work with Michael

Blackie at NeXT, which is as good a place to start as any, and so far he's living up to his billing. When it's available we always have the signature black cod in miso, but the lamb and duck make solid second choices. And if somebody else is paying, there are three excellent and extraordinarily expensive steaks (when last seen, the ribeye with bone-marrow bordelaise cost 55.00).

Open daily from 4.30 pm to 10.30 pm. Licensed. All cards.

OTTAWA   **MAP 135**
FAIROUZ   ☆
343 Somerset Street W   **$140**
(613) 422-7700

The original Fairouz at this address was a likeable place that served home-style Middle-Eastern food in the nineteen-nineties. It was owned by the family of Hussain Rahal, and became one of his first employers. A couple of years ago, when the old heritage house fell vacant again, Rahal—now a successful surgeon—decided to reinvent the family business as something entirely new to Ottawa: an upscale Middle-Eastern restaurant—falafel meets fine dining. The town's not short of shawarma, but none of it could be called haute cuisine. Fortunately he found the perfect chef in Walid El-Tawel, who had taken over from Matthew Carmichael at Restaurant Eighteen before leaving to work for the Aga Khan and others in Toronto. El-Tawel was excited to get a chance to cook from his roots, as he puts it—he was born in Abu Dhabi into a Palestinian family—and he created a menu that was at once authentic and original. A dinner here is a fascinating experience. Much of the food you've never eaten before, and the rest—things like baba ghanoush and falafel—you only think you have. The menu is a blend of small and large plates, both meant for sharing. Start with some falafel, so you can see just how poor the versions you've eaten before have been, and then try something new like the superb tuna maslouka with hibiscus gel, diced cucumbers and house-grown herbs. The showpiece large plate is always the lamb—perfectly tender pink chunks of loin sweetened with pomegranate molasses—but the duck breast with saffron and barberry comes a close second. We've also enjoyed the chicken livers, the lamb tartar, the kebabs and, of course, the baba ghanoush. This is a restaurant filled with new ideas, and it deserves to succeed.

Open Tuesday to Thursday 5.30 pm to 10.30 pm, Friday and Saturday 5.30 pm to 11 pm. Closed on Sunday and Monday. Licensed. Master Card, Visa.

OTTAWA   MAP 135
FAUNA
425 Bank Street   **$150**
(613) 563-2862

When Jon Svazas decided to open Fauna on Bank, he and Whalesbone had the street pretty much to themselves. But then, as everyone knows, two years went by in a nightmare of landlord litigation. By the time the Opening Soon paper finally came off Fauna's huge windows, Bank had almost as many fine-dining options as Wellington West. Svazas and his team had no choice but to buckle down and fight their way out of debt, and now, four years later, they're riding high. The high-ceilinged room—formerly home to Higgerty's shoe shop and Hackett the Shoemaker, and now stripped down to its basic bricks and timber—is filled with bright lights and the pleasing roar of commerce. Like so many other local chefs, Svazas used to work with John Taylor—the godfather of Ottawa cuisine—at both Domus and the Genuine Wine Bar. His menu offers five raw choices, five small plates and five main dishes. You can combine them how you will. Prices, except for the 80-day-aged ribeye at 80.00 for two, are reasonable. On the raw list we like the oysters and the beetroot tartar; among the small plates the daily soup and the tempura mushrooms with ponzu aioli; among the main dishes the black cod with shiitake and the lamb shoulder with harissa and mint sourcream. The wine-list is extensive, and everyone loves the pendant lights that hang over the bar like trailing lilies.

Open Monday to Wednesday 11.30 am to 2 pm, 5.30 pm to 10 pm, Thursday to Saturday 11.30 am to 2 pm, 5.30 pm to mid-

night, Sunday 5.30 pm to 10 pm. Licensed. Master Card, Visa. Book ahead if you can.

OTTAWA   MAP 135
FRASER CAFE   ☆
7 Springfield Road   **$145**
(613) 749-1444

Fraser's has been cherished since the day ten years ago when it first opened in cramped quarters on Beechwood Avenue. Like so many others, Ross and Simon Fraser had both cooked with John Taylor at Domus. They were hard-working and cheerful, and really seemed to like working together. The neighbourhood welcomed a serious restaurant, and they soon moved to a new and larger location nearby. Their customers followed them in droves, and the only time you can get a table now is late at night. Their food is not always perfect, but they do most things very well indeed, and the service is unerringly knowing and friendly. We like the pink shrimp with tomato ragout, the torchon of foie gras, the salmon and the striploin of beef. Their tuna is lovely and so is the charcuterie. As for their oysters on the half-shell—impeccably cleaned and served with horseradish and lemon—they're the best in the city. The wine-list is short but well designed. In 2015 they opened a second and similar restaurant called The Rowan downtown at 915 Bank Street (telephone (613) 780-9292). It's cheaper, but it misses the warmth and brio of the original.

Open Monday to Friday 11.30 am to 2 pm, 5.30 pm to 10 pm, Saturday and Sunday 10 am to 2 pm (brunch), 5.30 pm to 10 pm. Licensed. Amex, Master Card, Visa. Book ahead.

OTTAWA   MAP 135
THE GREEN DOOR   ☜🖐
198 Main Street   **$40**
(613) 234-9597

It's all about novelty now in the restaurant trade. New restaurants, new chefs, new recipes, new ingredients—

that's all anyone wants to talk about. Chefs who should be working in their kitchens go crawling through ditches and hedgerows in search of anything edible that hasn't been eaten before. In the midst of this madness, it's sometimes nice to go back to a simpler time. The Green Door has been serving vegetarian food on Main Street for almost thirty years. That's a lot of avocados. The buffet counters—one cold, one hot—hold about 65 choices: salads, dips, casseroles, quiches, pastas and sweets. The avocado salad is famous—its secret is umeboshi vinegar—and they bring out a dozen bowls a day. Meals are priced by the pound—you hand your plate to one of the cashiers in the middle of the room and she'll put it on a scale. It won't come to much, but if you're feeling poor, eat lettuce. The cashier will also pour you a carafe of wine if you want, though there's a limited selection. Everything on offer is made on the premises, and there's no set menu—the kitchen cooks what it can buy. Since you're helping yourself, you can have as much or as little as you want, with no waiting for menus, service or food. A kitchen staff of more than 40 people arrives everyday at 6 am, and dishes are replenished the minute they empty. Try the avocados, the daily dal, the lasagne, the mashed potato with kale or any of the several curries. To follow there are compotes, crumbles and an excellent tofu cheesecake.

Open Tuesday to Sunday 11 am to 9 pm. Closed on Monday. Licensed for beer and wine only. Master Card, Visa.

OTTAWA   MAP 135
ORTO
151 Second Avenue   **$170**
(613) 244-6786

René Rodriguez won a number of prizes on reality shows like *Top Chef Canada* and *Beat Bobby Flay* when he owned Navarra, a sophisticated little boîte in the Byward Market serving reinvented Basque and Mexican cuisine. After Navarra went the way of a lot of Ottawa fine dining, Rodriguez took a bit of a break before being tempted back to cook at Orto, a southern Italian restaurant in the premises off Bank Street vacated by the late and unlamented Urban Pear. There he's making new versions of old standards like pappardelle ai funghi and osso buco with polenta, and the place is packed every night. For now, anyway: Rodriguez is a gifted chef, and how long he will be content to cook an adopted cuisine in a restaurant that is not his own is anybody's guess.

Open Monday to Wednesday 11.30 am to 2 pm, 5.30 pm to 10 pm, Thursday to Saturday 11.30 am to 2 pm, 5.30 pm to 11 pm. Closed on Sunday. Licensed, all cards.

OTTAWA   MAP 135
THE POMEROY HOUSE   ☆
749 Bank Street   **$175**
(613) 237-1658

The Pomeroy House is essentially a mainstream restaurant, but that doesn't mean that the cooking is humdrum. It's not. Chicken is offered with gherkins and kale, Pacific salmon with pickled beets and yogurt, Fogo Island cod with kohlrabi, snap peas and chanterelles, rabbit with potato bread and syrup of balsam. A meal here is always novel and interesting. There's an extensive wine-list of 25 reds and 20 whites, and a bottle of Organized Crime costs only 54.00. The chef, Richard Wilson, comes from Beckta, and his partner, maîtrise d'hôtel Lindsay Gordon, from the Fraser Cafe. Their restaurant is one of a half-dozen ventures in Ottawa—others include Fraser's, the Rowan and Wilf & Ada's—funded by Ion Aimers, who earned his substantial fortune through the sale of the Works gourmet hamburger chain, and is now investing it wisely.

Open Tuesday to Saturday 11.30 am to 2 pm, 5.30 pm to 10 pm, Sunday 5.30 pm to 9 pm. Closed on Monday. Licensed, Master Card, Visa. Book ahead if you can.

If you wish to improve the guide send us information about restaurants we have missed. Our mailing address is Oberon Press, 145 Spruce Street: Suite 205, Ottawa, Ontario K1R 6P1.

RIVIERA
62 Sparks Street   **$140**
(613) 233-6262

Matthew Carmichael kept his head down for quite a while after leaving Restaurant Eighteen. When he finally opened El Camino, it was little more than a take-out taco window in a basement on Elgin Street. But the restaurant slowly expanded, and when a sister restaurant, Datsun, was added next door they took over the entire floor of the building. Elgin became a go-to destination and Carmichael and his co-chef Jordan Holley prospered. Inevitably they began to think about a third location, which led to the opening in 2016 of Riviera on the Sparks Street mall, in what used to be the old Imperial Bank building. It's a grand and handsome space, designed to inspire the same confidence in the cooking that customers used to have in the solvency of the bank. But the menu is a strange hybrid, offering black cod next to hanger steak, lobster pappardelle next to spaghetti bolognese and grilled octopus with blistered shishitos next to mushrooms on toast with an egg. The kitchen seems to want to be all things to all people. And of course, the results are mixed. A hanger steak will always be a hanger steak, and nothing can save spaghetti bolognese. But we like the other pastas, the cod, the prawn-and-scallop chowder and the fine lemon tart. And on a cold winter's night there really is a lot to be said for mushrooms on toast—particularly with an egg. It's hard to say how the chips will fall at Riviera, but Carmichael and Holley have just opened a second El Camino on Clarence Street, and four restaurants may prove to be more than even they can handle.

Open Monday to Friday 11.30 am to 2.30 pm, 5 pm to 11 pm, Saturday 5 pm to 11 pm. Closed on Sunday. Licensed. All cards. Book ahead.

Nobody can buy his way into this guide and nobody can buy his way out.

OTTAWA   MAP 135
STOFA   ☆☆
1356 Wellington Street W   **$140**
(613) 722-6555

Jason Sawision was chef de cuisine at Atelier for six years—"Atelier's secret weapon," Marc Lepine says. Before that he worked at Canoe and for Michael Stadtländer at Eigensinn Farm. It's an impressive resumé, and Stofa is an impressive restaurant. Really, the only thing we don't like is the name, which is apparently Old Norse and means "hearth." Sawision says he wanted to convey that his restaurant was comfortable and approachable in spite of its ambitious cuisine, and it is. The room is large, pale and sparsely decorated, but the tables are well-spaced, the noise level agreeable and the padded chairs soft and welcoming. Sawision has moved on from molecular gastronomy and tasting plates to a conventional kitchen and three-course menus. It is, he says, how he prefers to eat himself. What he has brought from Atelier is a gift for diverse combinations. Every ingredient on the plate can stand on its own, but Sawision mingles them together like a string quartet—you can taste each one and you can taste them all. Try the scallops with braised red cabbage, carrot-and-caraway purée, almond pudding and crispy chicken skin—an extraordinary dish—or the duck and buffalo-milk ravioli with beluga lentils and porcini foam. To start there's beef tartar with vindaloo spices and cardamom mayonnaise, celeriac soup with fennel, apples, pickled mushrooms and confit chicken or—our favourite—roast quail with chicken stuffing, vanilla-parsnip purée, pomegranate chutney and garam masala jus. If the sumptuous passionfruit soufflé is on the sweet list, make sure to order it in advance. Many people—and we don't disagree with them—think this is now the best restaurant in Ottawa.

Open Tuesday to Saturday 5.30 pm to 10 pm. Closed on Sunday and Monday. Licensed. Master Card, Visa.

Every restaurant in this guide has been personally tested.

OTTAWA　　　　　　　　　　　　　　　**MAP 135**
SUPPLY AND DEMAND
1335 Wellington Street W　　　　　　　　　**$135**
(613) 680-2949

You have to hand it to Joshua Bishop, he leaves his mark. We first met Steve Wall at Whalesbone, where he was backing up Steve Vardy and later running the kitchen on his own. Now Vardy is at the Adelaide Oyster House in St. John's (see below) and Wall is at Supply and Demand, and both Steves are modeling their approach on Bishop's. It's not so much the focus on seafood, or the casual service or the noise; it's more a matter of attitude, a commitment to the principles of sustainability and responsible consumption. These are people who take their food seriously. A good deal of the menu at Supply and Demand is raw. There are usually only two main courses, one meat and one fish (duck and cod the last time we were there). The rest of the list is small plates, built around vegetables or housemade pasta. It's tempting to order one of the main courses, but the smaller plates are often more interesting. Among the raw dishes we like the albacore tuna crudo, the beef carpaccio (which comes up Highway 7 from Tweed) and of course the oysters—anyone who has worked at Whalesbone will always serve oysters. The small plates change all the time, but are largely vegetarian: kale salad, roasted carrots or beets, squash salad, heirloom tomatoes with balsamic burrata. For sweet, corny or not, you have to go with the baked Alaska. The wine-list is large and the markups are small.
Open Tuesday to Saturday 5 pm to 10 pm, Sunday 5 pm to 9.30 pm. Closed on Monday. Licensed. All cards. Book ahead.

OTTAWA　　　　　　　　　　　　　　　**MAP 135**
WELLINGTON GASTROPUB
1325 Wellington Street W　　　　　　　　**$150**
(613) 729-1315

Everyone eats at the Gastropub. There's always someone tantalizingly familiar at the next table. (It once took us a whole lunch to recognize Jason Spezza.) And of course all these people know what they're doing. Chris Deraiche used to run the kitchen at Restaurant Eighteen, but he wanted something more real, more down-to-earth, something that felt like his own. So he and Shane Waldron opened the Wellie (as they call it) up a long flight of stairs in Westboro, and they've never looked back. For more than twelve years now, Chris Deraiche has made up a new menu every day. This is almost unheard of, but it's one of the reasons people keep coming back—to see what Chris will think of next. Scallops appear often, with couscous or lentils in winter, with fennel and apple in summer. They have the best pork in Ottawa and were one of the first to start cooking it rare. Beef short-ribs are a favourite, as is duck. Flavours are strong and colourful—this is pub food, not cuisine minceur. Potatoes are crushed (not mashed), tomatoes are roasted, soups are made out of white beans and bacon, breast of duck is served with fritters of thyme bread pudding. There is a wine-list, but most people drink beer. Shane grew up in Ireland, and like all Irishmen he knows his ales. There's a choice of about thirty Canadian craft beers, with another thirteen—none from further away than Collingwood—on tap.

Open Monday to Friday 11.30 am to 2 pm, 5.30 pm to 10 pm. Saturday 5.30 pm to 10 pm Closed on Sunday. Licensed. Amex, Master Card, Visa. Book ahead if you can.

OTTAWA   **MAP 135**
WHALESBONE   ☆
430 Bank Street   **$195**
(613) 231-8569

The Whalesbone on Bank Street is getting a bit old and worn, but between here and Elgin Street (see below), this is still the pick of the pair. There are hardly any tables—the restaurant is only 22 feet wide—and the soundtrack is Joshua Bishop's personal collection of vinyl LPs. The pictures on the walls are fading, and there can be drafts in the winter. And none of that matters, because the cooking never misses a beat. There aren't many main courses—lingcod, mackerel, lobster and steak (we like the lingcod)—but the appetizers more than make up. Of course there are the famous Thai mussels, without which Whalesbone wouldn't be Whalesbone. There's beef tartar with truffles and a quail egg, raw scallops with ginger and green apple, endive salad with pecorino and capers, clam chowder with bacon, dill, potato and leeks and (our favourite) torched albacore tuna with grapefruit, yoghurt, black garlic and sesame. The oysters on the half shell change every day and they're outstanding. The wine is still served in toothbrush glasses. Cafes like Whalesbone are a vanishing breed. Like one of the vintage Neil Young albums that Bishop spins on his ancient turntable behind the bar, it's raucous, noisy, uncomfortable and *real*. It's the most genuine evening in town.

Open Monday to Friday 11.30 am to 2 pm, 5 pm to 11 pm, Saturday and Sunday 5 pm to 11 pm. Licensed. Amex, Master Card, Visa. Book ahead.

OTTAWA   MAP 135
WHALESBONE ON ELGIN
231 Elgin Street   **$195**
(613) 505-4300

Whalesbone is prospering. The original restaurant at 430 Bank Street earned a star from us recently and it's always packed. Then they opened a second location at 231 Elgin Street, in a huge space that also fits in the Whalesbone supply shop that used to be over on Kent Street. Elgin is a hot address these days, and the new restaurant is crowded in spite of its size, but we don't find the cooking here as startling as it is on Bank Street. The menu is ambitious—yellowfin-tuna sashimi with wasabi, beef tartar, bone marrow with sea salt, Thai mussels in coconut milk (a perennial favourite at both locations), octopus and dry-aged striploin steak. You should come to Elgin Street if you can't get a table on Bank, or if you want to take advantage of the larger menu or buy from the shop. The noise in the restaurant was deafening when it opened, to the point where the staff couldn't hear people's orders, but dampening panels were put in the ceiling a few months later and they work beautifully.

Open Monday 11.30 am to 4 pm, 5 pm to 10 pm, Tuesday and Wednesday 11.30 am to 4 pm, 5 pm to 11 pm, Thursday and Friday 11.30 am to 4 pm, 5 pm to midnight, Saturday 5 pm to midnight, Sunday 5 pm to 10 pm. Licensed. Amex, Master Card, Visa.

OTTAWA *See also* CHELSEA.

OWEN SOUND, Ontario   **MAP 136**
THE FLYING CHESTNUT
199 Pellisier Street   **$100**
Eugenia
(519) 924-1809

To get to Eugenia, turn off Highway 26 at Thornbury and drive south on Highway 13 almost as far as Highway 4. This is the heart of Blue Mountain country, where you can go fishing on Lake Eugenia or visit Eugenia Falls, second only in height to the falls at Niagara. Shawn Adler has installed a big wood-burning stove in his kitchen and dedicated it to regional, organic cooking—even his beer and wine are local. Every night three appetizers and three main dishes are written up on a blackboard. Usually there's one fish, one meat and a vegetarian dish. The menu changes every week, but dinner usually ends with bread pudding, butter tarts or a fruit crumble. The Sunday brunch offers omelettes, pancakes and waffles for about 15.00, and portions are very generous. The dinner on Sunday is *prix fixe* and costs 40.00.

Open Thursday to Saturday 5 pm to 10 pm, Sunday 11 am to 2 pm (brunch), 5 pm to 10 pm. Closed Monday to Wednesday. Licensed. No cards. Book ahead if you can.

The price rating shown opposite the headline of each entry indicates the average cost of dinner for two with a modest wine, tax and tip. The cost of dinner, bed and breakfast (if available) is shown in parentheses.

PARRSBORO, N.S.   MAP 137
THE PORCHLIGHT   🗨
138 Main Street   **$65**
(902) 254-3111

The PorchLight is small, intimate and friendly. It's owned by Mitch and Kim White—he cooks, she serves (and makes friends). Most of their ingredients are local. Helpings are large and prices are low. They're rightly proud of their fish and chips, but they made their name with their huge hamburgers, which weigh about half a pound each. The biggest of all is the double cheddar and bacon—two patties, two slices of cheddar and six rashers of bacon, all for 13.00. Everybody admires the elegant salads and the sourdough toast. The kitchen is always ready to cater to gluten-free and other diets. All the pies are made on the premises, and the apple crisp is as good as your grandmother's.

Open Tuesday to Sunday 7 am to 7 pm and closed on Monday from 1 July until 30 September, Wednesday and Thursday 7 am to 2 pm, Friday and Saturday 7 am to 7 pm, Sunday 10 am to 7 pm and closed on Monday and Tuesday from 1 October until 30 June. Licensed. Master Card, Visa. ♿

PEMBROKE, Ontario   *MAP 138*

Most of the restaurants in Pembroke confine themselves to lunch. The Nook Crêperie at 26 Pembroke Street W (telephone (613) 735-4800) serves both savoury and sweet crêpes that change with the seasons. You can make a dinner out of some of them (like the lox or the Michelangelo). They've added a couple of lighter sweets for those who don't want to follow crêpes with more crêpes—things like vanilla crème brûlée. They're open all day every day but Sunday, when they're open only in the morning, and Monday, when they're closed all day. They have a licence and take most cards. Janna's Gallery Cafe at 20 Pembroke Street W (telephone (613) 631-0443) is known for its coffee and its sweets. It's open all day every day but Sunday, has a licence and takes most cards. Then there's Ullrich's on Main at 214 Pembroke Street W (telephone (613) 735-6025), which started out years ago as a butcher's shop, *branched out first into groceries, then into a deli and finally into a lunchroom, open from 11 am to 2.30 pm every day but Sunday. They offer two soups, a chicken quesadilla and a number of salads and sandwiches. Their chocolate cake is very good indeed and the service is quick and friendly. They have a licence and take most cards.* &

PEMBROKE
See also PETAWAWA.

PENTICTON, B.C.   MAP 140
VANILLA POD
Poplar Grove Winery   **$160**
425 Middle Bench Road
(250) 493-9463

Poplar Grove built this stylish new building in 2011, nearly twenty years after the business was founded. Soon afterward they invited Paul and Sheila Jones to bring over their Vanilla Pod restaurant from Summerland. The winery has a spectacular location on the Naramata Bench, with panoramic views from the restaurant over Penticton and Lake Okanagan. Bruno Terroso has been in the kitchen since the beginning, and his menu makes regular use of local suppliers as well as his own kitchen garden. The prawns with chorizo are a good place to start, as is the platter of salami and candied smoked salmon with mustard, garlic and goat cheese. The restaurant does well with seasonal seafood like salmon, halibut and mussels. Or there's the signature paella, filled with prawns, mussels, chicken, chorizo, bell peppers, red onion and pea shoots. If you'd rather stay out of the water there's lamb shank, confit of duck and an excellent organic ribeye steak from Cache Creek.
Open daily 11.30 am to 9 pm. Licensed. All cards. Book ahead. &

PENTICTON
See also OLIVER.

PERCE, Quebec   **MAP 141**
LA MAISON MATHILDE
Auberge les Trois Soeurs   **$120**
77 route 132
(800) 463-9700

La Maison Mathilde is a small, rather pretty house
attached to a 60-room hotel. Look for it at the east end of
the village, overlooking the beach, the sea and the rock.
They have a three-course menu specializing in fish and
shellfish (including lobster). Everything—the poached
salmon, the seafood pastry, even the tarte au sucre—is
beautifully presented and full of flavour, and the whole
meal costs less than 50.00 a head. The tables tend to fill up
quickly, so book ahead. We have found the service brisk,
but others have had long waits. Everyone agrees,
however, that the food should be served hotter.
*Open daily 7 am to 11.30 am, 4 pm to 10 pm from mid-June until
the end of September. Licensed. Visa. Book ahead.*

PERTH, Ontario   **MAP 142**
FIELD HOUSE   ☆
43 Herriott Street   **$45**
(613) 267-7474

The Field House was attractively renovated last year, and
now has seating for a dozen people inside to go with the
outdoor summer patio, not to mention longer hours, a
larger menu and a license. Unfortunately it still closes in
the middle of the afternoon, but one step at a time. People
like to say that the bakery is as good as any in the county.
Actually, everything is good and everything is cheap, perhaps because the chef got his start at Whalesbone in
Ottawa (see above). In the morning they serve housemade
granola, croissants, muffins and breakfast sandwiches (try
The Boss, with egg, bacon, cheese, roasted red peppers
and kale). Lunch is soup, salads and sandwiches—
porchetta, turkey and soppressata, chicken and brie—and
a chicken, porchetta or tofu noodle bowl. On Fridays
there's smoked trout with caramelized onion. You can

also order (at least 24 hours in advance) a variety of takeout pizzas, either one of the usual combinations or a Field House Special like Calabrian chili, kale and anchovy or walnut pesto with squash, caramelized onion and camembert.

Open Tuesday to Friday 9 am to 4 pm, Saturday 10 am to 3 pm. Closed on Sunday and Monday. Licensed. Master Card, Visa.

PERTH-ANDOVER, N.B.   MAP 143
WATERFRONT CAFE
878 Perth Main Street   **$90**
(506) 273-2878

Perth-Andover meant York's for so many years that it feels strange to start looking elsewhere. But the Waterfront Cafe gives pleasure to everyone who crosses its doorstep—or would if only it kept longer hours. The chef serves dishes that look as good as they taste. That doesn't mean high prices and small helpings. A brunch with a choice of eggs can be had for only 10.00. Diners find the flavours amazing, whether it's salmon cakes with a composed salad, jumbo shrimp with cranberry and goat-cheese, prime rib of beef with red wine or Atlantic salmon with hollandaise sauce. You can finish your meal with poached pears or New York cheesecake. Either will cost you just 5.00.

Open Wednesday and Thursday 9 am to 4 pm, Friday 8 am to 8 pm, Saturday and Sunday 9 am to 4 pm. Closed on Monday and Tuesday. Licensed. Master Card, Visa. Book ahead if you can.

PETAWAWA, **Ontario**   *(MAP 138)*
MADAMEEK   *¢*
1024 Victoria Street   *$80*
(613) 687-6872

Most people in the area know the story behind this restaurant. A soldier at Camp Petawawa named Marc Diab asked his parents if they would help him open a Lebanese restaurant in the town when he came back from Afghanistan. He wanted to introduce his new home and new friends to some of the food he had loved as a little boy in Lebanon. But Marc did not come back from Afghanistan. When they got the news, his parents decided to move from Toronto to Petawawa and open the restaurant for him. Madameek serves all the dishes Marc Diab wanted—shawarma, kibbeh, kabobs, fattoush and tabouleh salads—and more. Everything is prepared with all the care that you would expect. The restaurant is open every day of the week from 11 am to 8 pm, has no liquor and takes all cards.

PICTON, Ontario   **MAP 145**
BLUMEN GARDEN   ☆
647 Highway 49   **$150**
(613) 476-6841

A lot of people make a detour to stop at the Blumen Garden, both for the setting and the food. On a sunny day you can sit under the gazebo in the garden; on a chilly day you can warm up inside over a plate of pulled rabbit with housemade gnocchi. Whatever you order will be cooked with precision and care. You won't go wrong with the fish chowder—to which each separate fish is added at just the right time—or the rack of lamb or the Atlantic salmon. They always try to have a couple of vegetarian options—look out for the chickpea frites. Altogether there are five or six appetizers and eight or nine main courses, all generously served. The wines are mostly local, as are the beers and the cider on tap.
Open Monday and Wednesday to Sunday 11.30 am to 2 pm, 5 pm to 10 pm from 1 April until 15 October. Closed on Tuesday. Licensed. All cards. ♿

PICTON   **MAP 145**
MERRILL INN   ☆
343 Main Street E   **$150 ($400)**
(866) 567-5969

The Merrill Inn is probably the best place to stay now in Prince Edward County. The grand old mansion has been completely renovated to provide a dozen lovely bedrooms with a restaurant downstairs that is open only for dinner (though if you stay overnight there's breakfast as well). The menu is cautious and traditional. It starts with calamari, hot smoked trout and spinach-and-ricotta dumplings, and goes on to rack of lamb, osso buco with fennel and breast of duck with rostii potatoes. For sweet there's a tart cherry pie. The cellar offers a wide selection of unusual local wines from small vineyards, and you can get a pairing for each dinner course for 33.00.

Open Tuesday to Saturday 5.30 pm to 9 pm. Closed on Sunday and Monday. Licensed. All cards. Book ahead if you can.

PICTON
See also BLOOFIELD, WELLINGTON.

PICTOU, N.S.   (MAP 123)
STONE-SOUP CAFE
41 Water Street   **$80**
(902) 485-4949

The Stone-Soup Café prospers even in the winter when all the tourists have gone home. Barry Rundle and Camille Davidson have attracted a big local following with their generous all-day menu. Breakfast is mostly about benedicts, lunch and dinner are soups (housemade and served in gigantic bowls), salads, sandwiches (roast turkey and grilled chicken are the favourites) and, from the fryer, haddock, chicken wings, onion rings and sweet-potato fries. Some years ago the Café introduced international dinners—the most popular have been Italian and Korean—on Saturday nights, and they've been so successful that they're now offered on Fridays as well. People drive from 50 miles away. The sweets change daily—just look in the case and see what they have—and there's a small list of local wines and beers.

Open daily 7 am to 8 pm from 1 May until 15 October, 7 am to 3 pm from 15 October until 1 May. Licensed. Master Card, Visa.
&

Nobody can buy his way into this guide and nobody can buy his way out.

LA POCATIERE, Quebec   MAP 147
CAFE AZIMUT
309 4 avenue Painchaud   **$120**
(418) 856-2411

The Café Azimut celebrates its thirtieth anniversary in 2018, and for the last ten of those years it has been owned by Julie Levesque. La Pocatière is home to both a junior college and a Bombardier plant, and the menu offers pizza, hamburgers and housemade fries along with smoked sturgeon, filet mignon and fresh salmon. Everything is cooked à point—the duck just slides off the bone. The menu is extensive, but we prefer the table d'hôte. If you're lucky there'll be a tarte au sucre. The wine-list is full of private imports. Even the Michelin guide has called—they wrote that no-one visiting the lower St. Lawrence should miss the Café Azimut.
Open daily 9 am to 8 pm, later on weekends. Licensed. All cards.
&

POCOLOGAN, N.B.   MAP 148
BAYBREEZE MOTEL
1475 Highway 175   **$60**
(506) 755-3850

The old Highway 1, with the waves practically breaking on your car, is a lot more fun to drive than the new one. The Baybreeze is right on the shore overlooking the sea. John and Maria Lytras have owned it for almost 40 years. Their three-room motel is the best place to stay hereabouts, and the kitchen serves nothing but seafood and fresh, seasonal vegetables. The potato salad is remarkable, and the scallops and clams come straight from the sea. We usually ask for either the lobster roll or the lobster stew. The pastries are made with a very light hand, and the olives all come from trees that grow on the Lytras property in Greece, where John and Maria spend the winter.
Open daily 7 am to 10 pm from 1 May until 31 October. Licensed. All cards.

PORT CARLING, Ontario

MAP 149

LOONDOCKS
98 Joseph Street   **$140**
(705) 765-5191

The celebrities are fickle around Port Carling, and Loon-docks has done well to survive for five long years. It over-looks the small-boat locks from a height of land next to the Post Office, with a lovely open-air deck looking down on the water. Kevin Duynstee, the owner and chef, grew up in Muskoka and Muskoka still means a lot to him. At Loondocks he has a few small plates to start—spring-rolls, gnocchi with chorizo and a trout salad. Among his large plates there's breast of duck with blueberries, pickerel with béarnaise and chicken with chorizo, as well as vegetarian choices of risotto and pasta. There's also fillet of trout with maple and merlot and an excellent beef tenderloin (from Morley Stephen, Muskoka's best butcher) with mushrooms and brandy. The wine-list has been enlarged and there are now several good wines from California, Australia and the Niagara Region. The only thing threatening Loondocks is its own success: Kevin and his wife Brittany opened a second location down in Burlington in 2018, and everyone is wondering how much of their attention will get taken away from Muskoka.

Open daily 5 pm to 8.30 pm from early May until late October.
Licensed. Master Card, Visa. Book ahead if you can. &

PORT ELGIN, N.B.

MAP 150

LE CHAT BLEU
342 Highway 970   **$110**
(506) 538-0110

You'll find this picturesque old house in Baie Verte, which is a few miles from Port Elgin. The building began life as a church in the eighteen-thirties and was converted into a general store fifty years later. The current owners have treated the place with love and respect, and filled the inte-rior with treasures, among them a vintage motorcycle in the window. The menu is seasonal, relying heavily on neighbouring organic farmers. One traveller told us he came in because everything smelled so good. They offer such things as seafood cioppino, spanakopita, prawn-and-lobster cakes and chicken teriyaki. Many of the desserts are made by the owner's mother, like the rhubarb-and-strawberry pie and the pineapple-carrot cake, and there are local beers on tap.

Open Wednesday to Sunday 11 am to 8 pm from mid-March until Thanksgiving, Thursday to Sunday 11 am to 8 pm from Thanksgiving until 31 December. Closed on Monday and Tuesday in summer, Monday to Wednesday in fall, and from 1 January to mid-March. Licensed. Master Card, Visa.

PORT HOOD, N.S.   MAP 151
HAUS TREUBURG
175 Main Street   **$125 ($250)**
(902) 787-2116

Georg and Elvi Kargoll bought this old house in 1984 and restored it from top to bottom. Their menu seldom changes, their prices never do. Dinner comes in four courses unless you book the seven-course *menu surprise* in advance. Normally you start with house-smoked salmon or flammkuchen, an Alsatian version of pizza, followed by soup or a Caesar salad. Then there's a choice of meat, fish or a vegetarian dish. The meat might be beef stroganoff; the vegetarian dish might be lasagne. We ourselves usually prefer the fish. It used to be Atlantic salmon, but this year they are serving lobster instead. The meal ends with a fine apple strudel, made to an old family recipe and topped with real whipped cream. If you spend the night—the bedrooms are immaculate—you'll come down in the morning to what they call a German Sunday breakfast, which means farm-fresh eggs, homemade sausages, cereals, grains, hot buttered toast and homemade yogurt. The Haus Treuburg has its own sandy beach and some of the warmest water in Eastern Canada. *Open daily by appointment only from 1 June until 31 October. Licensed. Master Card, Visa. You must book ahead.*

PORT HOOD

See also GLENVILLE, NORTHEAST MARGAREE.

PORT MEDWAY, N.S.   MAP 152
THE PORT GROCER
1615 Port Medway Road   **$90**
(902) 677-2884

The old Port Medway grocer in the heart of town was taken over a few years ago by Deb Melanson and Annabel Singleton and transformed into a cafe, post office and general store. They serve lunch six days a week from 11 am to 2.30 pm, and brunch on Sunday from 10 am to 2 pm. Dinner is only on Friday, which is a pub night with live music and daily specials like creole chicken pasta and shrimp and sausage gumbo. At lunch we like the dragon bowl—grains, nuts and greens with chicken or shrimp in sesame dressing, all for 8.95—or the chowder brimming with seafood. There are also pies, pizzas and wraps, not to mention art classes and shows and local events.

Open Monday to Thursday 11 am to 2.30 pm, Friday 11 am to 2.30 pm, 6 pm to 10 pm, Saturday 11.30 am to 2.30 pm, Sunday 10 am to 2 pm (brunch). Licensed. All cards.

PORT STANLEY, Ontario   MAP 153
WINDJAMMER INN   ☆
324 Smith Street   **$130 ($290)**
(519) 782-4173

After ten years as the Windjammer innkeeper, Kimberley Saunders realized she wasn't just tired, she was tired of doing the same old things. She closed the inn for three months of renovations and used the time off to reinvent her menu. It's now centred around what she calls modern farmhouse cuisine. Everything possible comes from Elgin County, and much of it from the gardens surrounding the inn. A chef's harvest table with seats for twelve friends or strangers has been put in the library, with a daily prix-fixe menu; the regular à la carte is offered in the main dining-room. Fresh fish—perch or pickerel perhaps—is always

216

on the list, along with beef and chicken or duck. Before settling here, Kimberley worked in several important Toronto restaurants, and her dishes all look as they would in the big city. She also used to be a pastry chef, and makes most of the sweets out of her head. Port Stanley is an attractive lakeside town, with a fine beach within walking distance of the inn. The Windjammer was built in 1854 by a local ship's captain. It's been skilfuly restored and is now an attractive place to stay.

Open Tuesday 5.30 pm to 8.30 pm, Wednesday to Friday 11 am to 3 pm, 5.30 pm to 8.30 pm, Saturday and Sunday 9.30 am to 2 pm (brunch), 5.30 pm to 8.30 pm from early May until Thanksgiving (shorter hours in winter). Closed on Monday (and Tuesday in winter). Licensed. Master Card, Visa.

PRINCE ALBERT, Saskatchewan   MAP 154
AMY'S ON SECOND   ☆
2990 2 Avenue W   **$140**
(306) 763-1515

It's now 32 years since Amy came to Second Avenue. It hasn't all been smooth sailing, but right now she's excited about her new staff. Kyle Novicki, who has taken over the kitchen, worked at a number of two-star Michelin restaurants in France before coming to the River Café in Calgary. Amy says he will bring some new approaches to her menu, though nobody's favourites are going to disappear. Her new pastry chef has added a great chocolate cake and her own tiramisu. And finally, Amy's son Ian Harris has taken over the dining-room for her. She gets her vegetables from a local market gardener. Once a week the biggest supplier of fresh seafood in the province brings her tuna, wild salmon, Arctic char, even mussels. Pickerel comes from the northern lakes and it's a huge seller. The striploin is all handcut triple-A Black Angus. Brome Lake duck, bison and lamb all make regular appearances on the menu. The coffee is roasted locally. If Prince Albert lasts another 32 years, Amy's will still be there.

Open Monday to Friday 11 am to 9 pm, Saturday 5 pm to 9 pm. Closed on Sunday. Licensed. All cards. Free parking. &

PRINCE GEORGE, B.C.　　　　　　　　**MAP 155**
THE WHITE GOOSE　　　　　　　　　　　☆
1205 3 Avenue　　　　　　　　　　　　　**$165**
(250) 561-1002

Ryan Cyre loves what he's doing; in fact, he's passionate about it. He's felt that way ever since he arrived in Prince George in 2007. He now offers his magnificent five-course dinners seven nights a week and sells them for 60.00 a head. His express lunches, served six days a week, have gone up a dollar or two. He also has a regular à la carte and a food truck. Everything on his menus is the best he can find and everything is carefully and skilfully prepared. The triple-cream baked brie with pears and roasted garlic and the duo of duck never leave the menu. For that matter, you'll still find most of the old favourites there— braised-beef short-ribs, crab-cakes, ragout of bison and polenta. Cyre's mother still makes the chocolate cake, using an old family recipe, and she has no plans to stop. The wine pairings are all chosen with great care. The service is perfect.
Open Monday to Saturday 11 am to 2 pm, 5 pm to 9 pm, Sunday 5 pm to 9 pm. Licensed. Master Card, Visa. ⅃

PRINCE RUPERT, B.C.　　　　　　　　**MAP 156**
CARGO KITCHEN
101 1 Avenue E　　　　　　　　　　　　**$90**
(250) 624-8444

Cargo Kitchen has been a rewarding place to eat ever since the day it opened. It helps, of course, that it's right next door to the wonderful Museum of Northern History. Its first chef, Avi Sternburg, spent years training in Japan, after which he laid out a shortish menu of classic dishes with an Asian kick. For instance, karate chicken was his take on chicken karaage. Two chefs have come since, but without making any important changes to the menu. The halibut and salmon are always exceptional, but you won't go wrong either with the Moroccan chicken or the seafood risotto. A surprising number of people write to us about the grilled chicken on a bun, but we haven't yet tried it. They have the local Wheelhouse on tap; it's a nice pale ale and well worth a try.

Open Monday to Friday noon to 2 pm, 5 pm to 9 pm, Saturday and Sunday noon to 9 pm (shorter hours in winter). Licensed. Amex, Master Card, Visa. Book ahead if you can. &

PRINCE RUPERT   MAP 156
COW BAY CAFE   ☆
205 Cow Bay Road   **$95**
(250) 627-1212

It's extraordinary how this little restaurant has risen to the top and stayed there, despite having three different owners. The latest of these, Opa Sushi, has somehow created a kitchen that may soon rival their own. We thought the new menu would be built around local seafood, because there's no better fish anywhere in the province. But the fact is that what most diners are talking about is the authentic Italian cuisine, particularly the beef and the lamb. There's a chalkboard of daily specials as well as a regular menu. The dining-room may be small, but it has a very likeable atmosphere and fine views of Cow Bay. What is really surprising is the number of fine imported wines in the cellar. If you prefer to drink beer, they have that too, and have it in spades.

Open Tuesday to Friday 11.30 am to 2 pm, 5 pm to 9 pm, Saturday 5 pm to 9 pm, Sunday noon to 3 pm. Closed on Monday. Licensed. Visa. Book ahead.

PRINCE RUPERT   MAP 156
OPA SUSHI   ☆
34 Cow Bay Road   **$95**
(250) 627-4560

If you haven't tasted sushi made with really fresh seafood, come to Opa Sushi—they never have anything else in the kitchen. In season, they'll have salmon, squid, octopus, sweet shrimp and eel. Plus there are now four new specials, among them crab with avocado and tuna (called Firecracker) and crab with avocado, cucumber and curried honey (called Manila Vanilla). They have a sake bar, the only one in the Pacific Northwest. Opa Sushi is on the second floor of an old net loft, and it's one of the last of its kind. It seats just 35 people, so you should book ahead. If you ask for a table on the outside patio you may be able to watch the sea-eagles nesting overhead.

Open Tuesday to Friday 11.30 am to 2 pm, 5 pm to 9 pm, Saturday noon to 3 pm, 5 pm to 9 pm, Sunday 1 pm to 8 pm. Closed on Monday. Licensed. Visa. Book ahead.

QUALICUM BEACH, B.C.   MAP 157
GIOVANNI'S
180 2 Avenue W: Unit 4   **$120**
(250) 752-6693

Giovanni's is back in top form this year. That's partly because of its pizzas, which are the best north of Lantzville. Our favourites are the Thai chicken supreme and the Principessa with artichoke hearts, spinach and raw tomatoes. To start you should order the deep-fried squid marinara or the saltspring mussels steamed in white wine with garlic and tomatoes. After that, go for the char-broiled filet mignon with gorgonzola or the breast of chicken sautéed with oyster mushrooms. As usual, we recommend the flourless torte made with Callebaut chocolate. The service has only been at work a few months, and should improve. Unless you want to see the hockey game, sit away from the big-screen television—it's distracting.

Open Monday to Saturday 5 pm to 9 pm. Closed on Sunday. Licensed. All cards. ♿

QUALICUM BEACH
See also COOMBS.

☞ This symbol means that the restaurant is rated a good buy. This ♿ means that there is wheelchair access to both the tables and the washrooms.

220

QUEBEC, Quebec   MAP 158
APSARA   🤚
71 rue d'Auteuil   **$85 ($185)**
(418) 694-0232

There are, of course, more notable kitchens in Quebec
than the Apsara. But there are few so inexpensive or so
comfortable. Everybody leaves this place in a good mood.
Chau Mouy Youk has been in charge of the kitchen for at
least 30 years and she makes a virtue of consistency. The
menu includes several Thai and Vietnamese dishes as well
as Cambodian, and it never changes. There are a number
of vegetarian dishes, and they and everything else are surprisingly cheap. Some of the best dishes are the khemara
soup, the mini lat and mou sati from Sangker, the oudong
chicken and the Annam shrimp. The sorbets taste of real
fruit and are all wonderful. The lunch menu, which
changes daily, costs only 12.95. If you come with a com-
panion, there are several dishes on offer for two or more,
among them a starter of spicy pork with crisp noodles and
a main course of stir-fried chicken with ginger. They have
a few wines, but it's better, we think, to order a carafe of
hakutsuru sake, which is sold on draft. It comes cold and
clear and it's great.
Open Monday to Friday 11.30 am to 2 pm, 5.30 pm to 10.30
pm, Saturday and Sunday 5.30 pm to 11 pm. Licensed. Amex,
Master Card, Visa.

QUEBEC   MAP 158
INITIALE   ☆☆☆
54 rue St.-Pierre   **$275**
(418) 694-1818

Initiale is exquisite. It was established in an old bank
building in the Lower Town almost 30 years ago by Ivan
Lebrun and Rolande Leclerc. Lebrun comes from St.-
Malo, and he cooks Parisian French with the very best
local québécois ingredients. He's at his best with things
like venison with wild mushrooms and scallops with
mustard leaves, but everything is impeccably prepared

221

and served. The front of the house is artfully managed by Mme Leclerc. Dinners are expensive, but lunch is a much better buy.

Open Tuesday to Friday 11.30 am to 2 pm, 6 pm to 9 pm, Saturday 6 pm to 9 pm. Closed on Sunday and Monday. Licensed. All cards. Book ahead.

QUEBEC   **MAP 158**
LAURIE RAPHAEL   ☆☆☆
117 rue Dalhousie   **$290**
(418) 692-4555

This much-admired restaurant was established in 1991 by Daniel Vézina and his wife Suzanne Gagnon. It was named for their children, and Raphael is now the chef. Last year it went through extensive renovations that created an elegant new interior while cutting the number of tables in half, and the cooking moved to a whole new level. At noon and in the evening there are menus of three or five courses. The lunch menus cost 30.00 and 50.00, the dinner ones about three times that. A five-course evening menu might start with a superb rillette of tuna, and go on to tartar of venison, dorade, magret of duck, pastry and a sorbet. Everything is perfectly cooked and beautifully presented. The wine list is as large as the menu is small. We used to recommend the Macon Villages by Jean Thévenet. If that is still on the list, make no mistake and ask for a bottle; it costs 70.00, which is a bargain in this company.

Open Tuesday to Friday 11.30 am to 2 pm, 5.30 pm to 10 pm, Saturday 5.30 pm to 10 pm. Closed on Sunday and Monday. Licensed. All cards. You must book ahead. ♿

QUEBEC   **MAP 158**
LE SAINT-AMOUR   ☆☆☆
48 rue Saint-Ursule   **$260**
(418) 694-0667

It sometimes seems as if the Saint-Amour has always been the city's favourite restaurant. Each new redecoration has been more stylish—or over the top—than the last. But the cooking never changes, even when Jean-Luc Boulay is not himself in the kitchen. The table d'hôtes are amazing and there's a new one every day. The à la carte changes only three times a year—so forget it, even if it does list foie gras de canard done five ways. (The chef has majored in foie gras, it seems, all his life.) At noon, the Inspiration menu costs 68.00 for soup, a choice of two appetizers and two main courses, plus a cheese plate or gourmandises. In the evening, the Discovery menu offers seven courses for 125.00. We won't soon forget the sea-bass, the lamb or the venison. And in season, the Fundy salmon is a small miracle. The wines, however, are amazingly expensive. Ask the sommelier about wines by the glass.

Open Monday to Friday 11.30 am to 2 pm, 6 pm to 10 pm, Saturday 5.30 pm to 10 pm, Sunday 6 pm to 10 pm. Licensed. All cards. Free valet parking. Book ahead.

QUEBEC   **MAP 158**
TOAST   ☆☆
17 Sault-au-Matelot   **$265**
(418) 692-1334

Christian Lemelin, who learned his trade at the French Laundry in California, has been in charge of Toast since it opened. He's still known for pronounced flavours, but his cooking is surprisingly delicate and he always offers the freshest and best of local produce. Some things never leave the menu—foie gras, tartar of bison, scallops from the Magdalen Islands, loin of pork—but most of his recipes are new. A staple this year has been veal en croûte with mushrooms in sauce périgourdine. The fish might be walleye with scallops and brandade de morue or, less happily, swordfish. The vegetables are complex and exotic. The sweets are complex too and sometimes take 30 minutes to prepare. We remember one made up of macaroons, chocolate, cream cheese, blueberries, raspberries, strawberries and lime sorbet. Most of them actually work. In summer you can have lunch outside, where there's abundant greenery and masterly lighting. The wine list is large and unusual, but Toast is one of the few Eastern restaurants that offers such Okanagan wines as Burrowing Owl cabernet franc and Blue Mountain chardonnay. Burrowing Owl is expensive at 125.00 a bottle, but the Blue Mountain can be had for little more than half that.

Open daily 6 pm to 10.30 pm (later on weekends). Licensed. All cards. &

QUEBEC
See also ILE D'ORLEANS.

RADIUM HOT SPRINGS, B.C.   **MAP 159**
HELNA'S STUBE
7547 Main Street W   **$150**
(250) 347-0047

Radium Hot Springs has a year-round population of 800 and eighteen restaurants. Of these, Helna's Stube is certainly the best. It's a robust Austrian place offering unpretentious fine dining in a warm and welcoming room that opens onto an open fireplace in winter and two outdoor patios in summer. Best of the appetizers is the brie cheese baked in phyllo pastry with garlic and olive oil, though we also like the crêpes in herb sauce filled with chicken and white mushrooms. The main dishes are meant to be filling: lamb shank is braised with garlic and wine, the classic wienerschnitzel is made with loin of veal rather than pork, and the calf's liver comes properly smothered in bacon and onions. The service is careful and attentive, and the wine-list nicely balanced between the old world and the new.

Open daily 5 pm to 10 pm. Licensed. All cards. Book ahead. &

REGINA, Saskatchewan   **MAP 160**
TANGERINE
2234 14 Avenue   **$45**
(306) 522-3500

Tangerine is as fresh and lively as its name suggests. It offers a new menu every day, with a housemade soup, savoury tart and a hot lunch dish to go with the variety of salads and sandwiches they're known for. To follow there are at least a dozen wonderful pies, squares, croissants, cakes and cobblers. Come early to be sure of a table for lunch, but if you can't find one, get your lunch packed up to go—there are three nearby parks. The Saturday brunch is one of the best in town.

Open Monday to Friday 7 am to 6 pm, Saturday 8 am to 4 pm. Closed on Sunday. No liquor. Master Card, Visa. &

REGINA

MAP 160

WILLOW ON WASCANA
3000 Wascana Drive
(306) 585-3663

☆

$160

With its lake-front balcony, Willow on Wascana has a better view than any other restaurant in Regina. It also has first-class cooking, which is all about local, fresh and seasonal. Order the six-course tasting menu and see them at their best. There's a substantial wine-list, but the service is not up to scratch.

Open Monday to Saturday 11.30 am to 10 pm, Sunday 10.30 am to 1.30 pm (brunch). Licensed. All cards. Book ahead. &

REGINA

See also VIBANK.

REVELSTOKE, B.C.

MAP 161

WOOLSEY CREEK CAFE
604 2 Street W
(250) 837-5500

☆

$130

Woolsey Creek is located in the heart of Revelstoke, where it offers good food at reasonable prices to skiers and to anyone passing through the town on their way from Calgary to Vancouver. From the large menu you should probably begin with the tuna tataki, the pan-seared scallops or the parmesan gnocchi, and then go on to the Haida Gwaii wild halibut, the pork two ways or the free-range beef short-ribs. For vegetarians there's an excellent cauliflower soup with parmesan cheese, squash cappelletti, a cauliflower steak and a Thai green curry with tofu. Best of the sweets are the tiramisu and the pear crisp.

Open daily 5 pm to 9 pm. Licensed. All cards. Book ahead if you can. &

REVELSTOKE
See also HEDLEY.

RIMOUSKI, Quebec   MAP 162
LE CREPE CHIGNON
140 avenue de la Cathédrale   **$90**
(418) 724-0400

Nothing has come along in the last year or so to spoil Le Crêpe Chignon. It was started in 1998 by two local women as a crêperie with a conscience—everything is either recyclable or bio-degradable. The big, colourful menu offers fifteen or sixteen of their favourite crêpes, as well as the crêpe Breton, for which you choose your own filling from a list of several meats, vegetables and cheeses. They make all their own jams and their own yogurt and bake all their own bread. They also make fine omelettes and several Mexican dishes, but you're usually better with one of the crêpes. They have a licence, and you can have a glass or two of Orpailleur if you like, but we usually ask for the fresh-squeezed orange-juice or even a cup of the excellent coffee. The Cathedral of Saint-Germain is just down the street and the dazzling white interior looks like a painting by Saenredam. It's worth a visit.

Open Wednesday and Thursday 7 am to 10 pm, Friday 7 am to 11 pm, Saturday 8 am to 10 pm, Sunday 8 am to 9 pm. Closed on Monday and Tuesday. Licensed. Master Card, Visa. Book ahead if you can. &

RIMOUSKI
See also LE BIC.

226

RIVIERE DU LOUP, Quebec — MAP 163

CHEZ ANTOINE ★ ★
433 rue Lafontaine **$195**
(418) 862-6936

Chez Antoine has an extraordinary wine-list, with its countless tignanellos, sassicaias, solaias and ornellaias. The cooking matches the wine. The feuilleté of escargots comes to the table with its snails in beautiful puff pastry. The carpaccio of beef is a delight and so is the ris de veau. The filet mignon is perfectly tender, the fillet of salmon is moist and very fresh. Even at noon the menu is amazing. There's rognons de veau, tartar of salmon, entrecôte of beef and bouillabaisse of pink shrimp. The service is perfect.

Open Monday to Friday 11 am to 2 pm, 5 pm to 9 pm, Saturday 5 pm to 9 pm. Closed on Sunday. Licensed. All cards. ᗔ

RIVIERE DU LOUP — MAP 163

AU PAIN GAMIN ☞
288-90 rue Lafontaine **$45**
(418) 862-0650

This bakery café in the centre of town is just across the road from Chez Antoine. If you look over from there you can see its sidewalk tables and big umbrella practically inviting you in. There are other newer bakeries in town, but for over ten years now we've found this one special. The breads are all made on their hearth from the finest available flour: all-butter croissants, old-style sourdough, french fougasse, pizzas and pastries. If you order a ham sandwich, you'll find that the ham comes from their own smokehouse. A sandwich and a bowl of good homemade soup costs only about 17.00. The menu is bilingual and so are the waiters.

Open Monday to Friday 8 am to 6 pm, Saturday 8 am to 5 pm from late June until Labour Day, Tuesday to Friday 9 am to 6 pm, Saturday 8 am to 5 pm from Labour Day until late June. Closed on Sunday in summer, on Sunday and Monday in winter. No liquor. All cards.

ROSSEAU, Ontario **MAP 164**
CROSSROADS
2 Cardwell Road **$145**
(705) 732-4343

Rosseau is a small village at the north end of Lake Rosseau. Crossroads, the only restaurant in town, is owned by people who care. They have fresh fish, sometimes fresh lamb, always steak. The steak comes from a local farmer, who regularly brings them first-class beef. The pork is almost as good as the beef, and so is the Georgian Bay pickerel. The vegetables are all excellent too, though the sweets lack interest. The best of the wines is Leaping Horse from California, which costs only about 45.00 a bottle.

Open daily 11 am to 9 pm from Victoria Day until Thanksgiving, Wednesday to Sunday 11 am to 9 pm from Thanksgiving until Victoria Day. Closed on Monday and Tuesday in winter. Licensed. Amex, Master Card, Visa. No smoking. ♿

ST. ANDREWS, N.B. **MAP 165**
ROSSMOUNT INN ✩✩✩
4599 Highway 127 **$170 ($370)**
(506) 529-3351

The Rossmount may have stumbled, but this year it's back in top form, about as good as anything in the province. They do things like poached lobster on a bed of parsnip ravioli—an unlikely but highly successful dish—or civet of red deer flavoured with allspice and cloves and marinated for a week. The carpaccio is everything it should be—and more. The espresso crème brûlée and the lemon tart are both delicate dishes, and never too sweet. The service is local and surprisingly competent. This year the news here is all good.

Open daily 5.30 pm to 9.30 pm from 9 April until 31 December. Licensed. Amex, Master Card, Visa. Book ahead in season. ♿

We accept no advertisements. We accept no payment for listings. We depend entirely on you.

ST. CATHARINES, Ontario　　　MAP 166
WELLINGTON COURT　　　☆☆
11 Wellington Street　　　**$170**
(905) 682-5518

Wellington Court was opened by Claudia Peacock, who turned her father's little house on Wellington Street into a restaurant thirty years ago. Her son, Erik, who worked with his mother for some years, is a natural chef. He's imaginative, even daring, offering things like pink-radish salad with shrimp, avocado and goat-cheese. Every dish is freshly prepared on a menu that changes every couple of weeks. He and his wife, Dale, opened a second restaurant recently, in the Henry of Pelham winery at 1469 Pelham Road (telephone (905) 684-8423), which is open from early May until Thanksgiving. It serves three-course patio meals all week. At Wellington Court itself, fish is always a good choice, especially the Lake Huron pickerel, but you won't be disappointed in the strip-loin with triple-cooked chips and chimichurri. The vegetarian plates too are always well made. There are four Canadian cheeses, with fresh fruit and wines from Niagara. (If you bring your own bottle, the corkage is only 15.00.) In summer, you can sit in comfort outside on the verandah that encircles the house.
Open Tuesday to Saturday 11.30 am to 2.30 pm, 5 pm to 9.30 pm. Closed on Sunday and Monday. Licensed. All cards. Free parking. Book ahead in summer.

ST. CATHARINES
See also BEAMSVILLE.

STE.-FLAVIE, *Quebec*　　　*MAP 167*
LE GASPESIANA
460 rue de la Mer　　　*$95 ($225)*
(800) 404-8233

The cooking here may not be quite what it used to be, but the place is a godsend for anyone who comes to the Gaspé out of season. The bedrooms, all of which face the beach and the Gulf of St. Lawrence, are immaculate. The dining-room, which is open all

229

year, is expansive and well served. The kitchen majors in fish and shellfish: clam chowder, shrimp bisque, cod meunière and bouillabaisse. They have a good sugar pie, but otherwise the cooking isn't distinguished. The wine-list, which is rather small and conventional, has two great buys: the Kim Crawford sauvignon blanc at 9.00 a glass and 42.00 a bottle and the Liberty School cabernet at 46.00 a bottle. The hotel is only two kilometres from the Mont Joli airport and transportation is free. The restaurant is open all day every day, and serves lunch from 11 am to 4 pm and dinner from 6.30 pm to 9.30 pm. Licensed. Amex, Master Card, Visa. ⅋

ST.-HYACINTHE, Quebec   MAP 168
LE PARVIS
1295 rue Girouard o   **$95**
(450) 774-0007

The Parvis occupies an abandoned church that was built in 1878. It's right in the heart of town and painted brick red. Inside, the floors are bare and the tablecloths are white. The owner says his cooking is high end, and to prove it he has a special gourmet menu that costs nearly $200 a head, including a half-bottle of first-class wine. The prices on the regular menu are much more reasonable, offering a plate of appetizers for 20.00 and a bavette of beef for 24.50. Dinner might start with shrimps provençale or a terrine of wapiti in a peach coulis, and then go on to a pavé of salmon, chicken wings with green peppers, or a house-made pasta. Sweets are served buffet-style, and coffee comes with the meal. In summer, you can eat outside.
Open Monday 11.30 am to 2 pm, Tuesday to Friday 11.30 am to 2 pm, 5 pm to 9 pm, Saturday 5 pm to 9 pm. Closed on Sunday. Licensed. Master Card, Visa.

ST.-JEAN-PORT-JOLI, Quebec   MAP 169
LA BOUSTIFAILLE
547 avenue de Gaspé e   **$70**
(877) 598-7409

This small town of 3500 attracts a surprising number of tourists. Several of its woodcarvers have become famous.

The parish church dates from 1779 and has some very fine sculptures. In 2005 the town was declared the cultural capital of Canada. There are several restaurants here, of which the Libellule at 17 place de l'Eglise (telephone (418) 598-9644) is probably the best. It has great atmosphere, a great location and is open every day in season. Local people come here by the thousand, for the healthy food (try the soup) and the camaraderie. It's open daily 7.30 am to 9 pm from the first Friday in May to 31 October, B.Y.O.B., Master Card, Visa. Meanwhile, down the road to the east of town (next door to the theatre) is the Boustifaille, which opened in 1965 with the intention of providing habitant food to all comers at a fair price. After more than 50 years, the restaurant is still preparing such dishes as split-pea soup, tourtière, ragout de pattes et boulettes and, of course, sugar pie. With the passage of time the kitchen has lost some of its fire and spice, but it's never merely run-of-the-mill. They have a few wines and a couple of draft beers, and maple syrup is still sold in cans to take out.

Open daily 8 am to 11 pm from 1 June until 12 October (shorter hours in the spring and fall). Licensed for beer and wine only. Visa. No reservations. &

SAINT JOHN, N.B.   MAP 170
THE ALE HOUSE   ☜▯
1 Market Square   **$90**
(506) 657-2337

The Ale House is starting to get noticed right across the country. That's because Jesse Vergen is doing such a good job in the kitchen and behind the bar. He emphasizes local organic produce. His beef comes from Shipp Farms in Sussex; his fish mostly from New Brunswick. Some things are grown by Vergen himself in Quispamsis. Fish doesn't get any fresher than this and the beer-battered fish and chips is a steal at 9.45. The mussels, which come from Prince Edward Island, are also cooked with beer and the house-made pancetta and garlic are served with fries. Vergen has taken the bones out of his chicken but not the flavour, and his fried chicken fingers is one of the most popular items on the menu. Everything is cheap at the Ale House—everything, that is, but the lobster roll, which costs almost 40.00. They have the largest selection of beers in town, including drafts from Picaroon's in Fredericton and the Pump House in Moncton. Every Thursday Moosehead sends them a cask of real ale, and there are people who will drink nothing else. There's an all-Canadian wine-list that offers wines from Nova Scotia as well as Niagara and the Okanagan. You can sit upstairs in the formal dining-room if you like or downstairs in the pub.

Open Sunday to Thursday 11.30 am to 10.30 pm, Friday and Saturday 11.30 am to midnight. Licensed. All cards. No reservations. ♿

SAINT JOHN   MAP 170
EAST COAST BISTRO
60 Prince William Street   **$90**
(506) 696-3278

This is not the place to go for a surprise. They offer expert cooking and attractive presentation—nothing more. The bistro occupies a brick-walled space in the city's heritage district. It's run by Tim Muehlbauer and his wife, Kim Steele, both of whom have worked for years in high-end restaurants in Europe and the West Coast. They start their menu with gnocchi with pesto and tomato confit and cauliflower tempura with pickled jalapenos. They like salads and there are four of them, our favourite of which comes with beets, apples, blue cheese and spiced pecans. Main dishes are more conservative, including steak frites and a popular burger with caramelized-onion aioli. There's fresh fish every day of the week, often salmon glazed with Picaroon's beer and Crosby's molasses. All the sweets are made in-house, but everyone seems to order the sticky toffee pudding. The wine-list is compact and well-chosen. There are also several beers, among them Picaroon's Dark and Stormy ale, and the local Propeller Best Bitter.

Open Monday 11 am to 3 pm, Tuesday to Thursday 11 am to 9 pm, Friday 11 am to 10 pm, Saturday noon to 10 pm. Closed on Sunday. Licensed. Amex, Master Card, Visa. &

SAINT JOHN   MAP 170
ITALIAN BY NIGHT
97 Germain Street   **$135**
(506) 214-8259

Italian by Night started out at the Urban Deli around the corner on King Street, which used to transform itself four nights a week into an Italian trattoria. The venture was so successful that it moved into its own quarters last year—a bright, airy space that useed to be (for 110 years) Bustin's furniture store. There are seven house pizzas, including a Bianco with white sauce, parmesan, potato, pancetta and egg, and a San Marzano with housemade meatballs and roasted wild mushrooms. Or there's risotto di mare, gnocchi gorgonzola and—our favourite—penne con capesante with scallops, pancetta, sweet red pepper, baby spinach, garlic, herbs, white wine and cream. Michelle Hooten is particularly good with slow-cooked meats, and Italian By Night offers two excellent treatments: a brasati di barolo of braised beef short-ribs, and a classic osso buco. Both come with polenta fries. Best of the sweets is probably the pavlova, but the bread pudding with butter-scotch sauce comes a close second. The wine-list is small but reasonable.

Open Monday to Wednesday 5 pm to 9 pm, Thursday to Saturday 5 pm to 10 pm. Closed on Sunday. Licensed. Master Card, Visa.

SAINT JOHN   MAP 170
PORT CITY ROYAL   ☆
45 Grannan's Lane   **$95**
(506) 631-3714

Jakob Lutes opened Port City Royal in 2015 with the idea of reinterpreting Maritime home cooking using seasonal and local ingredients. And he's stuck to his guns. The menus here are short, unusual and frequently changed. Starters might include smelts fried in lard, beet salad with citrus and apple and a superb pâté of mushrooms marinated in cognac and spices and puréed with oat groats from the local Speerville mill. New Brunswick oysters are served with eye-dropper bottles of verjus and strawberry hot sauce. There are usually four or five main courses, always including a vegetarian option. The superb meat pie contains chunks of beef, pork and venison and is served inverted over a bed of whipped blue potatoes and vinegar gravy, garnished with tart pickled cauliflower. The fresh and creamy seafood chowder is filled with smoked haddock, salmon, cod, potatoes and salt pork. A perennial favourite is the striploin steak with sautéed kale and sunchoke purée. The most interesting of the two or three sweets is the so-called scouts: leftover trimmings of scone dough deep-fried, dusted with sugar and served with a strawberry-jam dip. They're hot and crisp outside, and soft and moist in the middle. At lunch there's a short list of soups, salads and sandwiches—try the hoagie of pork pâté with bacon jam. There are only a few wines, but many local craft beers.

Open Tuesday to Saturday 2 pm to 5.30 pm (lunch), 5.30 pm to 10 pm (dinner). Closed on Sunday and Monday. Licensed. Master Card, Visa. Book ahead.

SAINT JOHN   MAP 170
THE URBAN DELI
68 King Street   **$50**
(506) 652-3354

The deli menu here has changed very little over the years—it hasn't needed to. They offer a broad selection of soups and sandwiches. The soups include split-pea and a chowder, which costs 11.00 a bowl. They have smoked-meat and corned-beef sandwiches, as well as a Reuben with dijon mustard. And they have beef burgers (with garlic), as well as fish and veggie burgers. There's both wine and beer to drink.

Open Monday to Saturday 11.45 am to 3 pm. Closed on Sunday. Licensed. All cards.

ST. JOHN'S, Newfoundland

ADELAIDE OYSTER HOUSE
334 Water Street
(709) 722-7222

MAP 171
★
$150

Steve Vardy has been through the pages of this book for years—in Ottawa at Beckta, where he was the original chef, and at the Whalesbone Oyster House, which he made into one of the city's top kitchens; on Fogo Island at Nicole's Café, which he helped open for Zita Cobb; back in Ottawa at the Black Cat Bistro, which he helped open for Richard Urquhart; and back in Newfoundland at Atlantica, which he took over after Jeremy Charles left to open Raymonds. And now he finally has a place of his own. The Adelaide Oyster House seems to have drawn most of its inspiration from Vardy's Whalesbone years. It's small, crowded and noisy, with cramped wooden tables on plank floors, and a long bar along the brick wall where you may have to sit, since there are no reservations. The menu is eclectic—what Vardy calls "all over the map: I cook what I love to eat"—and the plates (at about 15.00 each) are small. Try the superb chicken-liver pâté with rhubarb compote, the popcorn chicken karaage or the beautifully constructed plank of scallops with pickled beetroot, peppers and shiitakes. Some things—like the Korean pork—are less successful, but none are without merit. There's usually only one choice of sweet, but if you're lucky it may be a perfect lemon panna cotta with bakeapple topping. And if you get carried away and order a round of beers for the kitchen (it's listed on the menu at 20.00) they will all come out and cheer and blow ear-splitting horns.

Open Tuesday to Sunday 5 pm to 10 pm. Closed on Monday. Licensed. Master Card, Visa. No reservations.

This is a guide to Canadian restaurants from coast to coast—the first ever published and the only one of its kind on the market today. Every restaurant in the guide has been personally tested. Our reporters are not allowed to identify themselves or to accept free meals.

ST. JOHN'S
BASHO
283 Duckworth Street
(709) 576-4600

MAP 171
☆
$175

Tak Ishiwata trained under the Tokyo celebrity chef
Nobu Matsuhisa, and brought many of Matsuhisa's recipes
with him to Canada. Not surprisingly, his standards at
Basho are high. All the sushi is prepared upstairs by Ishiwata himself, and it's all superb. But this is a fusion restaurant, and there's more to the menu than nigiri. To start
there are tempuras, croquettes, scallops three ways and
the restaurant's signature tuna tartar with roasted garlic,
avocado and essence of white truffle. Main courses
include filet mignon, striploin, rack of lamb and duck
breast, as well as two assorted plates of sushi—the second
one, for 5.00 more, is labelled "exotic." Best of the
desserts is the frozen goat-cheese cheesecake. The restaurant is known for its martinis, particularly the premium
martini of the week which features various combinations
of fruit.
Open Monday to Saturday 6 pm to 10 pm. Closed on Sunday.
Licensed. All cards. Book ahead. ♿

ST. JOHN'S
CHINCHED BISTRO
5 Bates Hill
(709) 722-3100

MAP 171
☆☆
$175

Since people always ask, we explain every year that
chinched is Newfoundland slang meaning stuffed so full
you can't find room for more. In 2017, the bistro moved
from Queen Street to larger and more attractive quarters
on Bates Hill. There's even room now for a delicatessen
where you can buy their housemade condiments and charcuterie. Shaun Hussey works closely with local suppliers
to make sure that nothing but the freshest and best ingredients gets into his kitchen. The menu changes with the
seasons, but you can usually count on miso-chili roasted
cauliflower, pig-ear fries, char-broiled squid and the

restaurant's signature dish of potato-wrapped cod. Plates are small and meant for sharing—most people order three or four. Make sure that one of them is charcuterie. Hussey even makes his own pasta, and his co-owner and partner Michelle LeBlanc makes all the sweets, which are superb. The wine-list is small but very inexpensive. This is a friendly place and everyone is made to feel welcome.
Open Tuesday to Saturday 11 am to 3 pm, 5.30 pm to 10 pm. Closed on Sunday and Monday. Licensed. Master Card, Visa. Book ahead.

ST. JOHN'S MAP 171
THE HUNGRY HEART
142 Military Road **$50**
(709) 738-6164

The Hungry Heart is part of Stella's Circle, a non-profit organization that provides assistance to people who cannot play a normal role in the community. They serve breakfast and lunch during the week and brunch on Saturday and Sunday. They also feature theme nights, offering cuisines from Italy, Turkey, Thailand and Vietnam. Typically, there's a new menu every Monday, posted on Facebook. There are usually half a dozen entrées on the list, including pasta, curried seafood, local meats and two or three vegetarian dishes. Everything is made from scratch, even the salad-dressings and their amazing sweets. The Hungry Heart is a great place to stop for a cup of strong coffee and a scone. The scones are very good and are available, like the coffee, to take out.
Open Monday to Saturday 9 am to 2 pm. Closed on Sunday. Licensed for beer and wine only. Master Card, Visa. Book ahead. &

ST. JOHN'S MAP 171
INTERNATIONAL FLAVOURS
4 Quidi Vidi Road **$45**
(709) 738-4636

This tiny, owner-operated restaurant never seems to change. If you're looking for a bargain, you'll find it here at the foot of Signal Hill. They make curries of all sorts, as well as dal, samosas and naan. And they sell spices, so you can make curries at home if you like. Everything is full of flavour and everything is very inexpensive.

Open Tuesday to Saturday noon to 7 pm. Closed on Sunday and Monday. No liquor. Master Card, Visa. No reservations.

ST. JOHN'S   **MAP 171**
MALLARD COTTAGE   ☆☆
Quidi Vidi Village   **$150 ($430)**
8 Barrows Road
(709) 237-7314

Quidi Vidi has become one of the most popular destinations in St. John's. The tour buses coming down Signal Hill all turn away from the city now to head out to this impossibly quaint and ramshackle little hamlet perched on either side of a narrow inlet well protected from the sea. They visit the artisanal workshops at the new Quidi Vidi Village Plantation, and take tours of the Quidi Vidi Brewing Company, Newfoundland's largest craft brewery. And they try to find a free table at Mallard Cottage. Every year the reputation of this small white heritage house gets bigger and bigger. Todd Perrin's menu is scrawled on a blackboard that is posted on Instagram every day. This is not fussy food: portions are ample and the flavours are comforting and rich. Co-owner Stephen Lee says they wanted to create "a place where everybody could come and feel comfortable, because the typical fine-dining environment isn't for everybody, but access to good food should be." What interests Perrin is reinventing traditional Newfoundland cuisine using wild game, local fruits and vegetables and seafood fresh from the sea. And the result is an appealingly unpretentious experience. Even the antique cutlery is deliberately mismatched. In 2017, the Inn by Mallard Cottage was added to the property: two guest houses next door to the restaurant, each with four stylish rooms. Unfortunately, the Inn is as expensive as the restaurant is cheap.

Open Wednesday 4 pm to 9 pm, Thursday to Saturday 10.00 am to 9 pm, Sunday 10.00 am to 7 pm. Closed on Monday and Tuesday. Licensed. Master Card, Visa. Book ahead.

ST. JOHN'S

RAYMONDS
95 Water Street
(709) 579-5800

MAP 171
★★★
$295

It's not been that long since eating out in St. John's meant deciding what fish to have with your chips. And look at it now: bistros and wine bars on every streetcorner, and fine dining on offer at places like Chinched, the Adelaide Oyster House, Mallard Cottage and, above all, Raymonds, which is routinely called the best restaurant in Canada. It may or may not be that, but Jeremy Charles and Jeremy Bonia have created something quite remarkable in the short time since they came here from Atlantica in Portugal Cove. (Since everyone asks, the restaurant is named for Charles's grandfather Raymond and Bonia's father Raymond—which is why there is no apostrophe.) To begin with, it's a beautiful building in a beautiful location, with high ceilings, long curtains and tall windows that look out at the supply ships for the oil rigs coming and going in the harbour. The service is extraordinarily well-informed—as it needs to be, since the menu is best described as terse. You choose between dinners of three, five or seven courses—at 85.00, 115.00 and 135.00—with no more to go on than "Tomato: ricotta / Pasta: moose / Halibut: cauliflower / Pork: squash / Tuna: beans / Beef: sunchokes." And the food—which bears as much resemblance to its descriptions as a Mozart concerto does to "Music: violins"—is extraordinary. The menu constantly changes, but the combinations are always exciting and convincing. Everything is terroir of course, and much of it is foraged or caught—Charles is deeply involved in both fish and game (he even dives for scallops). The sweets are as inventive as everything else: our last meal ended with an exquisite apple-cider-vinegar mousse. The best way to experience the wine-list is to try Bonia's pairings at 50.00, 70.00 and 90.00 for the three, five and seven courses.

Open Tuesday to Saturday 5.30 pm to 10 pm. Closed on Sunday and Monday. Licensed. All cards. Book ahead. ♿

ST.-LUNAIRE-GRIQUET,   (MAP 6)
Newfoundland
DAILY CATCH   ☆
112 Main Street   **$90**
(709) 623-2295

Global warming has brought more, not fewer, icebergs to the bay at St.-Lunaire. The Daily Catch in the village is close to the Viking settlement at Anse-aux-Meadows, which is worth seeing. Terry Hedderson comes from a long line of fishermen, and a cousin or two still bring him fish from their daily catch. Cod and lobster occur locally, but salmon and halibut come in from Labrador. Crab-cakes and crab au gratin are often on the menu. Cods' tongues are also usually available, as are pan-fried cod and scrunchions. The chips are always cut by hand and fried in the kitchen. Christmas cake, made to an old family recipe, is offered all summer long, along with apple crisp and fresh-fruit pies. They have a wine-list, but most people seem to drink Iceberg beer or one of the local berry wines. *Open daily 11 am to 9 pm from 1 June until 30 September. Licensed. All cards.* ♿

ST. MARYS, Ontario   (MAP 192)
LITTLE RED'S
159 Queen Street E   **$130**
(226) 661-2233

Chris and Mary Woolf have a long history in the Stratford area. Having closed Woolfy's at Wildwood, they've reappeared at this small (50-seat) pub and eatery right on the main street of St. Mary's. Here they have a short bistro-style menu and a large blackboard of daily specials, with nearly everything coming from nearby suppliers. People talk about the cheeseburger with bacon from a bison farm just outside town, but one diner praises his summer trout, which, he says, was beautifully cooked and served with impeccable vegetables. Everything, even the tomato ketchup, is made from scratch on the premises and you'll be pleased with both the salads and the fries. Perth County pork might appear in a tourtière with Stonetown cheese as an appetizer. There are a number of traditional sweets, among them a pavlova made with real whipped cream and a crème brûlée made with local berries. The dining-room is noisy, but the service is calm and poised and the parking is ample. The wine-list is novel and interesting and there's a good selection of local craft beers.

Open Tuesday to Saturday 11 am to 2 pm, 4.45 pm to 9 pm. Closed on Sunday and Monday. Licensed. All cards. &

ST. MARYS (MAP 192)
WESTOVER INN
300 Thomas Street **$160 ($360)**
(519) 284-2977

St Marys is one of the loveliest small towns in Ontario. William and Joseph Hutton built the Westover in 1867, as well as six other limestone buildings in what is now referred to as Stonetown. The Inn occupies a wooded estate at the edge of town. If you want to spend the night, book a room in the main house or in Thames Cottage. Anthony Gosselin has been the chef here for almost 25 years, and these days some of his dishes are better than others. The most expensive is the rack of lamb. There's also a grilled organic striploin with chimichurri, but over the years, the chef seems to have been most successful with pork. Meals always start well with a spinach salad, mussels or scallops. The dining-room is dignified and handsome; the service sometimes is not.

Open daily 11.30 am to 2 pm, 5 pm to 8 pm. Licensed. All cards. Book ahead.

Where an entry is printed in italics this indicates that the restaurant has been listed only because it serves the best food in its area or because it hasn't yet been adequately tested.

ST. PETER'S, N.S.

MAP 177

BRAS D'OR LAKES INN
10095 Granville Street
(800) 818-5885

☆
$140 ($295)

We never expected Jean-Pierre Gillet to retire, but he's still very much involved and some of his dishes, such as the daily mussel creation (steamed in beer with lime and ginger) will probably never leave the menu. The dinner menu offers two courses for 25.00 and three for 30.00. Recently they introduced lunch until 4 o'clock, and they plan to serve breakfast every day from 8 o'clock to 10. The new dinner menu will feature a seafood platter with mussels, clams, shrimps, scallops and crab, all from nearby waters. Breast of chicken has been joined by quail and the stuffed pork chops have been replaced by roast duck. Don't miss the scallops provençale or the local lamb. We still hanker for the apple pie with caramel, but others prefer the gâteau St.-Honoré. Most nights there's live gaelic music.

Open Monday to Saturday 8 am to 10 am, 11 am to 4 pm, 5 pm to 8 pm, Sunday 11 am to 2 pm (brunch), 5 pm to 8 pm from early May until mid-October, Wednesday to Saturday 8 am to 10 am, 11 am to 4 pm, 5 pm to 8 pm, Sunday 11 am to 2 pm (brunch), 5 pm to 8 pm from mid-October until mid-December. Closed on Monday and Tuesday in the fall. Licensed. Amex, Master Card, Visa.

ST. PETERS BAY, P.E.I.

(MAP 37)

THE INN AT ST. PETERS
1668 Greenwich Road
(800) 818-0925

☆
$180 ($425)

We've said it before: the success of the Inn at St. Peters is largely down to the innkeeper. Karen Davey may have become Karen Milligan over the winter, but her amazing attention to detail is still the same. Most of the cottages overlook the sea and there's a beautiful view from the dining-room windows. The chef, Chris Campbell, is committed to local produce, and the inn has a large organic vegetable garden. There are mussels from the bay and local scallops; oysters come from South Lake and the trout is smoked in-house. In season lobster is boiled in the traditional way; North Shore halibut is served with a jalapeno aioli. And from the land there's island beef and island pork. There are always choices for vegetarians as well. The kitchen makes all its own sorbets and ice creams.

Open daily 5 pm to 8.30 pm from 26 May until 16 October. Licensed. All cards. &

ST.-PIERRE-JOLYS, Manitoba MAP 179
OMA'S SCHNITZEL STUBE
601 Sabourin Street S **$45**
(204) 433-7726

The village of St.-Pierre-Jolys is in a French-speaking area of southern Manitoba, 30 minutes south of Winnipeg. The cuisine at Oma's, however, is resolutely German, the atmosphere surprisingly upbeat. The Zimmerman family, who own the place, come from Wald-katzenbach in Baden-Wurttemberg. Their schnitzels have all kinds of fillings. They also have bratwurst, rouladen, dumplings and spaetzle, as well as thick soups, strudels and hefty tortes. On weekends there are buffets, the price of which will remind you of days long gone— they cost just 18.00 for adults, and half that for children of six or more—children of less than six eat for free. To drink there are German beers and a few wines.

Open Wednesday to Sunday 11 am to 8 pm. Closed on Monday and Tuesday. Licensed. Master Card, Visa. &

SALT SPRING ISLAND, B.C. (MAP 211)

Salt Spring Island has always been known for its lamb and cheese and shellfish. More recently it's been known for its wineries, for its abundance of organic produce and for its bakeries. Try either Jana's Bake Shop at 149 Fulford Ganges Road (telephone (778) 353-2253) for fresh muffins, fabulous butter tarts and mini-quiches or the Embe Bakery at 174 Fulford Ganges Road (tele-

phone (250) 537-5611) for great cookies and pies. Fresh bread for a picnic can be had from Barb's Buns at 124 McPhillips Avenue in Ganges (telephone (250) 537-4491), and David Wood's celebrated goat cheese and sheep's-milk cheese can be found at the Cheese Farm Shop at 285 Reynolds Road (telephone (250) 653-2300). Long a favourite for fresh pasta, Del Vecchio at 149 Fulford Ganges Road (telephone (250) 537-8588) has added a top-end espresso maker so you can sit and enjoy a cappuccino with one of their delicious cannelli. The best way to get to know what's available on the Island is to visit the Farmer's Market in Ganges, which is held every Saturday morning from Easter until Thanksgiving. If you drive south out of Ganges you'll soon come across the Garry Oaks and Salt Spring Island wineries. Both offer tours and tastings. Smoked salmon and crab or salmon pâtés are available right in Ganges itself from a shop called Sea Change. If you have to wait for the ferry to Swartz Bay, you can get something good to eat close to the terminal at the Rock Salt Cafe at 2921 Fulford Ganges Road (telephone (250) 653-4833). If you're going to Vancouver Island through Crofton via Vesuvius, stop for the fish and chips at the Seaside on Vesuvius Road (telephone (250) 537-2249). The restaurant in Hastings House is, we think, too expensive for most of our readers. Piccolo at 108 Hereford Avenue (see below) is closer to the mark and attracts visitors by the boatload.

SALT SPRING ISLAND (MAP 211)
HOUSE PICCOLO ☆☆
108 Hereford Avenue **$140**
(250) 537-1844

What can we say about this charming little place that we haven't said before? There are few changes from year to year. The Finnish-born chef, Piccolo Lyytikainen, cooks with more than a hint of his Scandinavian background. The Pacific crabcakes are terrific and well worth sharing (if you can be sure of getting at least half), and the baked chèvre salad features goat's cheese from David Wood. Keep an eye out for the gorgonzola tart, the gravlax and the beef carpaccio. The Queen Charlottte sablefish meunière is always perfectly cooked and presented, and the pan-seared sea scallops run it a close second. The sauce on the fillet of beef can be peppercorn or a decadently creamy gorgonzola. There's also a lobster risotto and locally sourced lamb and duck. The sweets are all fabulous—chocolate terrine, pear-and-almond tart, warm Belgian-chocolate timbale, cardamom crème brûlée. The wine-list is outstanding and quite fairly priced.

Open Wednesday to Sunday 5 pm to 9.30 pm. Closed on Monday and Tuesday. Licensed. Master Card, Visa. Book ahead.

SASKATOON, Saskatchewan   MAP 182
AYDEN   ☆☆
265 3 Avenue   **$140**
(306) 954-2590

Dale MacKay has named his restaurant after his son. It's housed in a graceful downtown building, where he practises his innovative urban style of cooking six nights a week, usually playing to a full house. Snacks are offered at noon and that means house-made charcuterie, popcorn prawns and Thai-style chicken wings. In the evening they have a rib-eye steak and freshly-ground hamburgers. These two are always on the menu, while the chicken, pork, fish and pasta change every day. Dinner ends with a soufflé and one or two of Proust's madeleines. Take them both.

Open Monday to Saturday 5.30 pm to 10 pm. Closed on Sunday. Licensed. All cards. You must book ahead. &

SASKATOON   MAP 182
THE ODD COUPLE
228 20 Street W   **$100**
(306) 668-8889

The Odd Couple is modern, relaxed and friendly. Andy Yuen has joined his father in an effort to create an upscale but affordable Asian-style restaurant. The interior of the Odd Couple was inspired by the Chinese film, *In the Mood for Love*. Outside there's a double-happiness symbol;

inside the message is *just eat together*. The food is simple but fresh and well prepared. There are several dishes to share and a number of vegetarian options. Traditional dishes like won-ton soup, fried rice, chicken and gailan are somehow made to seem exciting. Not that they don't have innovative dishes as well—dishes like eggplant with ground pork, chicken with shimeji and oyster mushrooms, sweet chili chicken and, for sweet, sesame rice with chocolate. There's a good wine-list, as well as Sapporo beer on tap.

Open Monday to Thursday 11.30 am to 2 pm, 4.30 pm to 11 pm, Friday and Saturday 11.30 am to midnight. Closed on Sunday. Licensed. Master Card, Visa. &

SASKATOON   **MAP 182**
ST. TROPEZ
298 2 Avenue S   **$160**
(306) 652-1250

St.-Tropez has been a favourite with local people ever since it opened in 1979. And the reasons aren't hard to find. It's quiet—you can actually talk—and serene, the service is attentive and charming and the food is very good. Much of what is served comes from the restaurant's own farm or its large rooftop garden, and the rest is locally sourced. Everyone's favourite dinner here is the salmon with chipotle sauce followed by the classic crème caramel. The wine-list is very expensive—you'll probably want to settle for a glass.

Open Wednesday to Sunday 5 pm to 10 pm. Closed on Monday and Tuesday. Licensed. All cards. &

SASKATOON   **MAP 182**
SUSHIRO   ☆
737 Broadway Avenue   **$100**
(306) 665-5557

Megan Macdonald may have moved to Vancouver, but she returns regularly, and still owns half of the restaurant. Perhaps for that reason, there seem to have been no

important changes here—though the prices are higher and the portions smaller. The fish is still beautifully fresh, and the sushi is the best in town. The chili squid is simply fabulous. They have Hakutsuru sake on draft, as well as two or three premium sakes by the bottle.
Open Monday to Saturday 5 pm to 10 pm. Closed on Sunday. Licensed. All cards. &

SASKATOON   MAP 182
TRUFFLES   ★★
230 21 Street E   **$150**
(306) 373-7779

Truffles is everything its name implies. It's located in the old Birks building in downtown Saskatoon. Inside it's bright and lavish and very *au courant*. This is one place where the table d'hôte could be regarded as the specialty of the house. There's almost always a first-rate eight-ounce striploin with wonderful truffled fries, or perhaps steelhead trout from Diefenbaker Lake. But Lee Helman is a trained French chef, and there are those who think it would be a mistake to stick to things like steak or steelhead trout, even if they are cheap. If you feel that way, ask for the breast of duck or perhaps the house-made ravioli. Everything is made from scratch, even the tomato ketchup. He makes all his own bread and all his own sweets. His soups are exquisite. But he could still use more wines by the glass.
Open Monday to Friday 5 pm to 10 pm, Saturday 10 am to 2.30 pm (brunch), 5 pm to 10 pm, Sunday 10 am to 2 pm (brunch). Licensed. All cards. &

SAULT STE.-MARIE, Ontario   MAP 183
ARTURO'S   ★
515 Queen Street E   **$185**
(705) 253-0002

There are lots of Italian restaurants in the Sault—restaurants that flourish and then fail. That doesn't happen to the restaurants run by the Comegna family. Arturo

Comegna came here from Abruzzo in Italy, fell in love with the city, and has repaid it with three fine kitchens. The flagship restaurant, which is probably the best place for fine dining in town, is now in the hands of his sons, Thomas and Christopher. Thomas runs the front of the house, and Christopher is the chef. Try the fresh lobster ravioli, the seafood risotto (made from an old family recipe) or the pickerel in lemon butter. If you don't like seafood, you won't go wrong with the saltimbocca, always made with milkfed veal. Start with the zucchini-flower fritter. The wine-list is short, but there's plenty of parking.

Open Tuesday to Saturday 5 pm to 10 pm. Closed on Sunday and Monday. Licensed. All cards. &

LA SCIE, Newfoundland   MAP 184
THE OUTPORT TEAROOM
Highway 414   **$45**
(709) 566-2090

There were no roads to the outports in the old days. There's a road to La Scie now, but a visit to the Outport Tearoom will give you an idea of what Newfoundland used to be like. Valerie Whalen has said that she and her husband, Larry, would feed anyone who came to their door, no matter what time of day it was. And that was true. She did all the cooking while Larry played old Newfoundland songs on his accordion or guitar. The Whalens converted their family home into a museum and then opened a tearoom on the verandah that runs the length of the house. At first they served nothing but berry tarts, tea-buns, rhubarb crumble and a family-style chocolate cake. Later they added such traditional dishes as pea soup with dumplings, cod chowder, fishcakes and jiggs dinner. La Scie is special; find the Outport Tearoom if you can.

Open Monday to Saturday 8 am to 8 pm, Sunday 1 pm to 5 pm from 1 June until 15 September. No liquor. Master Card, Visa.

Our website is at www.oberonpress.ca. Readers wishing to use e-mail should address us at oberon@sympatico.ca.

SHAUNAVON, Saskatchewan   MAP 185
HARVEST   ☆
492 Centre Street   **$135**
(306) 297-3315

Garrett Thienes says Harvest serves gourmet comfort food. People beat a path to his door from as far away as Swift Current, and even the CBC have called his hamburgers the best in the province. Shaunavon is a picturesque town in the middle of cattle country and the restaurant's signature dish is beef brisket, slow-cooked with a maple-and-bourbon glaze. Striploins are well-aged and hand carved. There are also various treatments of duck breast and lamb, as well as a smoked cauliflower steak with béarnaise sauce for vegetarians. The crème brûlée is the most popular sweet, but we ask for the apple-pie cheesecake with praline crust. Coffee is ground to order, and the wine-list, which comes about equally from both sides of the Atlantic, has been chosen by the chef, who will be happy to talk about any vintages you haven't heard of. Recently Harvest added a fresh market shop with a separate entrance at the back that gets turned into a private dining-room at night.

Open Tuesday to Saturday 4 pm to 10 pm. Closed on Sunday and Monday. (The shop is open Tuesday to Saturday 10 am to 5 pm.) Licensed. All cards. Book ahead. ♿

SHELBURNE, N.S.   MAP 186
CHARLOTTE LANE CAFE   ☆
13 Charlotte Lane   **$140**
(902) 875-3314

Shelburne is one of the most picturesque Nova Scotia towns, and the Café is a good reason to linger. Kathleen and Roland Glauser have been operating this colourful little restaurant for many years now, but they've lost none of their energy. In fact, Kathleen recently took on a second careeer as a singer-songwriter. Roland's cooking is always innovative and usually effective—some years ago, Charlotte Lane was named the best small restaurant in the province. The kitchen makes a lot of use of local ingredients, from garden greens and red cabbage to asiago cheese. The lunch menu is much the same as dinner, with the addition of some soups, salads and sandwiches. Both meals offer large portions of rich and often spicy food. Regulars say the cooking just gets better every year. Everybody likes visiting Charlotte Lane—there's even a gift shop.

Open Tuesday to Saturday 11.30 am to 2.30 pm, 5 pm to 8 pm from early May until late December. Closed on Sunday and Monday. Licensed. Master Card, Visa. Book ahead if you can.

SHELBURNE
See also CLARK'S HARBOUR.

SIDNEY, B.C. (MAP 211)
DEEP COVE CHALET ☆☆☆
11190 Chalet Road **$165**
(250) 656-3541

The Deep Cove Chalet was built on six acres of waterfront land in 1913 by the B.C. Electric Company, but for more than 40 years now it has been run as a restaurant by chef Pierre Koffel and his wife Beverly. The Chalet serves classical French country cuisine—Koffel was born in Strasbourg—using local ingredients. They make their own bread, pâtés and sweets, and smoke their own salmon. The main courses will be familiar to anyone over fifty: breast of duck with cherries, fillet of beef in red wine, quails normande with apples and calvados, rabbit with prunes, rack of lamb provençale, beef Wellington and lobster américaine. And they taste even better than they used to. There's usually a daily catch, which may be a fillet of sablefish en croûte or a Dover sole meunière—both are not to be missed. If you come for lunch, try the hot avocado with prawns and scallops in a creamy curry sauce. The wine-list has few equals anywhere: Mouton-Rothschilds, Lafites and Latours, all listed at staggering prices, together with much less expensive fine wines from the Okanagan—wines like Poplar Grove, Wild Goose, Blue Mountain and Burrowing Owl. It takes an hour to get to Deep Cove

from Victoria by Highway 17. Start on Blanshard Street and turn left at Swartz Bay on Land's End Road.
Open Wednesday to Sunday noon to 2 pm, 5.30 pm to 9 pm. Closed on Monday and Tuesday. Licensed. All cards. Book ahead. &

SINGHAMPTON, Ontario **MAP 188**
EIGENSINN FARM ☆☆☆
449357 Townline 10 **$800**
(519) 922-3128

Michael Stadtländer and his wife, Nobuyo, have been running Eigensinn Farm for 22 years. This year again they plan to be open only on Friday and Saturday, and since there are only twelve seats in the dining-room you should book at least three months in advance and pay when you book. It's a long way to go from almost anywhere, even for an eight-course dinner. The price of a meal is 300.00 a head, plus tip and tax. As for wine, you must bring your own bottle. Michael Stadtländer ranks with the best chefs in the world. He was born the son of a farmer, and here he has a vegetable garden so big that he has had to employ a full-time gardener. He has two farm ponds, where he raises speckled trout and crayfish. He breeds ducks and sheep. He grows fruit trees. All these things eventually find their way onto his table. To get to Eigensinn Farm, head west from Singhampton on Townline 10 and remember, if you bring your own bottle there's no charge for corkage.
Open Friday and Saturday at 7 pm by appointment only from 1 May until 15 October. Closed Sunday to Thursday. Bring your own bottle. No cards. You must book ahead.

SOOKE, B.C. **(MAP 211)**
POINT NO POINT
10829 West Coast Road **$120**
(250) 646-2020

Point No Point is back in this guide after going through a bit of an identity crisis. They have settled now on a limited menu based on what the farms, pastures and waters of Vancouver Island have to offer. You can start with a local salad of romaine, brie and pear, an Asian-fusion duck confit with moo shu pancakes or fresh side-stripe shrimps with chorizo and cornbread fritters. Popular entrées include a roasted breast of local chicken, marinated wild salmon with polenta and garlic aioli, and a perfectly grilled beef tenderloin with mushroom spaetzle and truffle beets. At lunch there's a variety of west-coast seafood, housemade soups and sandwiches. The restaurant is located some distance west of Sooke on the road to Port Renfrew, and the seaside setting is spectacular.

Open Monday and Tuesday 11.30 am to 3.30 pm, Wednesday to Sunday 11.30 am to 3.30 pm, 5.30 pm to 8.30 pm. Licensed. All cards. No reservations for lunch, book ahead for dinner. &

SOOKE   (MAP 211)
WILD MOUNTAIN
1831 Maple Avenue S   **$90**
(250) 642-3596

Wild Mountain may not look like much from the street, but every detail of the two snug rooms inside has been chosen and arranged with care, from the artwork to the candleholders to the flowers. And so has the menu, which changes seasonally—Oliver Kienast and his wife, Brooke Fader, are both keenly interested in locally foraged organic produce. We usually begin with the figs topped with cheese, paper-thin ham and drizzled honey, or the chanterelle risotto with squash, spinach, apple and grana padano, and go on to the local Metchosin lamb with bacon, mushrooms, and a puree of corn and onion or the seared wild sole with a potato-and-yam brandade in a lemon verbena emulsion. The wine-list features only B.C. wines and the cocktails feature locally-distilled spirits. There are also of course an impressive number of local craft beers, and in summer you can take one outside with a plate of charcuterie to admire the harbour views.

Open Wednesday to Sunday 5 pm to 9 pm. Closed on Monday and Tuesday. Licensed. All cards. Book ahead. &

SOURIS, P.E.I. (MAP 37)

21 BREAKWATER
21 Breakwater Street   **$90**
(902) 687-2556

21 Breakwater is unassuming, comfortable and inexpensive. And it might be the best place to eat fish on the Island. Sadly the scallops that came fresh from the harbour are no longer on the menu; they've just become too expensive. Console yourself with the excellent fish and chips. Fresh haddock is available everywhere, but seldom cooked this well. The menu is small, because Pedro Pereira and Betty Macdonald limit themselves to general favourites, plus a daily special or two—a fish chowder full of crab perhaps, or mussels, clams and hake. Not that you have to eat fish: the beef is just as good. They like their deep-fried Mars bar, but don't you believe them. Go with the blueberry cobbler instead. The view from the restaurant is lovely and most people are in no hurry to leave. In fact, lunch is so crowded that you'll be lucky to get in the door unless you have a reservation.

Open Monday to Saturday 11.30 am to 8 pm from 1 June until 30 June, daily 11.30 am to 9 pm from 1 July until 31 August, Monday to Saturday 11.30 am to 8 pm from 1 September until 30 September, Monday to Thursday 11.30 am to 8 pm from 1 October until 31 May. Licensed. Master Card, Visa. &

STELLARTON, N.S. (MAP 123)

ANDRE'S SEATS
245 Foord Street   **$75**
(902) 752-2700

André is good at marketing. Every day, for example, he has a different lunch deal: from Sunday to Thursday you can take 25% to 33% off, Friday and Saturday have pizza discounts and Tuesdays are tax-free. He started with a pizza takeout at 243 Foord Street, and business was so good that he expanded next door and opened this full-service restaurant with seats (hence the name). There's an extensive menu, a wide assortment of cocktails, imported

253

and domestic beers with two local breweries on tap, and a variety of wines, including some from Nova Scotia. The tomato-and-cheese soup is one of the best we've ever been offered, and the seafood chowder is chock-full of haddock, salmon, mussels and lobster. The sweets, unfortunately, are a bit hit-and-miss. André has lined the walls with posters from the eras of Elvis Presley and the Dave Clark Five, the glass-topped tables are covered with ticket stubs from concerts of the time, and there's a real jukebox on the floor.

Open Monday and Tuesday 11 am to 8 pm, Wednesday and Thursday 11 am to 9 pm, Friday and Saturday 11 am to 10 pm, Sunday 4 pm to 8 pm. Licensed. All cards. &

STRATFORD, Ontario   MAP 192
THE BRUCE HOTEL
89 Parkview Drive   **$225**
(519) 508-7100

The Bruce Hotel is a new beginning for Stratford. It has a sumptuous setting, surrounded on all sides by expansive lawns and a field-brick wall. The dining-room is all white, with soft grey cushions and chairs. Dinner begins with sushi with koji, wild ginger and local sake, foie gras with peanut brittle and green strawberries, or beef tongue with wild laurel oil and caramelized garlic. Main dishes start with ivory salmon with edamame and sea-asparagus and leg of lamb in hemp sauce vierge. Boileau venison costs 53.00 and comes with blueberries and spruce butter. It's an exciting menu, if only because Arron Carley and his team forage for native plants and make a point of buying from local suppliers. There are some interesting wines from the Simulkameen and the Russian River valley.

Open Tuesday to Saturday 5 pm to 10 pm. Closed on Sunday and Monday. Licensed. Amex, Master Card, Visa. &

This is a guide to Canadian restaurants from coast to coast—the first ever published and the only one of its kind on the market today.

STRATFORD
THE PRUNE
151 Albert Street
(519) 271-5052

MAP 192
★★
$225

There's always talk of it closing but the Prune soldiers on, though Bryan Steele's back has finally given out and the kitchen is now in the hands of his sous-chef, Michael Fry, under the direction of Ryan O'Donnell, the executive chef of all Windsor Hospitality's holdings (The Prune, Bar One Fifty One, Mercer Hall). People like to say that the measure of a man is what he leaves behind, and what Bryan Steele left behind is a kitchen that isn't missing a beat. Dinner begins with some really interesting complimentary hors d'oeuvre, and goes on to things like citrus-cured albacore tuna, seared squid and smoked Boon Run trout, followed by charred salmon with shiso mustard, roasted skate wing, smoked breast of duck and seared Cornish game hen. Now that Rundles has gone, the Prune is as expensive as anything in town, which means 75.00 for three courses or 85.00 for four. Try for a table in the garden room.

Open Tuesday to Saturday 5 pm to 8 pm from late May until mid-October. Closed on Sunday and Monday. Licensed. Amex, Master Card, Visa. Free parking. Book ahead.

STRATFORD
RED RABBIT
64 Wellington Street
(519) 305-6464

MAP 192
$135

Red Rabbit is one of the few downtown restaurants open on Monday. Sean Collins and Gen Zinger came here from Mercer Hall and spent about a year converting the old store—it once sold wedding dresses—into a restaurant. Red Rabbit, which is just off the town square, is a happy-go-lucky place with creative cooking and a number of delectable dishes, among them fried chicken with spices and Thai duck curry with sticky rice. One diner wrote to say how nice it was to get things that were too much trouble to make at home. The lunch menu is offered all day on

Sunday and Monday, but from Thursday to Saturday dinners include pickerel, pork-sausage gnocchi and falafel. There are fixed-price menus for two, three or four courses—all for the theatre crowd as they take last orders no later than 6:30 pm.

Open Sunday 11 am to 7 pm, Monday noon to 7 pm, Thursday noon to 9 pm, Friday and Saturday noon to 10 pm. Closed on Tuesday and Wednesday. Licensed. Master Card, Visa.

STRATFORD
See also ST. MARYS.

SUMMERSIDE, P.E.I. (MAP 37)
SAMUEL'S COFFEE HOUSE
4 Queen Street **$60**
(902) 724-2300

Samuel's starts with splendid coffee, but it does a lot more than that. It makes a good breakfast and lunch as well. Home-baked scones and cinnamon rolls are prepared each morning and become lunchtime specials at noon. Of course, there are other things as well: corn chowder, cream-of-potato soup, vegetarian chilis and a variety of sandwiches—grilled ham-and-brie, smoked local turkey, bacon, chicken with pesto. Sit over some of the best espresso you've ever had and have a slice of raspberry pie, or a wedge of gluten-free coffee-cake you won't soon forget. Samuel's has recently opened a second location in Avonlea village at 8779 Highway 6 (telephone (902) 963-3330).

Open Monday to Thursday 7.30 am to 5 pm, Friday 7.30 am to 8 pm, Saturday 8 am to 5 pm, Sunday 9 am to 5 pm. Licensed. Master Card, Visa.

SUMMERVILLE BEACH, N.S. MAP 194
QUARTERDECK GRILL
7499 Highway 3
(800) 565-1119 **$135**

One thing we can all agree on, and that is that Summerville Beach is spectacular. It's a mile of white sand that nobody should miss.

The Quarterdeck Grill is right on the beach, and if you stay in one of their attractive new bedrooms, you can stroll along it from your doorstep. Greg Whynot, the new owner, has removed every trace of quaintness from the place. The floors are now polished concrete, the tables and chairs stark white. But he still buys his fish fresh from the wharf at Port Mouton, his vegetables from the Annapolis Valley and his wines from the best local vineyards. This year the restaurant was closed for two months, until mid-March. In summer it should be open daily from noon to 8 pm, but nobody seems quite sure. They have a licence and take all cards. ♿

SUNDRIDGE, Ontario   MAP 195
DANNY'S JUSTA PASTA   ☆
367 Valleyview Road   **$125**
(705) 384-5542

There are those who don't agree with us when we say that Danny Galekovic makes the best pastas in the province. They should just come and take a look at the lineups at the door. Highway 11 may have been altered to leave Danny's out in the cold, but no matter, the world still beats a path to his door. Danny opened Justa Pasta in 1983, so he's been here for more than 30 years. Thirty years is nothing to the Galekovic family—Danny's parents ran the Sundridge Steak House far longer than that. We've always liked Danny's chicken penne and we still do, but these days we're recommending his linguine, which comes with your choice of smoked salmon or fresh Atlantic salmon with onions, tomatoes and leeks in a dill cream sauce. The helpings are certainly big, but everything on the plate is so light that you wouldn't notice it. Start your meal with pâté maison and warm herb bread. As for sweets, they change almost daily. Outside, Justa Pasta looks pretty plain and prices have certainly risen, but what do you expect? Do you want him to cut corners and lower his standards?

Open Monday to Thursday 11 am to 8 pm, Friday and Saturday 11 am to 9 pm, Sunday 11 am to 8 pm from 1 April until 31 October, Thursday 11 am to 8 pm, Friday and Saturday 11 am to 9 pm, Sunday 11 am to 8 pm from 1 November until 31 March.

Closed Monday to Wednesday in winter. Licensed. All cards. No reservations. Free parking.

SYDNEY, N.S.   **MAP 196**
GOVERNORS
233 Esplanade   **$165**
Cape Breton
(902) 562-7646

This is now about the best place to eat in Sydney. They have first-class filet mignon and excellent Atlantic salmon with maple sugar. Everything is cheap—the fish and chips battered with beer costs an incredible 14.00 and the filet mignon itself costs only 35.00. For rather more than that—they don't give the price—they'll bring you a fresh naked lobster. Dinners begin well with crab-cakes, or with shrimps or mussels. The wine-list is small (seven labels) but choice. They have Tidal Bay from Grand Pré and Nova 7 from Benjamin Bridge. The reds are less exciting, but there is a Leon Millet from Grand Pré, and it's one of their best.
Open daily 11 am to 11 pm. Licensed. Master Card, Visa. ♿

SYDNEY   **MAP 196**
THE OLIVE TREE   ☞
137 Victoria Road   **$75**
Cape Breton
(902) 539-1553

The Olive Tree used to be a pizzeria, but these days there isn't a pizza in the house. It's become a Mediterranean bistro, a place casual enough that you can drop by on impulse—there are no reservations. It's best to choose your time though, because it's become hugely popular. The portions are the right size at the right price, the service is friendly and fast, and nobody will hurry you out. The redecorated interior is bright and colourful, right down to the artificial plants. Go for the Blue Plate special, which changes daily, but might be something like chicken fettucine with tomato, basil and lemon. There are

also a number of wraps, sandwiches and salads, as well as Maltese haddock and lamb souvlaki.
Open Wednesday and Thursday 11 am to 8 pm, Friday and Saturday 11 am to 9 pm. Closed Sunday to Tuesday. Licensed. Amex, Master Card, Visa. No reservations.

SYDNEY
See also NORTH SYDNEY.

TATAMAGOUCHE, N.S.   **MAP 197**
TRAIN STATION INN
21 Station Road   **$150 ($300)**
(902) 657-3222

The dining-car here was one of the railway carriages used by immigrants making their way west from Pier 21 in Halifax. Jimmie and Shelley LaFrense found it in Winnipeg 25 years ago, and brought it home to Tatamagouche. Lobster pot-pie is the specialty of the house, but—think what you like—many people seem to prefer the lobster mac-and-cheese. Fortunately, there are other daily specials, like the excellent seafood chowder with house-made biscuits. They grow their own vegetables and know just how to cook them. There are only a few wines from Jost to drink, plus one or two quite ordinary beers. There might be raspberry pie to finish, and if you like, you can spend the night in the caboose.
Open daily 11 am to 2.30 pm, 5 pm to 9 pm from 20 May until 31 October. Licensed. Master Card, Visa. Book ahead if you can.

TEMISCOUATA-SUR-LE-LAC, Quebec MAP 198
AUBERGE DU CHEMIN FAISANT   ☆☆☆
12 rue Vieux Chemin   **$225**
Cabano
(418) 854-9342

Cabano has now merged with Notre-Dame-du-Lac and become Témiscouata-sur-le-Lac. The Chemin Faisant has six bedrooms, all different and all decorated in the *art-déco* style. Every evening the chef, Hughes Massey, offers an eight-course *menu de dégustation,* featuring products of the Bas St.-Laurent: red-tuna tartar, saddle of rabbit with sautéed chanterelles and date purée, and grilled trout with sour cream and garlic. At noon the menu is simpler and smaller, offering little but fruit salad, poached egg with hollandaise sauce and tapioca with lemon and lavender. From time to time he brings in crab from the Magdalens and regularly buys red deer, scallops and foie gras wherever he can find them. There are about 150 labels in his cellar and they're all constantly changing. Meanwhile, he likes to play the piano, which he does most evenings after dinner.

Open daily 6 pm to 8 pm from 1 June until Labour Day, Saturday 6 pm to 8 pm from Labour Day until 31 May. Closed Sunday to Friday in winter. Licensed. All cards. &

TEMISCOUATA-SUR-LE-LAC   MAP 198
AUBERGE MARIE-BLANC   ☆
2629 rue Commerciale s   **$150**
Notre-Dame-du-Lac
(418) 899-6747

The Auberge Marie-Blanc was built in 1905 by a New York lawyer for his mistress, Mlle. Marie-Blanc Charlier, who lived here until her death in 1949. Guy Sirois and his wife, Jeannine, bought the place in 1960 and ran it for more than 40 years. Many people thought it was the only dependable place to break a journey from Fredericton to New York. The motel units were plain but tidy, and everybody had breakfast on their porch overlooking Lake Témiscouata. The evening menu was simple in its early days, but it grew over the years into a four-course table d'hôte. Finally Guy's daughter took charge of the kitchen. She had never heard of sweetbreads, but her father lived just long enough to teach her. Guy Sirois may be gone now, but his kitchen is still there, turning out raw oysters, seafood salads—and sweetbreads. Main courses include tuna niçoise, magret de canard, fillet of beef béarnaise and, an unusual dish, young wild boar. For a few dollars extra, they give you a wedge of local cheese, a fruit

sorbet and a cup of filter coffee.
Open Monday 8 am to 10 am, Tuesday to Saturday 8 am to 10 am, 5.30 pm to 8.30 pm, Sunday 8 am to 10 am from early June until mid-October. Licensed. Master Card, Visa.

THUNDER BAY, Ontario   **MAP 201**
BISTRO ONE   ☆
555 Dunlop Street   **$170**
(807) 622-2478

Jean Robillard runs a tight ship at Bistro One. His chef de cuisine has been with him for 23 years. So had the patissière, Maria Costanzo, until her recent departure. Samantha Turner, Maria's replacement, knew better than to meddle with Maria's celebrated molten-chocolate cake, but she's added some touches of her own, like apple fritters and salted-caramel pots-de-crème. The roasted fillets of Alberta veal have been replaced by a veal T-bone chop, but the fresh New Zealand rack of lamb with gorgonzola butter is here to stay, and so are the wonderfully tender Angus filet mignon and the breast of duck flavoured with brandy. Nothing is ever overstated or overcooked. The wine-list offers several wines that no-one else seems to carry; they're expensive but good drinking.
Open Tuesday to Saturday 5 pm to 10 pm. Closed on Sunday and Monday. Licensed. All cards. ♿

THUNDER BAY   **MAP 201**
THE SILVER BIRCH   ☆☆
28 Cumberland Street N   **$160**
(807) 345-0597

Darlene Green has a fierce attachment to Thunder Bay, which is where she was born and grew up. When she needed a chef for the Silver Birch, she never considered looking farther afield. She hired Jamie Minaker, one of the local college's most outstanding students, and he has turned her kitchen into a force to be reckoned with. Darlene calls their food Northern Inspired Cuisine, and that means walleye, pike and perch from Lake of the Woods, bison, elk and duck from local woodlands, wild mushrooms and locally made cheeses. Everybody likes the mushroom tart, which is made with puff pastry and aged local gouda, the shaved zucchini strips with honey and lemon, and the seafood chowder. Darlene ran a respected catering business for 25 years before she opened the Silver Birch, and she still makes all the sweets herself. The saskatoon-berry tart never leaves the menu.

Open Tuesday to Saturday 5 pm to 10 pm. Closed on Sunday and Monday. Licensed. All cards. &

THUNDER BAY   MAP 201
THE SOVEREIGN ROOM
220 Red River Road   **$110**
(807) 343-9277

It's getting hard to find an empty table at the Sovereign Room. The menu is attractive, the cooking is accomplished and the prices are reasonable. The small wood-lined room has a comfortable, casual feel, and for once you can hear yourself think. The menu ranges from stone-baked pizzas—try the one with fig, prosciutto, gorgonzola and honey—to burgers (both meat and vegetarian) and prime rib. To start there's duck-confit poutine or buttermilk-fried chicken with chipotle mayonnaise. And you could spend an evening sampling the beers—some of them you will never have heard of.

Open Tuesday to Thursday 4 pm to 11 pm, Friday 4 pm to midnight, Saturday 4 pm to 11 pm, Sunday 11 am to 3 pm (brunch), 4 pm to 11 pm. Closed on Monday. Licensed. Master Card, Visa. No reservations.

THUNDER BAY   MAP 201
TOMLIN   ☆☆
202 Red River Road   **$150**
(807) 346-4447

Tomlin is still pretty near the top of the heap in Thunder Bay. Steve Simpson is a creative chef and his menu evolves with the seasons. Everything is made in house from local ingredients. When they buy a pig they eat every part of it. Most of the time that works, sometimes it doesn't. The menu is small, unless you go for the chef's tasting menu, reserved for parties of four or more. The daily specials are a good bet: try the chicken karaage with honey. The chef's charcuterie board is always outstanding, and everyone loves the cocktails and the coffee. The restaurant is small, but not too noisy, and the waterfront location is attractive.

Open Tuesday to Saturday 5 pm to 10 pm. Closed on Sunday and Monday. Licensed. All cards. No reservations. &

TOFINO, B.C.　　　　　　　　　　　　　　MAP 203
ICEHOUSE OYSTER BAR　　　　　　　　　　　　☆
81 West Street　　　　　　　　　　　　　　　　**$135**
(250) 725-4239

Tofino is a favourite destination for surfers and sightseers; more than that, it's a great place to get some of the freshest seafood in the country—salmon, tuna, cod, halibut, crabs, prawns, oysters and clams. But until very recently Tofino had no real fisherman's wharf restaurant. The Icehouse is located right on a pier in the heart of the city, and it has a great salad of grilled octopus rubbed with paprika and fennel, flash-fried calamari in a ginger-beer tempura with candied salmon, and tsunami oysters with marmite mayonnaise. There's also lightly-battered fish and chips, seafood risotto and pan-seared local salmon on steamed nappa cabbage with daikon and pickled shiitakes in a very light dashi broth. The cajun crab boil, expensive at 85.00 for two, is made with Dungeness crab from Clayoquot Sound, local clams, fresh salmon and cod in a cajun ginger butter broth. To finish, we really like the bread-and-butter pudding. The Icehouse has a few good wines, but the food goes better with one of the local craft beers.

Open daily 12.30 pm to 11 pm. Licensed. Master Card, Visa.

The map number assigned to each city, town or village gives the location of the centre on one or more of the maps at the start of the book.

TOFINO   MAP 203
KUMA
120 4 Street: Unit 101   **$90**
(250) 725-2215

Sadly, the Spotted Bear closed a year or two ago, and Kuma (which means Bear in Japanese) has taken its place. Kuma is warm and friendly, with 28 seats including eight at the bar. Rob Leadley and Mitsumi Kawai opened a similar restaurant on Bowen Island in 2014, and Mitsumi's parents still run the Basho Cafe on East Hastings Street in Vancouver. Kuma has a happy hour from 4 pm till 5, and there's always a lineup for it at the door. Ask for the chicken karaage while you wait. Most of the dishes on the regular menu come tapas-style, and the best of the lot is the miso-braised beef with fried rice, kale and miso mustard. It's wonderful. Almost is good is the jig-caught local tuna, served with tamari and truffle vinaigrette in an avocado purée with green onions and pickled shallots. We also like the miso eggplant, which comes with togarashi, and of course their signature dish—Osaka-style pancakes with Japanese mayonnaise, tonkatsu sauce and bonito flakes. To drink there's local craft beer and hot and cold sake.
Open daily 4 pm to 10 pm. Licensed. Master Card, Visa. Book ahead if you can.

TOFINO   **MAP 203**
THE POINTE
Wickaninnish Inn   **$200**
500 Osprey Lane
(250) 725-3106

Under the guidance of Warren Barr, the menu at the Pointe continues to feature local (or foraged) salmon, halibut, prawns, crab, evergreen huckleberries, wild mushrooms, sea truffles and gooseneck barnacles. It was recently one of eight winners of the University of Guelph's Innovation Awards. Breakfasts here (they call them brunches every day) are hearty and expensive. Try the mushrooms on toast, which come with two poached eggs, truffle hollandaise and foraged wild mushrooms, or the short-rib omelette with goat cheese and caramelized onions. Lunches begin with clam chowder and end with albacore tuna. In the evening there are baked oysters, side-striped-shrimp salad, suckling pig, curried scallops and roasted sablefish (expensive at 45.00 or more). The sweets are sumptuous.

Open daily 8 am to 9 pm. Licensed. All cards. Book ahead if you can. &

TOFINO   **MAP 203**
TACOFINO CANTINA
1184 Pacific Rim Highway   **$35**
(250) 726-8288

Tacofino has expanded to Victoria and Vancouver now, but it all began right here in this orange truck. You place your order at the window and take it to one of the many picnic tables, or carry it home or out to the beach. The cooking is from Baja California—try the lingcod tacos with chipotle mayo, the tuna tacos with wasabi and ginger or the pulled-pork burritos stuffed with salsa, cabbage and beans. The helpings are big and you probably won't be able to eat everything at once. If the weather is cold, order the tortilla soup filled with chicken, cheese, avocado and sour cream. There are lineups up all day long, and you can tell from the BMWs and Porsches in the parking-lot that people aren't just here for the prices.

Open daily 11 am to 5 pm. No liquor. Master Card, Visa.

TOFINO   **MAP 203**
WILDSIDE GRILL
1180 Pacific Rim Highway   **$90**
(250) 725-9453

Wildside has no liquor, no reservations and no indoor seating. All it has is plenty of good food—which, unless you're careful, you'll find yourself sharing with nearby crows. They cook Mexican dishes like pulled pork and lingcod tacos with chipotle mayonnaise, and a large number of meat and seafood burgers stuffed with oysters, tuna and salmon, flavoured with wasabi and served with homemade fries, onions and chili. They also do a great job with fish and chips, panko-crusted and served with tartare sauce. On a cold night, try a bowl of Louisiana chowder, filled with pink shrimp and chorizo sausage. The service is fast and friendly.

Open daily 11 am to 11 pm. No liquor, no reservations. Master Card, Visa.

TOFINO   MAP 203
WOLF IN THE FOG
150 4 Street   **$90**
(250) 725-9653

Wolf in the Fog was called Canada's best new restaurant in 2014. That may no longer be true, but the restaurant is still a force to be reckoned with. In the evening there are a number of tapas-style dishes, like smoked-beef back ribs with onions and bone marrow and chicken-liver parfait with tea jelly. Among the larger (and more expensive) plates we like the mustard-glazed sablefish and the Fraser Valley breast of duck with orange and quinoa. Best of the sweets are the butterscotch crème brûlée and the dark chocolate ice cream with huckleberries. For lunch there's a first-rate lentil burger, and an excellent beef burger with fries and horseradish mayo. The bar offers a number of amazing cocktails, as well as a remarkable list of single malts.

Open Wednesday and Thursday 9 am to 10 pm, Friday and Saturday 9 am to midnight, Sunday 9 am to 10 pm. Closed on Monday and Tuesday. Licensed. Amex, Master Card, Visa. Book ahead for dinner. &

TOFINO
See also UCLUELET.

Nobody can buy his way into this guide and nobody can buy his way out.

TORONTO, Ontario   **MAP 204**
ALO   ★★★
163 Spadina Avenue: Floor 3   **$275**
(416) 260-2222

Two years ago Patrick Kriss opened what has to be the best restaurant in Toronto. Here he offers a five-course tasting menu priced at 89.00 a person. With wine, service and taxes an evening at Alo costs almost 300.00—and it's worth every penny. The critics all say, and it's true, that what makes Alo is Kriss himself. His cooking is superlative. He begins with a corn sorbet with buttermilk and amaranth, foie gras with king oysters and veal trotters, dungeness crab with lime and spices, hamachi with barese cucumbers and continues, without taking a breath, with rack of Yorkshire pork and Dorset shoulder of lamb and ends with a dark chocolate ganache or a yellow-plum sorbet with bulgur and bitter almond. It's hard to pick and choose among these pleasures, but our favourites are the pain au lait (made with butter churned in-house and a glass of madeira) and the dungeness crab with Carolina-gold rice and lime. All these dishes are meticulously thought out and prepared in classical Parisian style. The wine-list is spectacular; the service superb.
Open Tuesday to Saturday 5.30 pm to 10.30 pm. Closed on Sunday and Monday. Licensed. Amex, Master Card, Visa. Book ahead. &

TORONTO   **MAP 204**
BAR BUCA
75 Portland Street   **$100**
(416) 599-2822

This is the third Buca in Toronto. They started on King Street, then opened a second in Yorkville (see below). This one is deliberately uncomfortable in the best modern style. They take no reservations and, once you get a table, you climb onto a high chair to sit down. The staff are all friendly and relaxed, however, and they're quick to offer you a glass of Italian wine. There are twenty reds and ten whites. The menu is short and the best thing on it is either the bianchetti (small fried smelts) or, if you come in on a weekend, the nova rossa, which combines egg yolk with crisp potatoes and scallions. The critics also admire the focaccia with roast pork and farm-fresh eggs, but there's too much focaccia for our taste and too little pork. The best of the sweets is the bombolone with vanilla cream and lemon, and it's famous all over town.

Open Monday to Friday 7 am to 2 pm, Saturday and Sunday 10 am to 4 pm. Licensed. Master Card, Visa. No reservations. ♿

TORONTO **MAP 204**
BUCA ☆
53 Scollard Street **$200**
(416) 962-2822

Never mind the Scollard Street address: look for the entrance to this uptown Buca at 60 Yorkville Avenue. It's a modern Italian restaurant, majoring in appetizers like octopus salami with lemon, smoked rainbow trout and cured Ahi tuna. Main courses—black cod, raw steelhead trout and pork belly—are broadly similar. Gorgonzola cheese is offered as a sweet, along with tiramisu and panna cotta. The list of Italian wines is huge. The interior is all cool glass and steel, which makes it look impersonal, but the service, as it happens, is very friendly. This is a sister restaurant to the original Buca at 604 King Street W (telephone (416) 865-1600). Rob Gentile is in charge of both restaurants, but the chef de cuisine on King Street is now Jorge Fiestas. He has good salumi, lamb's brains, gnocchi ripieni, divers scallops, goose sausages and a variety of pizzas. If you like glass and steel, go to Yorkville. If you like being underground, go to King Street.

Open Monday to Wednesday 11 am to 3 pm, 5 pm to 10 pm, Thursday and Friday 11 am to 3 pm, 5 pm to 11 pm, Saturday 5 pm to 11 pm. Closed on Sunday. Licensed. Amex, Master Card, Visa. Book ahead.

If you use an out-of-date edition and find it inaccurate, don't blame us. Buy a new edition.

TORONTO   **MAP 204**
BYBLOS
11 Duncan Street   **$165**
(647) 660-0909

Charles Khabouth says Byblos is a celebration of the eastern Mediterranean seaboard, which seems to mean from the Middle East to north Africa. (He and executive chef Stuart Cameron also run Patria a few blocks west on King Street; its Spanish cuisine is presumably making a start on the western seaboard.) Byblos is on two floors: the ground floor is lively, the upstairs quieter. Both have the same menu: crispy deep-fried eggplant with tahini, roasted beets with labneh, hand-rolled couscous, black cod, squid-ink tuna with Turkish dumplings, whole roasted sea bass, octopus, rib-eye steak, duck kibbeh and Persian flatbread. We particularly like the fried eggplant, the duck kibbeh and above all, the whole sea bass (don't be tempted to have the black cod instead). To follow try the lovely orange-blossom mousse.
Open daily 5 pm to 9.30 pm. Licensed. All cards. Book ahead. &

TORONTO   **MAP 204**
CAMPAGNOLO
832 Dundas Street W   **$150**
(416) 364-4785

Campagnolo is Italian and very chic, but, as we've said before, the best things on the menu aren't Italian at all. There's raw hamachi, for instance, crisp pork belly, water-buffalo carpaccio, roasted bone marrow, roasted venison and seared king salmon. Of course, they have spaghetti in tomato sauce as well, agnolotti (made with kale), rigatoni bolognese and rabbit spezzatino. The best of the sweets, we think, is the salted-caramel budino, and there's always plenty of sherry, port and grappa. The cooking has always seemed to us more pleasant than remarkable, but the service is very, very friendly and the ambience delightful. It's easy to enjoy an evening at Campagnolo. Last year Craig Harding opened a second restaurant, La Palma, just down the street at 849 Dundas Street W (telephone (416) 368-4567), and from the first day it's been an immense success. Over there the cooking is unequivocally Italian, simple dishes cooked with imagination and care.

Open Wednesday to Sunday 6 pm to 9 pm. Closed on Monday and Tuesday. Licensed. Master Card, Visa. Book ahead.

TORONTO   **MAP 204**
CANIS   ☆☆
746 Queen Street W   **$240**
(416) 203-3317

Canis opened in 2016 and quickly became one of the best new restaurants in town. A dinner here is an exciting experience: everything is beautiful and everything is interesting. The room is minimalist but warm, with a Scandinavian feel—lots of pale wood and clean lines. The knives and forks are in the classic Danish style, and a number of the attractive ceramics were made by a potter who happens to be Henri Matisse's great-grandson. And the food has no difficulty holding its own in these surroundings. Every course is imaginative, thoughtful and perfectly executed. Take, for example, the East Coast uni with soy and crème fraîche, served in a thin, crisp pastry shell. The different textures and flavours exist in perfect harmony, and something you might have thought you didn't like—like sea urchin—is miraculously transformed into something wonderful. Ferments play a big role at Canis, particularly in the winter: oysters come with fermented carrot, cabbage is fermented with plums and crispy shallots in a bone-marrow broth, and local Ontario soft cheese is served with fermented plum preserve. If you used to class ferments with sea urchin (and perhaps cabbage as well), Jeff Kang will convert you with ease—each one is better than the last. Five courses costs 68.00, but with cooking like this you want all the courses you can get. Spend another 20.00 to add three more. Wine pairings are 55.00 for five courses and 68.00 for eight, and you'll be given some wines you've never managed to discover before.

Open Tuesday to Saturday 5.30 pm to 10 pm. Closed on Sunday and Monday. Licensed. All cards. &

TORONTO   **MAP 204**
CANOE   ☆☆
Toronto–Dominion Centre   **$250**
66 Wellington Street W
(416) 364-0054

Canoe has an astonishing view of Toronto, from the islands in the south all the way out to the west end of the city. But there's much more to it than that. The menu is interesting and the cooking accomplished. They make mistakes, of course: the ivory salmon is dull and tasteless, and we don't much admire the panna cotta. But their oysters are superb, and the mushroom soup is the real thing. The smoked breast of duck and the Arctic char are both remarkable, and you can always depend on the beef, the lamb and the lobster. The wine-list is stupendous, if expensive. If you're excited by champagne, try the Blue Mountain sparkling white cabernet—one of the best of its kind we've ever tasted. Or there's always Benjamin Bridge—at a price. And to follow there is still a charming passion-fruit sorbet.

Open Monday to Friday 11.45 am to 2.30 pm, 5 pm to 9 pm. Closed on Saturday and Sunday. Licensed. All cards. Book ahead. &

TORONTO   **MAP 204**
CARISMA
73 King Street E   **$175**
(416) 864-7373

Carisma is dark, dark, dark: black walls, black tables, black chairs. But the menu is brightly Italian: gnocchi, orecchiette, pappardelle, porcini risotto, osso buco Milanese, vitello al limone. The cooking is straightforward and vigorous, with strong, clearly defined flavours. Michael and Margi Pagliaro aren't young. They came out of retirement to take on this project, and everything is done their way. No cucina nuova here. There's an exceptional list of chardonnays, and excellent wines by the glass at modest prices. The service is relaxed and efficient. *Open Monday to Friday noon to 3 pm, 5 pm to 10 pm, Saturday 5 pm to 10 pm. Closed on Sunday. Licensed. All cards.*

TORONTO   **MAP 204**
CARMEN   ☆
922 Queen Street W   **$130**
(416) 535-0404

Carmen was one of the ten best new restaurants in Toronto in 2013. The chef is Spanish and his menu features tapas and four or five paellas. Our favourite tapas are the fried artichokes with aioli, the pork tenderloin with piquillo jam and the fried green tomatoes with red peppers and feta cheese. The paellas, which are expensive, come to the table in a hot pan and are big enough for four. The wines are Spanish, some of them quite rare in this country.
Open daily 5 pm to 11 pm. Licensed. All cards. Book ahead. ♿

TORONTO   **MAP 204**
CAVA   ☆
1560 Yonge Street   **$195**
(416) 979-9918

Chris McDonald has sold Cava to chef Doug Penfold and Niall McCotter, and its easy to say things aren't quite the same. The Iberico ham for instance seems to have lost some of its magic, and the roasted sablefish is no longer really worthwhile. But there are still many reasons to come here, as there always have been. The tapas-style menu ranges effortlessly from pinchos of foie gras and ceviche of scallop to octopus with hazelnut romesco, paella of duck and clams, empanadilla of beef with prunes and chili and loin of lamb with savoy cabbage and lemon cream. The meal ends well with a valhrona-chocolate soufflé, even if it needs more coffee sauce, and there are many excellent sherries.

Open daily 5 pm to 10 pm. Licensed. Amex, Master Card, Visa.
&

TORONTO   **MAP 204**
THE CHASE
10 Temperance Street   **$250**
(647) 348-7000

The Chase is down a dark alley off Temperance Street, and upstairs (there's an elevator) on the fifth floor. The service is ingratiating and the wine-list large. They keep many single malts in stock, as well as brandies and grappas. The menu has several unusual things like madai, brown rice and burrata. The madai is a better bet than the salmon, which may be overcooked. It comes with jade radish, bee pollen and white truffles in an anise-and-shallot dressing. The oysters aren't particularly appealing; better the roasted cauliflower for a few dollars more. The albacore tuna is served with wild rice and sheep's yogurt, the lobster with squid ink, tarragon and lemon. The cooking at Chase can be demanding—don't come here looking for soup and mashed potatoes.

Open Monday to Friday 11.30 am to 5 pm (lunch), 5 pm to 11 pm (dinner), Saturday 5 pm to 11 pm, Sunday 10.30 am to 3 pm (brunch). Licensed. Amex, Master Card, Visa. Valet parking. Book ahead. &

TORONTO   **MAP 204**
DANDYLION
1198 Queen Street W   **$175**
(647) 464-9100

Dandylion continues to flourish on West Queen West, perhaps because Jay Carter makes it so easy to enjoy yourself. The room—a former furniture shop that he renovated with his father—may be long and narrow, but the exposed brick, high ceilings and shelves of succulents climbing the walls make it feel calm and welcoming. For once, you won't have to shout across your table—and nor will you have to

273

part with the better part of ten dollars to be given some bread. Instead, a warm, house-baked boule with fresh cheese will arrive, and perhaps an excellent glass of house-brewed kombucha. The menu is as tightly controlled as ever, offering only three choices per course. But don't worry—you'll still have a hard time deciding. Terrine of pork with apple and celery root is fresh and light; confit of chicken with lentils and sunchokes simply perfect. Even the potato dumplings with kale and raclette are remarkably delicate. The passionfruit tart is well made, but liquorice ice cream with mango is the surprise showstopper. Don't miss it, even if you think you don't like liquorice.

Open Tuesday to Saturday 5.30 pm to 10.30 pm. Closed on Sunday and Monday. Licensed. Master Card, Visa.

TORONTO MAP 204
EDULIS ☆☆
169 Niagara Street **$240**
(416) 703-4222

Edulis is becoming almost as difficult to visit as Alo. Right now they're booking a month in advance, which pretty much rules out casual dining. But this is not an ostentatious place. It's run by an extremely hard-working husband and wife, Michael Caballo and Tobey Nemeth, who are in the restaurant all day every day for fifteen or sixteen hours, assisted by a staff of five. The room is small, with only 32 seats, and the cost is not unreasonable for what you're getting: a five-course (65.00) or seven-course (85.00) tasting menu of typically elaborate and intricate dishes—things like bigeye tuna with black garlic, poached lobster with pumpkin seeds, milk-fed lamb with morels and green garlic and roasted quails smoked in apple wood. If you want to spend more, you can come in the winter to sample one of the supplementary truffle menus—the season for white truffles is November to December and for black truffles January to February.

Open Wednesday to Saturday 6 pm to 10.30 pm, Sunday noon to 1.30 pm, 6 pm to 10.30 pm. Closed on Monday and Tuesday. Licensed. All cards. You must book ahead. ⅙

TORONTO   **MAP 204**
ENOTECA SOCIALE
1288 Dundas Street W   **$120**
(416) 534-1200

Enoteca may be a long way out west, but it's well worth
the trip. Basically this is a pasta house, with very little fish
and meat, but everything is done with style. Most people
think the whole grilled sea-bass is the best thing they do,
though there's also a fine Haldimand County rib-eye
steak at 46.00. The seven pasta dishes are all less than
twenty dollars, which makes them an attractive alternative—try the bucatini or the gnocchi. To begin there's a
root-vegetable salad, brussels sprouts, trout and beef
crudo and a chicken-liver mousse. Everyone likes the
roasted parsnips with stracciatella and gremolata. There
are plenty of open wines, and many first-class imported
cheeses.
*Open daily 5 pm to 11 pm. Licensed. Amex, Master Card, Visa.
Book ahead.*

TORONTO   **MAP 204**
THE FAT PASHA   ☞▯
414 Dupont Street   **$95**
(647) 340-6142

The Fat Pasha is fun if you take things slowly, one at a
time. The star of the menu has always been the whole
roasted cauliflower, though they've had to market price
it since the cost of cauliflowers started seesawing all
over the place. If you really don't want that much
cauliflower (and it's huge) start with some cabbage with
caraway or, if you're hungry, some za'taar chicken.
Next comes tabouleh or falafel. Don't bother with the
hummus, which is oily and heavy. Instead, finish your
meal with some bread pudding with maple syrup,
which is a lot lighter than the sticky-date pudding.
White wine goes better with this style of cooking (Jewish, Middle Eastern) and they have a couple of useful
white wines from Prince Edward County. Ask for the

Norman Hardie. The Fat Pasha is usually crowded and always noisy. Just point to what you want on the menu, and with luck you'll get it. Last year Anthony Rose expanded his empire on Dupont (Rose and Sons, Big Crow, The Fat Pasha, Schmaltz) with the addition of Bar Begonia, just east of Spadina. Like all his venues it's ridiculously popular, but most of the food there is drink.

Open Monday and Tuesday 5 pm to 11 pm, Wednesday to Sunday 11 am to 3 pm, 5 pm to 11 pm. Licensed. Master Card, Visa. Book ahead if you can. &

TORONTO   MAP 204
THE GALLERY GRILL
Hart House   **$140**
7 Hart House Circle
(416) 978-2445

The Gallery Grill is a lovely place for lunch. Sit by the windows if you don't like heights; otherwise there's a fine view down from the gallery. The food is bright and modern—this is not a refuge for professors looking for the comfort foods of their youth. Suzanne Baby presents an attractive and accessible menu, with plenty of vegetarian, vegan and gluten-free options—none of which feels forced. Small plates include a soup of roasted eggplant, tomatillo and lime, and a roasted paillot de chèvre with persimmon salad. Grilled lamb belly comes on a toasted brioche with charred tomatoes, kale and preserved lemon; Icelandic cod-cake comes with a poached egg, salsa verde and a warm frisée salad. To drink you should try the cinnamon-mulled tart cherry cider, or maybe the St. Ambroise oatmeal stout. For sweet there are housemade ice creams and sorbets, or perhaps a maple-syrup crème brûlée or citrus posset. After lunch you can see what's on display at the art galleries in Hart House and University College next door.

Open Monday to Friday 11.30 am to 1.30 pm, Sunday 11 am to 1.30 pm (brunch). Closed on Saturday. Licensed. Amex, Master Card, Visa. &

TORONTO MAP 204
GEORGE ☆☆
111C Queen Street E **$200**
(416) 863-6006

Not that it really matters, but George is not the name of
the chef. It's the name of the man who designed the
restaurant for free—the owner was so grateful he used his
name. The chef is Lorenzo Loseto. He's won a number of
prizes, including the Canadian Culinary Championships
a few years ago, and they were well-earned. Loseto comes
from Bari, and his menu is his distinctive take on his
Italian roots. He used to work with Susur Lee and says, "I
learned from him that food is very personal; it is putting
your personality on a plate. When you eat at his restaurant
you know you're eating his food, and I wanted to be like
that." These days his dinners begin with trout, Wagyu
beef tataki and lobster, and go on to short-ribs, Fogo
Island cod, Cornish hen, ribeye of beef, venison and halibut. Seasonal vegetarian options are available for each
course. The tasting menus are a good idea, if you can
afford 120.00 for five courses, 140.00 for seven courses or
160.00 for ten. The room is graceful and warm, the
service is impeccable, the table linen immaculate, the
porcelain Villeroy & Boch.
Open Monday noon to 2 pm, Tuesday to Friday noon to 2 pm,
5.30 pm to 9.30 pm, Saturday 5.30 pm to 9.30 pm. Closed on
Sunday. Licensed. Amex, Master Card, Visa. Book ahead.

TORONTO MAP 204
HONEST WEIGHT ☆
2766 Dundas Street W **$125**
(416) 604-9992

Honest Weight is a fishmonger first and a restaurant second, like a Maritime fish shack. It's a tiny space (there's
room for about eight tables), with the menu written on
chalkboards at the counter. John Bil used to be a seafood
importer (and oyster-shucking champion) and even now
his fish is supplied to a number of top-end Toronto

restaurants. Or you can eat it here for half the price. The butter drenched clam chowder is justly famous, as is the okonomiyake, a Japanese seafood pancake with bonito, smoked trout, fried onions and microgreens. What follows depends on the day and the season: it might be Ontario trout, Newfoundland cod, Arctic char, PEI salmon, BC halibut or Winnipeg pickerel (Bil has a wide range of contacts from his days as an importer). Don't miss the pickerel if it's offered. The restaurant stays open all day (except Monday) and though there are no reservations on weekends you can call ahead and they'll tell you when you're likely to get a table. Honest Weight is the sort of place this book is all about.

Open Tuesday and Wednesday 11 am to 9 pm, Thursday to Saturday 10 am to 10 pm, Sunday 10 am to 9 pm (brunch on Saturday and Sunday from 10 am to 3 pm). Closed on Monday. Licensed for beer and wine only. Master Card, Visa. No reservations on Friday and Saturday.

TORONTO   MAP 204
INDIAN STREET FOOD COMPANY   🦐
1701 Bayview Avenue   **$80**
(416) 322-3270

There's a formula for Indian restaurants in Canada. You'd think they all had the same owner. They all look the same, smell the same and offer the same menu. Every third customer orders chicken korma, every second a hot, fluffy naan. Indian Street Food isn't like that at all. Chicken korma isn't even on the menu. Nor are saag lamb, pork vindaloo, chicken tikka masala, beef madras, vegetable biryani or any of the other clichés. Instead there are things like sweet potato chaat, aloo tuk and chili calamari—the sort of snack food that Hemant Bhagwani remembers from roadside stands and railway cafes in India. Mixed with this street food are local specialties like Kerala prawns, dishes Indian chefs cook up for their staff, like pan-fried chicken with coconut—even Bhagwani's mother's grilled bhindhi. The restaurant recently introduced tasting menus, three courses for 50.00 or six

278

courses for 60.00, which are a great way to cover new ground. Try the spicy lamb chops in Lucknawi marinade, charred and served with fenugreek and mint, the light and subtle dal mordabadi with puffed rice, sev and cucumber, the eggplant bhartha with cherry tomatoes, pea shoots and green peas, or the roasted fish with tamatar masala wrapped in a banana leaf, and you won't be sorry you took the road less travelled on.

Open Monday to Thursday 5 pm to 10 pm, Friday to Sunday 11.30 am to 3 pm, 5 pm to 10 pm. Licensed. Master Card, Visa.

TORONTO   MAP 204
JACQUES
126A Cumberland Street   **$120**
(416) 961-1893

Jacques has been cooking in Yorkville for more than 30 years. There used to be a number of restaurants like his in Toronto: small, inexpensive, with the owner at the stove. Now there's only one—this one. Typically, it's upstairs, with the chef's wife in charge of the front of the house. They won't be serving focaccia or merguez sausages here. What they really like to serve (their traditional omelettes aside) is a first-class entrecote or fillet of salmon, with fresh vegetables, together with a glass or two of wine. To start there might be cold asparagus soup or terrine maison. For sweet, how about a housemade tarte au citron or perhaps a tarte tatin? You'd like a table for two by the window? Ask for one when you book. Jacques has everything and it doesn't cost very much. What more could you ask for?

Open Tuesday to Saturday noon to 3 pm, 6 pm to 11 pm. Closed on Sunday and Monday. Licensed. Amex, Master Card, Visa. Book ahead if you can.

This is a guide to Canadian restaurants from coast to coast—the first ever published and the only one of its kind on the market today. Every restaurant in the guide has been personally tested. Our reporters are not allowed to identify themselves or to accept free meals.

279

TORONTO   **MAP 204**
KAJI   ★★★
860 Queensway   **$325**
Etobicoke
(416) 252-2166

Mitsuhiro Kaji has been in a kitchen since he was thirteen
years old. First he apprenticed in Japan for ten years, then
he came to Canada in 1980. He's still in the kitchen today,
working five nights a week, offering two seasonal
omakase dinners, one featuring Wagyu beef, the other
lobster tempura. Course after course appears at your table
and everything is beautiful. The sushi is all flown to
Canada the day the fish is caught and it's served in the
restaurant the next day. It's all achingly tender. Kaji
thinks the commercial soy sauce is too salty, so he makes
his own. The vinegar is all imported from Japan. Before
he goes home for the night he throws away all the
leftovers. The toro tuna has been on his menu for years, as
have the lobster, the abalone, the sea bream and the udon
noodles. Spanish mackerel is a new delicacy. The menu
keeps changing, so you never know just what's coming
next. A taxi from downtown Toronto costs 60.00, but
you can avoid that by simply driving west on the Gardiner
to Islington, turning north on Islington and east on the
Queensway. Kaji is on the left.
*Open Wednesday to Sunday 6 pm to 9 pm. Closed on Monday
and Tuesday. Licensed. All cards. Free parking. Book ahead.*

TORONTO   **MAP 204**
NORTH 44°   ★★
2537 Yonge Street   **$250**
(416) 487-4897

The prices at North 44° are high, but no longer higher
than other restaurants of its calibre, like Canoe or Nota
Bene. Certainly they spare no expense, starting dinner
rather grandly with things like Ahi tuna and watermelon
(now a fashionable combination), steak tartar, foie gras,
organic Irish salmon and tagliatelle with poached lobster,

and going on to Dover sole, bison tenderloin, Pacific halibut, scallops, veal, chicken and duck. Some things—like the halibut—can be disappointing, and the Dover sole is certainly wildly overpriced at 70.00. But everyone likes the beef, which is aged for eight weeks and can be had with cilantro aioli—a nice touch. Try it with the house mashed potatoes. The wine-list is strong on wines from California and Australia, but surprisingly weak on wines from Canada—there are only three or four from Niagara and none from the Okanagan, which now cultivates some of the best wines in the world.

Open Monday to Saturday 5 pm to 10 pm. Closed on Sunday. Licensed. Amex, Master Card, Visa. Valet parking. Book ahead. &

TORONTO   MAP 204
NOTA BENE   ★★
180 Queen Street W $225
(416) 977-6400

Nota Bene is as elegant as ever, with its pale leather seats and tumbleweed hanging from the ceiling. The cooking remains exceptional, the service accomplished. Matzoball soup is delicate and lovely. The tartar of bigeye tuna comes in a small pool of Scotch bonnet sauce, and the Shelter Valley striploin can be cut with a butter knife—the restaurant doesn't even have steak knives in stock. Be sure to order the Mediterranean sea-bass at noon—it's perfectly cooked with lemon, butter and spinach and beautifully presented. We like the sticky toffee pudding best of the sweets, but if you prefer, there are also several fine cheeses from Quebec. The best buy on the large wine-list is probably the Tawse dry Riesling at 65.00. And if you want a cold drink, there are twelve gins, three tonics and three kinds of ice—amazing!

Open Monday to Friday 11.30 to 2.30 pm, 5 pm to 11 pm, Saturday 5 pm to 11 pm. Closed on Sunday. Licensed. Amex, Master Card, Visa. Book ahead. &

Every restaurant in this guide has been personally tested.

TORONTO   **MAP 204**
PAI
18 Duncan Street   **$80**
(416) 901-4724

All the Thai talk in Toronto these days is about the Regulars. Nuit Regular met her husband Jeff while he was backpacking in Thailand. They came back to Canada in 2008 to open Sukhothai, which is still run at three locations by Jeff's parents. Jeff and Nuit moved on to Khao San Road, to Sabai Sabai and then to Pai, a crowded basement in the theatre district festively dressed in teak, brick and strings of bright pennant flags. The menu runs through a selection of the usual Thai favourites—spring-rolls, satays, pad Thai, green curry (served inside a whole coconut) and a tasty treatment of massaman beef carpeted in deep-fried shallots. But it's the northern Thai specialties you come for (Nuit Regular grew up in north Thailand)—things like the khao soi, made with egg noodles in golden curry, or the gaeng hunglay, a sweet-and-sour ginger curry of oxtail, or the grabong, a mountain of Thai tempura made from kabocha squash. As with all of Nuit's restaurants, everything is made for sharing, and it's okay to eat with your hands. Last year the Regular family welcomed a new restaurant called Kiin, three blocks west at 326 Adelaide Street W (telephone (647) 490-5040), an upmarket dining-room serving the delicate and intricate Royal Thai cuisine of the country's aristocracy, something Nuit has always wanted to learn. First reports are encouraging, but this time round you probably can't eat with your hands.
Open Monday to Thursday 11.30 am to 10 pm, Friday and Saturday 11.30 am to 10.30 pm, Sunday 5 pm to 10 pm. Licensed. Master Card, Visa.

TORONTO   **MAP 204**
PATRIA
478 King Street W   **$225**
(416) 367-0505

Patria isn't easy to find, even if you're carrying a smart

phone. Look for the tall iron gate next to the Green-P parking-lot. Inside it's dark and very noisy, which isn't surprising given Charles Khabouth's background in the club scene. The menu is large and authentically Spanish. To start there's acorn-fed black-hoof Iberico if you can afford the price (which was last seen at 34.00), plenty of cheeses, and an excellent shaved-fennel salad. The empanadas are particularly welcome on a cold evening. But with the larger plates, the kitchen seems to run into trouble. A whole salt-baked branzino arrives full of promise, but the waiters aren't up to the job of breaking open and filleting and serving it—we were left with a pile of fish flakes mixed with bones, eyes and salt that was only a glimpse of what might have been. And the meat in your paella—which will take 45 minutes to prepare—may not be properly trimmed. Things get much better with the sweet course. Coffee ice cream comes sandwiched between nut wafers, with black-olive marmalade and spiced cream, Santiago cake comes with tangy hot custard, leche merengada ice cream and just a hint of quince jam. The long list of Spanish wines is arranged by region, and you can drink your way around the country exploring them. Most of the bottlings are private imports that you can't buy at the store, so grab your chance.

Open Monday to Saturday 5.30 pm to midnight, Sunday 10.30 am to 2.30 pm (brunch), 5.30 pm to midnight. Licensed. Amex, Master Card, Visa. Book ahead.

TORONTO   MAP 204
PLANTA
1221 Bay Street   **$130**
(647) 348-7000

David Lee, formerly of Nota Bene, has opened this sleek, black-and-white vegan restaurant on the site of the old Pangaea. The mandate is strict: they won't even sell you cream for your coffee. But the restaurant devotes a lot of energy to trying to replicate the things you can't have: there are so-called crab cakes made with hearts of palm, hot pots with truffle fries, burgers made from black beans, lentils and beetroot, "no-noodle lasagne" and the painfully named "18-carrot dog," which really does have a carrot inside in place of a wiener (though thankfully not eighteen of them). Some of these imitations work better than others. You should avoid the crab cakes and the carrot dog, but David Lee spent a long time working on his burger recipe, and it's surprisingly likeable, as are the pizzas. Or you can try the watermelon poké, which is fast becoming the restaurant's signature dish.

Open Monday to Wednesday 11.30 am to 2.30 pm, 5.30 pm to 9.30 pm, Thursday and Friday 11.30 am to 2.30 pm, 5 pm to 10 pm, Saturday and Sunday 11.30 am to 2.30 pm (brunch), 5 pm to 10 pm. Licensed. Amex, Master Car, Visa. Book ahead if you can.

TORONTO   MAP 204
RICHMOND STATION   ☆
1 Richmond Street W   **$150**
(647) 748-1444

There's always something to admire and enjoy at Richmond Station. Carl Heinrich's menu changes regularly, but if you're lucky it might start with something like pumpkin soup with toasted sesame seeds or sweet-potato fritters with maple aioli and a hint of cayenne, deep-fried on the outside and meltingly soft inside. Best of the main courses is probably the Berkshire pork three ways, which comes with fried terrine and shredded cabbage on a celeriac purée. We also admire Heinrich's mushroom agnolotti with Swiss chard, and the charcuterie that's on the menu all day. He has an excellent sangiovese for 170.00, but his Daniel Chotard sauvignon blanc is good enough for anybody at just 17.00 a glass. Everything his kitchen touches is perfect in its way.

Open Monday to Friday 11 am to 10 pm, Saturday 5 pm to 10 pm. Closed on Sunday. Licensed. Amex, Master Card, Visa.

Every restaurant in this guide has been personally tested. Our reporters are not allowed to identify themselves or to accept free meals.

TORONTO   **MAP 204**

SABAI SABAI

81 Bloor Street E   **$75**

(647) 748-4225

Nobody in Toronto these days can seem to get enough small plates, and if those plates can't be Spanish they might as well be Thai. Jeff and Nuit Regular saw this coming several years ago, when they opened Sabai Sabai as a stylish tapas bar at Church and Dundas. Recently they moved the restaurant upmarket to Bloor Street just east of Yonge, a stone's throw from Yorkville and a short block from the Hudson's Bay Centre, Manulife and Rogers. It's a little hard to find, tucked unobtrusively under a forgettable Firkins pub, but everyone has been there before. Sabai Sabai is a favourite of Regular regulars for a couple of reasons. First, unlike Pai (see above), it takes reservations for all of its tables. And second, its small-plates format is particularly suited to Thai food, where everyone wants to try a bit of everything. Nothing on the menu costs more than 15.00, and most of Nuit Regular's trademark dishes are here—squash fritters, papaya salad, stir-fried pad gra prao, massaman beef, morning glory and of course the famous golden khao soi. There are also a number of less familiar Laotian specialties, though none is as popular as the Beerlao lager, made from jasmine rice and available nowhere else in Canada. *Open Monday to Thursday 11 am to 10 pm, Friday and Saturday 11 am to 11 pm, Sunday 4 pm to 10 pm. Licensed. Master Card, Visa.*

TORONTO   **MAP 204**

SCARAMOUCHE   ★★

1 Benvenuto Place   **$240**

(416) 961-8011

Scaramouche, as everyone knows by now, has a stunning view of the city by night. But there's a lot more to Scaramouche than the view. Keith Froggett is still in charge of the kitchen and he has a very handsome menu and does some beautiful things with it. His steak tartar, for instance, tastes exactly as it should, which is rare in Canadian restaurants. His grilled-octopus salad is a delight. And his yellowfin-tuna sashimi is wonderful. At his best, Keith Froggett is brilliant. But of course he's not always at his best. His warm lobster with ginger and sesame is a good example. Lobster is, of course, an important luxury, but it's hard to deal with, hard for a kitchen that wants to handle its dishes with real delicacy. Froggett's lobster is just like the lobster you'll get in any Maritime road house. But one has to admit that his pasta is all housemade, his sea-bass fresh and lightly cooked. As for his wine-list, it's long and very splendid. If money is a problem—and Scaramouche is certainly expensive—ask for a couple of half-glasses of the Proprietary bordeaux. It costs 23.00 for two half-glasses, which is cheap for a wine of this quality. If you insist on a whole bottle, we can't help you.

Open Monday to Saturday 5.30 pm to 9.30 pm. Closed on Sunday. Licensed. All cards. Free valet parking. Book ahead.

TORONTO   **MAP 204**
YASU   ☆☆
81 Harbord Street   **$250**
(416) 477-2361

Yasu is small and simple. There's nothing inside but a plain white sushi bar with twelve seats facing three sushi chefs, each serving four diners. There's a list showing several sakes by the glass and the bottle together with a few wines, but there is no menu—this is an omakase restaurant. After you've chosen your wine or sake, you sit back and watch the chefs at work, and work they do for exactly two hours, creating identical sushis for each of the twelve diners. Most of these sushis few Canadians have seen before. There's lobster, scallop, cod, salmon, striped Jack with ginger from Japan, monkfish liver, sea-trout from Scotland, red shrimp from Argentina, mackerel from Iceland, sea-urchin from British Columbia, bluefin from Mexico and bonito and sea-eel from Japan. The meal ends with a dish of black-sesame ice-cream. It's an extraordinary experience. Whether or not it's worth the money is up to you. But don't decide to come at the last minute: Yasu is usually booked at least two weeks in advance.

Open Monday to Thursday at 6 pm and 8.15 pm (two sittings), Friday to Sunday at 5 pm, 7.15 pm and 9.30 pm (three sittings). Licensed. Master Card, Visa. You must book ahead.

TORONTO   MAP 204
ZUCCA
2150 Yonge Street   **$150**
(416) 488-5774

Zucca is a small restaurant with a big-time chef. Andrew Milne-Allan isn't getting any younger, and there are those who think he's not the man he used to be. Which of us is? He still has a fine menu, featuring appetizers like gnocchi di ricotta with shaved truffles, white asparagus with balsamic vinegar and grilled octopus with new potatoes, followed by squid-ink noodles, braised rabbit, sea bream, brick-pressed Cornish game hen and, the specialty of the house, grilled whole fish with lemon and extra-virgin olive-oil. The asparagus is served hot raw in the modern style, but the New York steak comes with good seasonal vegetables. There's a decent selection of Italian wine at reasonable prices.

Open Monday to Saturday 5.30 pm to 10 pm, Sunday 5 pm to 9 pm. Licensed. Amex, Master Card, Visa.

TORONTO
See also CREEMORE, MARKHAM.

TRINITY, Newfoundland   MAP 205
THE TWINE LOFT   ☆
Artisan Inn   **$150**
57 High Street
(709) 464-3377

Everyone stops at the Artisan Inn, to stay or to eat—and usually both. Trinity is easily the most beautiful spot in

Newfoundland, and the inn is the first place you should visit. Once you've checked in, walk a short distance back along the road (the Gows will give you directions) and climb up the side of Gun Hill; from halfway up, the view of the heritage village spread out in all its varied colours against the backdrop of Trinity Bay is unforgettable. Tineke Gow came here from Holland a long time ago, and fell in love with the town, which she calls "a little bit of the Old World tucked into the New." And indeed people have been living here for more than 500 years, which is about as far back as Canada goes. The Gows opened their first bed-and-breakfast house in 1992, and have been adding houses and guests ever since. Before long they turned an old storage building at the water's edge into the Twine Loft restaurant, with room for about 25 people at each of two sittings. (It takes reservations from outside the inn, but only if there's room, so you must call ahead if you're coming in from elsewhere.) The three-course menu offers a choice of two starters, two main courses, one sweet and tea or coffee for about 50.00. The starters are usually a soup— apple and turnip perhaps, or carrot and orange or tomato and gin—and a salad, made with local greens, dried cranberries, fruits and cheese. To follow there's a choice between meat and fish. The fish is often cod, en papillote perhaps. Salmon is another favourite, baked in a walnut-dijon crust. The meats may be pork with apple brandy and mushrooms, chicken with maple syrup and blueberries or lamb shank braised in Quidi Vidi brown beer. The inn grows its own rhubarb, which appears in a number of sweets, but there's also an apple spice-cake with warm screech sauce, pecan tart with crème brûlée and warm cinnamon waffles with housemade blueberry ice cream. It all seems even more remarkable when you look out the window at the waves a few feet away. If the weather is warm enough you can sit with a drink before or after dinner on the small front deck over the water. And if it isn't warm enough, the Gows will give you a blanket to wrap yourself up in. The Artisan Inn is that sort of place.

Open daily at 5.30 pm and 7.45 pm (two sittings). Licensed. Master Card, Visa. Book ahead. ♿

TROUT RIVER, Newfoundland   MAP 206
SEASIDE
263 Main Street   **$100**
(709) 451-3461

It's been almost 40 years since May Hann persuaded her husband to turn his old shed into a snack bar she could run. It was a simple place, and served a lot of ice cream, but May's standards were always high. Over the years her cafe got bigger and better until it grew into the Seaside, which has been managed ever since by her daughter Jenny Parsons. The restaurant sits right on the beach in Trout River, with nothing to the west before Labrador. The fittings are straightforward and old-fashioned, as they should be, and the menu features half-a-dozen different fillets of fish perfectly pan-fried (though you can have your halibut or salmon poached instead if you want to get fancy). The vegetables are plain, but the small roast potatoes more than make up for them. Get a table by the window and watch the sun set over the western headland, and you'll be glad you came.
Open daily noon to 10 pm from mid-May to mid-October. Licensed. Master Card, Visa. Book ahead if you can.

TRURO, N.S.   MAP 207
BISTRO 22
16 Inglis Place   **$100**
(902) 843-4123

Truro has never been a restaurant town. But as we've said before, Dennis Pierce changed all that. He's a local boy who went to Winnipeg for his Red Seal, and then stayed in Manitoba for eleven more years before returning home. This is his first restaurant, and he does all the cooking himself. He's even been known to prepare the sweets between lunch and dinner. His reputation may rest on his sandwiches and paninis, but you should also try one of the soups or salads. Our favourite is still the mixed green salad on the dinner menu, which is filled with goat cheese, avocado and walnuts. Pierce does very good things with meat and fish. The salmon is gently cooked, and the boeuf bourguignon as good as any to be had in France. Make sure to try the wonderful mashed potatoes. The wines are mostly Nova Scotian and so are the beers.

Open Tuesday and Wednesday 11 am to 2 pm, Thursday to Saturday 11 am to 2 pm, 5 pm to 8.30 pm. Closed on Sunday and Monday. Licensed. All cards. &

TWILLINGATE, Newfoundland   MAP 208

DOYLE SANSOME & SONS
25 Sansome's Place   **$60**
Hillgrade
New World Island
(709) 628-7421

Doyle Sansome and Sons is a fish-processing business on a remote shore of New World Island with a lobster pool big enough to swim in (but don't). Next to the pool is a small windowed café on the wharf over the water that is ably and charmingly run by Doyle's daughter-in-law Eileen. It's a simple place with a simple menu—your choice of lobster, snow crab, cod and scallops, with squid rings, chowder, mussels and crab rolls to start—but everyone loves it. The lobster is their showpiece dish, and they will give you a net to scoop your own out of the pool. Out of season Eileen will tell you she likes the snow crab even better, and help you take it apart. And their cod and chips is quite possibly the best in the province. To follow there are excellent housemade blueberry and partridgeberry pies. In summer you can sit even further out on the wharf on the small front deck, with water underneath and the ocean all around you. The views out to Black Island and the open sea are unforgettable. This is Newfoundland: fresh seafood, friendly people, no pretensions, perfect scenery.

Open daily 10 am to 9 pm from early May until mid-September. Licensed. No cards. Book ahead if you can.

UCLUELET, B.C.   (MAP 203)
NORWOODS   ☆☆
1714 Peninsula Road   **$200**
(250) 726-7001

The good news is that Norwoods is still one of the best restaurants in the country. The bad news is that it's getting so expensive only a few of us can afford to eat there. The appetizers are still, in our opinion, the highlight of the meal. Our favourite is the tender, lightly grilled Pacific octopus with truffled potato purée and ginger and chili sauce. Or you can try the Taste of the West Coast sampler, which includes smoked salmon, oysters, tuna ceviche, octopus, clams and black cod. Main courses run to seared albacore tuna with mushroom dashi and roasted ramen, or miso-glazed Alaska black cod with clams and chili. For sweet, look for dishes that feature local fruits and berries. There's an excellent list of B.C. wines, featuring Blue Mountain and Blue Grouse.

Open Monday and Tuesday and Friday to Sunday 6 pm to 11 pm. Closed on Wednesday and Thursday. Licensed. All cards. Book ahead. ♿

VANCOUVER, B.C.   MAP 209
L'ABATTOIR   ☆
217 Carrall Street   **$125**
(604) 568-1701

We used to have l'Abattoir in *Where to Eat in Canada*, but deleted it because the noise there reached a level that we thought was intolerable. But the young people who patronize the place don't seem to mind, so here we are again. Cocktails aside, the meal starts with poached shrimp, a terrine of smoked foie gras, pan-friend veal sweetbreads and olive-dusted albacore tuna. They're all delicious. Lamb neck follows or scallops in brown butter, steak Diane with bone-marrow butter, or roast duck with black beans and peppercorns. The meal ends very well with roasted pears with burnt-honey custard. The noise, however, is no better.

Open Monday to Thursday 5.30 pm to 10 pm, Friday 5.30 pm to 10.30, Saturday and Sunday 10 am to 2 pm, 5.30 pm to 10 pm. Licensed. Master Card, Visa.

VANCOUVER　　　　　　　　　　　　MAP 209
ABSINTHE　　　　　　　　　　　　　　☆☆
1260 Commercial Drive　　　　　　　　**$125**
(604) 566-9053

If you go to Absinthe for dinner, you'll soon see why it's considered one of Vancouver's best restaurants. It's small and intimate. Its menu is short and carefully crafted by Cory Pearson. The list changes daily but always offers three appetizers, three main courses and three sweets. There are two *prix-fixes*, one offering two courses for 36.00, the other three courses for 45.00. Appetizers run to things like tuna cured in lemon juice and chicken-liver terrine. The main courses favour scallops and duck, which recur in varied forms. Most recently the scallops came with roasted cauliflower and pommes anna, and the duck with a Belgian waffle, a pecan glaze and goat cheese. Pearson's favourite sweets are rice pudding with caramel sauce, chocolate lava cake and crème brûlée. Well selected B.C. vintages fill the wine-list, all at very reasonable prices.
Open Wednesday and Thursday 5.30 pm to 8.30 pm, Friday and Saturday 5.30 pm to 9 pm, Sunday 5.30 pm to 8.30 pm. Closed on Monday and Tuesday. Licensed. Master Card, Visa. Book ahead.

VANCOUVER　　　　　　　　　　　　MAP 209
ACORN　　　　　　　　　　　　　　　☆☆
3995 Main Street　　　　　　　　　　**$120**
(604) 566-9001

British Columbia has the highest percentage of vegetarians in Canada, and of course Vancouver leads the way. This may be one reason why Acorn was recently ranked among the world's top ten vegetarian restaurants. The flavours Brian Luptak creates are like nothing we've ever been offered. The best way to appreciate them is to order the Chef's Menu, which covers most of the night's choices. Look for the beer-battered halloumi cheese served on a bed of minted peas, the raw zucchini linguine with mint and walnut pesto, the caramelized onion tart and the eggplant risotto. The sweets are splendid: try the apple cannoli, the poached peaches with ice cream, the lavender crème brûlée or the raspberry cashew cheesecake. The wine-list is small but carefully chosen. *Open Monday to Friday 5.30 pm to midnight, Saturday and Sunday 10 am to 2.30 pm (brunch), 5.30 pm to midnight. Licensed. All cards.* &

VANCOUVER   MAP 209
ANCORA   ☆
1600 Howe Street   **$130**
(604) 681-1164

Ancora has a beautiful setting overlooking False Creek and Granville Island, in the premises once made famous by C. Its cuisine is an unusual mix of Japanese and Peruvian influences, using only sustainable seafood and some of the best ingredients the west coast has to offer. We like the lobster chupe, a rich Peruvian bisque blended with corn, quinoa and egg, the beef tartar yukke with Asian pear and sesame and the lobster risotto with cauliflower, peas and preserved lemon. Sablefish is glazed with aji panca, a smoky red chili pepper that is an important ingredient in many Peruvian dishes. Haida Gwaii halibut comes with chorizo, shellfish, Peruvian corn and an emulsion of smoked paprika. To follow there are spiced picarones, deep-fried soft doughnut rings made from pumpkin and sweet potato. The elaborate Sunday brunch offers things like duck cassoulet with poached eggs, paella with sablefish croquettes and a benedict of Dungeness crab. There's a fine list of sparkling wines. *Open daily 3 pm to 11 pm. Licensed. All cards. Book ahead.* &

Our website is at www.oberonpress.ca. Readers wishing to use e-mail should address us at oberon@sympatico.ca.

293

VANCOUVER   **MAP 209**
ANNALENA
1809 1 Avenue W   **$125**
(778) 379-4052

This is a hot new restaurant run by Michael Robbins,
assisted by Erin Searle, who cut her teeth at Bacchus and
Diva at the Met. Together they blend west-coast modern
and traditional French cuisine to create an impressive
array of small plates. There's a savoury duck liver on sourdough, squid in romesco, pan-seared lingcod (small but
perfectly cooked), glazed pork belly, shelled mussels in
garlic cream and buttermilk fried chicken (with dashi aioli
and shishito peppers). If you like, you can sign up for the
daily tasting menu at $75, but it's only offered until 8.30
pm. Best of the sweets is the cream puff filled with
bourbon ice cream and lemon curd. The wine-list is
expensive; its best buy is probably the cabernet sauvignon
from Washington State, but even that runs to 65.00.
Open daily 5 pm to midnight. Licensed. All cards. Book ahead.
&

VANCOUVER   **MAP 209**
ASK FOR LUIGI
305 Alexander Street   **$130**
(604) 428-2544

Ask for Luigi is a haven of comfort food in a neighbourhood that needs it. They take no reservations, and if you
arrive after 5:30 you'll have no choice but to walk around
the East Side waiting for their call. That can take up to
two hours, and these are not streets where you want to
walk for that long. Once inside, you'll find the amenities
basic—it's an old building—and the noise levels high. But
the food will help you forget. There's no Luigi in the
kitchen—Luigi is the grandfather of one of the owners.
This is a pasta house and it always has fresh homemade
rigatoni, spaghetti and gnocchi on hand, as well as panna
cotta and bunido (bunido is a flourless chocolate cake and
it's much better than the panna cotta). Gluten-free

options are always available. You can start with chicken-liver terrine or pork belly and kale, and finish with a cold glass of prosecco.

Open Tuesday to Thursday 11.30 am to 2.30 pm, 5.30 pm to 10.30 pm, Friday 11.30 am to 2.30 pm, 5.30 pm to 11 pm, Saturday 9.30 am to 2.30 pm, 5.30 pm to 11 pm, Sunday 9.30 am to 2.30 pm, 5.30 pm to 9.30 pm. Closed on Monday. Licensed for beer and wine only. All cards. No reservations. ♿

VANCOUVER   MAP 209
BAO BEI   👉
163 Keefer Street   **$80**
(604) 688-0876

Bao Bei is a perfect example of Chinese-Canadian fusion cuisine. If you can stand the noise, stop here after work for some house-made Taiwanese pork sausage or szechuan fried chicken. You can stay at the bar as long as you like, sampling Chinese pickles, oyster mushrooms or eggplant marinated in soy, garlic and ginger and served with bean-curd skin. Or you can take a table and settle down to a dish of steak tartar with mustard root, a salad of spicy smoked duck or a helping of wheat noodles with sesame and pork fat. And if you feel like an exotic cocktail, they have them all.

Open Tuesday to Saturday 5.30 pm to midnight, Sunday 5.30 pm to 11 pm. Closed on Monday. Licensed. Master Card, Visa. No reservations.

VANCOUVER   MAP 209
BARBECUE MASTER   👉
4651 No. 3 Road: Suite 145   **$45**
Richmond
(604) 272-6568

Barbecue Master is a hole-in-the-wall serving Hong-Kong-style food at startlingly low prices. There are only a few spartan tables and the meals are rock-bottom basic: soup, a roasted meat and rice. But there's still a long line at the door. Most people come for the char siu, three layers of roasted pork—skin, fat and belly—served over freshly made steaming white rice. Or there's roasted duck, fresh or smoked, and a moist and tender soy-sauce chicken. The restaurant can be a bit hard to find in the Superstore parkade—look for the lineup—but at least there's lots of free parking. Most people take their meals away to save waiting, but if you do eat in, the lychee tea is delicious.

Open Monday, Tuesday and Thursday to Sunday 11 am to 8 pm. Closed on Wednesday. No liquor, no cards. No reservations.

VANCOUVER   MAP 209
BAUHAUS   ☆☆
1 W Cordova Street   **$250**
(604) 974-1147

Bauhaus is owned by the German film director, Uwe Boll, who has lived in Vancouver for some time, and its innovative menu offers contemporary takes on German cuisine. The restaurant is located in Gastown, one of Vancouver's oldest neighbourhoods, and the original timber, brick and stone have been retained as part of its minimalist Bauhaus design. The menu changes every two months. If it's offered, order the spectacular wild boar pastrami, a paper-thin carpaccio warmed sous-vide with lavoche and Japanese mushrooms and served in a bell jar filled with smoke. One diner thought it was the best thing he had ever eaten. Main courses range from German comfort foods like rouladen with dumplings and sauerbraten with cabbage to more expensive creations like sturgeon with beets, blini and kale, roast pheasant with root vegetables and a 30-day dry-aged striploin. The selection of wines comes mainly from the United States and Europe.

Open Monday to Thursday 11.30 am to 2.30 pm, 5 pm to 10.30 pm, Friday 11.30 am to 2.30 pm, 5 pm to 11 pm, Saturday 5 pm to 11 pm, Sunday 5 pm to 10.30 pm. Licensed. All cards. Book ahead. &

We accept no advertisements. We accept no payment for listings. We depend entirely on you. Recommend the book to your friends.

VANCOUVER
BISHOP'S
2183 W 4 Avenue
(604) 738-2025

MAP 209

$150

Bishop's was a *Where to Eat in Canada* regular until a few years ago, when we came to feel that it had been overtaken by too many of the new restaurants that were appearing in the city. Fair enough, but 30 years of consistent cooking and excellent service should count for something—and they do. The menu is impressive, starting with a perfect crab risotto and excellent pan-seared scallops. Halibut comes from Haida Gwaii and is well served with cauliflower, fava beans and fennel. Sockeye salmon comes in a wine broth with chorizo. Bison is grilled rare with garlic aioli and pommes frites. The wines are of two sorts: well chosen and inexpensive local vintages or astronomically expensive labels from France. Does this sound like a restaurant that has no place in *Where to Eat*? We don't think so.

Open Tuesday to Sunday 5.30 pm to 10 pm. Closed on Monday. Licensed. All cards. Book ahead. &

VANCOUVER
BLUE WATER
1095 Hamilton Street
(604) 688-8078

MAP 209

☆☆☆
$225

It's hard to get a seat at the raw bar at Blue Water these days. Indeed, it's hard to get a seat anywhere. Vancouver's best seafood restaurant draws a full house almost every night for its fusion-influenced cuisine. The raw bar features acres of clams, oysters, prawns, scallops, crab and lobster that are given both western and Japanese treatments. If you're sitting away from the bar, you can order one of the seafood towers to be brought to your table— two tiers for 89.00 or three for 159.00—or settle for a platter (they call it a plateau) at 28.00. The pick of the hot plates is still the Arctic char with braised leeks, Dungeness crab, trout caviar and pearl couscous, though the sablefish, the lingcod, the sturgeon and the scallops are almost its equal. For people who want to stay on the shore there's kobe-style shortribs with fresh horseradish gremolata and chicken stuffed with sauvagine cheese. Side dishes are extra: truffle-and-parmesan fries are 9.50, baby spinach with lemon and garlic 8.00. The sweets are rich and elaborate: cassis-and-yuzu cheesecake with nougatine chantilly, apple-toffee pudding with nutmeg gelato, panna cotta with morello-cherry compote, brandy and ice cream. And the wine cellar is of course enormous. Blue Water is an amazing accomplishment.

Open daily 5 pm to 11 pm. Licensed. All cards. Valet parking. You must book ahead. &

VANCOUVER   **MAP 209**
LA BUCA   ☆
4025 Macdonald Street   **$180**
(604) 730-6988

La Buca has the smallest kitchen we have ever seen, but nothing seems to faze the chefs. For our money, this is the best Italian restaurant in Vancouver. Start with the rich and creamy veal tonnato or the orecchiette with rapini and chili. Then there's roast breast of duck with corona beans and pancetta and braised beef cheeks with a lovely wild-mushroom risotto topped with gremolata. Best of the pastas is probably the pappardelle with hedgehog mushrooms, sausage and cipollini. The panna cotta is lovely, and the wines are all carefully chosen—so go for broke.

Open Monday to Thursday 5 pm to 9.30 pm, Friday and Saturday 5 pm to 10 pm, Sunday 5 pm to 9.30 pm. Licensed, Master Card, Visa. Book ahead. &

VANCOUVER   **MAP 209**
BUFALA
5395 West Boulevard   **$80**
(604) 267-7499

Bufala was named one of Canada's ten best restaurants in 2014, and the quality of food and service is still very high four years later. To start, we like the arugula and beet salad almost as much as the burrata with compressed pears, honey, basil and prosciutto. If you're hungry, there are Italian meatballs with ricotta, basil and tomato. If you're not, try the bison carpaccio with smoked salt, horseradish and pickled shallots. Of course, everything turns on the pizzas, which are a matter of taste. Will it be the Finocchiona with fennel sausage, caramelized onions and smoked provolone, or the bianco funghi with roasted mushrooms and goat cheese? Or perhaps the bianco pesto, or the artichoke and olive with fior di latte? It's your call—they're all equally good. To follow, you'll find the lemon curd hard to beat. The selection of Italian reds is outstanding, and there's a good choice of local craft beers as well.

Open daily 11.30 am to 10 pm. Licensed. All cards. No reservations. &

VANCOUVER   MAP 209
CAFE KATHMANDU
2779 Commercial Drive   **$85**
(604) 879-9909

The menu here will be unfamiliar to many readers. For an appetizer, just ask either for the bhatmaas, which are toasted soybeans with minced ginger, garlic and chili, or for the choilaa, which are shredded chicken or pork simmered with lemon, garlic and coriander. Then go on to a goat curry with yellow dal and sweet-and-sour chutney. Cafe Kathmandu has a big vegan menu. Vegans won't do better than the raaio or mustard greens slow-cooked with gently-spiced potatoes. Nothing here costs more than 15.00 and beer is always on hand.

Open Monday to Saturday 5 pm to 10 pm. Closed on Sunday. Licensed for beer and wine only. Master Card, Visa. &

If you wish to improve the guide send us information about restaurants we have missed. Our mailing address is Oberon Press, 145 Spruce Street: Suite 205, Ottawa, Ontario K1R 6P1.

VANCOUVER

MAP 209

CHAMBAR
☆
568 Beatty Street
$170
(604) 879-7119

Noise has always been a problem at Chambar. We've complained about it for years, but their new location is no better than the old. The largely hipster crowds don't seem to mind though, so perhaps the restaurant knows what it's doing. Chambar used to be all about mussels—with or without Belgian beer—and they are still hugely popular, though at almost $30 a lunchtime plate close to pricing themselves out of the market. These days we prefer to have the beer—the list has now grown to two pages—with something that's better value. Breakfast is served seven days a week, starting at 8 am, and features things like a tagine of spicy merguez sausages with stewed tomatoes and poached egg, or (on weekends only) a savoury waffle covered with salmon gravlax, yuzu and pea shoots. Lunch is nearly as expensive as dinner, and offers miso tuna, a venison burger that isn't worth $21 unless you're very well off, and poached chicken with cardamom, puy lentils and fresh pomegranate. In the evening we like the fish, especially the Arctic char, the salmon and the halibut. To start there are frogs' legs, raclette, squid, foie-gras terrine and, of course, brussels sprouts. Come here with someone you don't want to talk to, and you'll leave happy.
Open Monday to Wednesday 8 am to midnight, Thursday to Saturday 8 am to 2 am, Sunday 8 am to midnight. Licensed. All cards. Book ahead. ♿

VANCOUVER

MAP 209

CINARA
350 W Pender Street
$130
(604) 428-9694

The cuisine at Cinara could be called modern European with an Italian accent. Lucais Syme and Gill Book make as many things as possible in the kitchen, including breads, pastas, preserves and cheeses. Regulars like the sous-vide fennel and shrimp, the chicken-liver parfait, the duck breast with lentils and the halibut-stuffed ravioli with shrimp on the side. We prefer the strozzapreti with duck confit and anchovy ragu and the rabbit wrapped in prosciutto. If you're feeling adventurous, there's even a nettle risotto. Best of the sweets is the yogurt panna cotta with coronation grapes. The well-chosen Italian wines cost upwards of 50.00 a bottle, with a corkage fee of 30.00 if you bring your own.

Open Monday 11 am to 2 pm, Tuesday to Friday 11 am to 2 pm, 5 pm to 10 pm, Saturday 5 pm to 10 pm. Closed on Sunday. Licensed. Book ahead if you can. &

VANCOUVER   **MAP 209**
CIOPPINO'S   ☆☆☆
1133 Hamilton Street   **$250**
(604) 688-7466

Pino Posteraro is still on the floor here every night, and often in the kitchen as well, which is probably why Cioppino's remains such a good restaurant. Their best dish is still the cioppino itself, a medley of fresh fish in a spicy bouillabaisse topped with rouille. Lobster figures prominently on the menu: it's served with saffron-lemon gnocchi, with a Genovese pesto risotto, with prawns and scallops and with chicken-and-lobster sausage in a light butter sauce (this dish is called Lobster Heaven). And where there's lobster, steak can't be far behind—triple-A Alberta rib-eye served sliced in the Tuscan style with arugula and parmigiano. There's also wild boar, osso buco, rack of lamb and fillet of sablefish. To start you can choose between octopus, squid, prawns, carpaccio of beef and a charcuterie board—or treat yourself to Iberico ham for $88. The wine cellar is one of the best in Vancouver, and has won the Wine Spectator's Award of Excellence for the last twelve years in a row.

Open Tuesday to Saturday 5 pm to 10.30 pm. Closed on Sunday and Monday. Licensed. All cards. Valet parking. You must book ahead. &

VANCOUVER MAP 209

DIVA AT THE MET ☆

645 Howe Street **$165**

(604) 602-7788

Considering how convenient it is to the Queen Elizabeth Theatre, the Vancouver Opera, BC Place and the Rogers Arena, Diva is not that expensive. Dinner appetizers, all under 20.00, include seared sea scallops with cauliflower couscous, wild prawns with artichokes, pork belly with raisins and beef tartar with black-garlic crostini. Main courses are more elaborate: wild prawn pappardelle with arugula, garlic, lemon thyme and lobster cream; spice-rubbed sakura pork chop with Fraser Valley corn, sweet potato hash and bourbon sauce; smoked black cod with potato puree, fennel marmalade and a celery nage. But the cooking is always apt and to the point, the service friendly and efficient. The wine-list is as good as ever, if not better, and reasonably priced—most of the bottles cost less than 55.00.

Open Monday to Friday 6.30 am to 10 pm, Saturday and Sunday 6:30 am to 11 am, 5 pm to 10 pm. Licensed. All cards. Free valet parking. Book ahead. &

VANCOUVER MAP 209

ESPANA

1118 Denman Street **$95**

(604) 558-4040

At España you can get Iberico or serrano ham, imported from Spain at great expense. If you can't afford either, there's always pork belly with hummus, grilled octopus with white-bean-and-potato purée or the very authentic patatas bravas in tomato aioli. These are all exciting dishes, and the paella is another; it's served in the traditional Valencian style, with fish, chicken, squid and a great many other things. They make a good sangria, and there are several fine sherries, sold as a flight. Ask for that every time, because the list of Spanish wines is not as good as it should be. On weekends they're open till two in the morning, just as they would be in Barcelona.

Open Sunday to Thursday 5 pm to 1 am, Friday and Saturday 5 pm to 2 am. Licensed. Amex, Master Card, Visa. No reservations. &

VANCOUVER   MAP 209
FABLE   ☆
1944 W 4 Avenue   **$140**
(604) 732-1322

Fable means Farm-to-Table. Trevor Bird is the chef and he buys fresh food at his kitchen door every day—the suppliers come and he buys. His restaurant is spare and simple, with old brick walls and wooden beams salvaged from the Cecil Hotel. There's a long bar looking into the kitchen, and that's the place to have dinner. You can't eat lunch at the bar, but it costs only about 20.00 a head for an ambitious menu featuring chickpea fritters, albacore tuna, lingcod brandade and lemon-meringue parfait. In the evening you can expect things like octopus salad and duck meatballs to begin with, followed by local seafood of all sorts, house-made chorizo, onion gnocchi, smoked breast of duck and loin of pork with polenta and mushrooms. The amazing thing is that no main course ever costs more than 30.00. The wine-list is small and features B.C. vintages. Even Venturi-Schulze is sold by the glass as well as the bottle.

Open Monday to Friday 11.30 am to 2 pm, 5.30 pm to 10 pm, Saturday and Sunday 10.30 am to 2 pm, 5.30 pm to 10 pm. Licensed. Amex, Master Card, Visa. Book ahead. &

VANCOUVER   MAP 209
GO FISH   ☞
1505 W 1 Avenue   **$45**
(604) 730-5040

Chances are you'll wait a long time for your meal at this little shack on Fisherman's Wharf, no matter when you come. And the service could be kinder. But people keep coming back because of the food. The tourists all order fish and chips, and they're not wrong. But it's a pity to miss things like the deliciously tangy Thai soup, the charcoal-grilled salmon and the seared ahi tuna salad. If you just want a sandwich, try the po-boy, filled with deep-fried oysters, sweet onions, chipotle cream and tartar sauce.

Open Tuesday to Friday 11.30 am to 6.30 pm, Saturday and Sunday noon to 6.30 pm. Closed on Monday. No liquor. Master Card, Visa. No reservations. &

VANCOUVER   **MAP 209**
HAWKSWORTH   ★★★
Hotel Georgia   **$285**
801 W Georgia Street
(604) 673-7000

Hawksworth has now become the most expensive restaurant in Vancouver. Starters range from 25.00 to 30.00 and main courses from 40.00 to 60.00. Obviously this raises expectations that the kitchen may not always be able to meet. And some people feel that David Hawksworth's attention has been distracted by Nightingale, his new (and much more economical) venture over on W Hastings Street (see below). But this is still a formidable operation, with an exciting menu, faultless cooking and impeccable service. Not to mention an absolutely unbelievable wine-list. The menu is filled with ideas: hamachi ceviche with sea buckthorn, passion-fruit, avocado and crisp rice; Humboldt squid with peanut, nashi pear and crispy pork; duck breast with beets, horseradish and chamomile; sturgeon with a mushroom crust, kale, sunchoke and lingonberry. You can keep it simple and get the Alberta ribeye with wild mushrooms, bone marrow and green peppercorns for 130.00 for two, or go the whole hog and order the chef's tasting menu of six elaborate courses for 118.00 a person (196.00 with wine).

Hawksworth is a place for special occasions, for an evening you want to remember.

Open Monday to Friday 11.30 am to 2 pm, 5.30 pm to 11 pm, Saturday and Sunday 10.30 am to 2.30 pm (brunch), 5.30 pm to 11 pm. Licensed. All cards. Valet parking. Book ahead.

VANCOUVER   **MAP 209**
JAPADOG   🖝
530 Robson Street   **$25**
(604) 569-1158

Japadog has been growing steadily for twelve years now, a testament to the popularity of Asian-fusion food. They approach the humble hot-dog with a passionate devotion to unami, the Japanese culinary concept that can be roughly translated as "pleasant savoury taste." Their signature dish is the terimayo dog, which comes with mayo, seaweed and teriyaki sauce. Have it with kurobuta sausage—the pork equivalent of kobe beef. Try also the ebi tempura dog, which features tempura shrimp on rice. Avocado dogs are available for vegetarians, and the fries are first-rate. This is the only storefront Japadog in Vancouver, but there are four roadside stands around town: one at Burrard and Smithe Street, where it all began in 2005, a second at Waterfront Station, a third at Westminster Highway and No. 3 Road in Richmond and a fourth at 10275 135 Street in Surrey. There's also a lunchtime trailer at Burrard and Pender in the business district, and a bright red Japadog truck that travels between Kerrisdale, Kitsilano and the Olympic Village. Not content with all of this, Japadog has recently expanded into California, with outlets in Los Angeles and on Santa Monica Pier.
Open Monday to Thursday 11 am to 10 pm, Friday and Saturday 11 am to 11 pm, Sunday 11 am to 10 pm. No liquor. Master Card, Visa. No reservations.

VANCOUVER   **MAP 209**
KINGYO IZAKAYA   ☆
871 Denman Street   **$95**
(604) 608-1677

Izakaya restaurants are essentially Japanese tapas bars, with an extensive selection of small plates and a wide range of drinks. Kingyo is crowded and noisy and running on energy. Minoru Tamaru, the owner and chef, directs his kitchen team like a samurai army, demanding precision and perfection at every turn. He shops daily for such key ingredients as fresh wasabi and yuzu (a Japanese citrus fruit); whatever else he finds determines what gets added to the restaurant's chalkboard. The best seafood choices remain the aonori calamari, the ebi-mayo (tempura prawns in chili mayo) and the outstanding sake-kasu black cod. The meats are stone-grilled: kobe beef, beef tongue and marinated pork cheek (a nice variation on the usual pork belly). The sushi and sashimi can get expensive: stick to the raw starters, like tuna tataki or ahi tuna and avocado carpaccio. The sweets tend to be fusion versions of old friends: crème caramel with caramelized soy sauce, and frozen green-tea crème brûlée with red bean sauce.

Open Monday to Thursday 11.30 am to 2.30 pm, 5.30 pm to 11.30 pm, Friday and Saturday 11.30 am to 2.30 pm, 5.30 pm to midnight, Sunday 11.30 am to 2.30 pm, 5.30 pm to 11.30 pm. Licensed. All cards. Book ahead. &

VANCOUVER   MAP 209
KISSA TANTO
263 E Pender Street   **$110**
(778) 379-8078

Kissa Tanto is a Japanese-Italian fusion restaurant (a kissa is a Japanese café) popular with young professionals. Tannis Ling, the owner of Bao Bei, took her inspiration from the jazu-kissa or jazz bars of Tokyo in the nineteen-sixties. You can drink a cup of sake or a glass of Italian wine while listening to Japanese and Western jazz from the large stack of vinyl records on the bar. Or you can try some of the restaurant's unusual combinations, like the lasagne made with kasu-braised pork and smothered in miso béchamel, the gnocchi with kombu dashi, the parmesan croquette with plum curry sauce or the garlic eggplant fritters with yuzu gribiche. Some work better than others, but they all work. We're not so sure about one or two of the cocktails, like the amaretto-and-plum-wine sour. Fortunately there's also a selection of local craft beers.

Open Tuesday to Saturday 5.30 pm to midnight. Closed on Sunday and Monday. Licensed. All cards. You must book ahead.

VANCOUVER   MAP 209
LONGTAIL KITCHEN
810 Quayside Drive: Unit 116   **$90**
New Westminster
(604) 553-3855

Longtail is located in a food court; you order and pay at the counter and then look for a table. Everything is as fresh as it gets; there are no heat lamps. This is not fine dining, but it doesn't pretend to be. Given its location, it's unusual in having a liquor license, which features Steel and Oak craft beer. The fried chicken wings rival those at Phnom Penh. The curried mussels with turmeric and the gai lan pork belly are also worth remembering, but the pad Thai, like the pad Thai at Maenam, is rather too bland. Helpings are small, the service all it should be. They close early, but the truth is they often run out of ingredients before then.

Open Sunday to Thursday 10 am to 7 pm, Friday and Saturday 10 am to 8 pm. Licensed. Master Card, Visa. ♿

VANCOUVER   MAP 209
MAENAM   ☆
1938 W 4 Avenue   **$225**
(604) 730-5579

Maenam has always been our favourite Thai restaurant in Vancouver, but lately things seem to be slipping. It may be that Angus An has become over-extended, with both Longtail Kitchen in New Westminster and Fat Mao in Chinatown to look after. Prices here have risen even as the food has become less reliable. And a number of our favourite dishes have disappeared from the menu—things like the stir-fried aubergine, the red curry of duck and the braised beef short ribs. We still like the steamed mussels with Thai basil and lemongrass, the hot and sour chicken soup, the squid and green mango salad, the crisp-fried eight-spice fish and the green curry of halibut cheeks. Don't bother with the pad Thai. Maenam can serve a fine dinner, but it's no longer at the top of the Thai tree in Vancouver.

Open Monday 5 pm to 10 pm, Tuesday to Thursday noon to 2.30 pm, 5 pm to 10 pm, Friday and Saturday noon to 2.30 pm, 5 pm to 11 pm, Sunday 5 pm to 10 pm. Licensed. All cards. Book ahead. ♿

VANCOUVER
MASAYOSHI SUSHI
4376 Fraser Street
(604) 428-6272

MAP 209
☆
$240

Masayoshi Baba worked for years with Tojo Hidekazu in Tojo's iconic restaurant. The customers at the sushi bar kept telling him he should start his own place, and two years ago he decided to take their advice and opened this tiny—it seats only 30 people—out-of-the-way bar on an out-of-the-way stretch of Fraser Street in Vancouver's East Side. Masayoshi is an omakase restaurant, and Masa sees himself as a performer, creating art in front of a live audience. His rice is mixed to order with vinegar and salt in a wooden bucket, as it should be, and the fish—much of which comes from Japan—is never less than perfect. You can ask for fourteen pieces for 80.00 or sixteen for 110.00, or try the Original Creation Omakase, a seven-course meal of both hot and cold choices that costs 120.00 and must be ordered three days in advance. You might start with chopped raw oyster with foie gras before sampling the many choices of sushi—butterfish, red snapper, bluefin tuna, isaki, mackerel, sablefish, needlefish, squid, scallop, uni, shrimp, geoduck and more. To follow all that there's fish soup and a tea-infused pudding. This is a very serious restaurant.

Open Monday to Saturday 6 pm to 10 pm (sittings at 6 pm and 8 pm). Closed on Sunday. Licensed. All cards. You must book ahead.

MEDINA CAFE
780 Richards Street   **$75**
(604) 879-3114

Medina is one of the few restaurants we know of that
makes a specialty of breakfast. This means great egg
dishes and Belgian waffles with unusual toppings. If
you're really hungry, ask for either the Tagine, which
comes with two poached eggs, a spicy merguez sausage
and a stew of chickpeas, black olives and preserved
lemon, or the Boulettes, which has poached eggs with
spicy Moroccan lamb meatballs, tomato stew and raita,
served with grilled focaccia. Our favourite dish—we're
getting too old to be really hungry—is the fricassée of
mushrooms with two fried eggs, roasted potatoes,
smoked cheddar and caramelized onions. After 11 in the
morning they serve rare albacore tuna, white beans and
quinoa salad with tahini dressing and Aleppo butter.
Their Liège-style waffles come with a remarkable array of
house-made toppings, including chocolate, lavender,
rosewater, fig marmalade and ice cream. The espresso is
strong, dry and very inexpensive.
*Open Monday to Friday 8 am to 3 pm, Saturday and Sunday 9
am to 3 pm. Licensed. Amex, Master Card, Visa. No reservations.* &

MY SHANTI   ☆
15869 Croydon Drive   **$135**
Surrey
(604) 560-4416

This is Vikram Vij's third restaurant, and he himself is
often seen here. The menu has expanded recently and
now reads like a culinary map of India. Our favourite
appetizers are the fish pakoras in a spicy chili sauce with a
mint-onion chutney, the lamb kebabs and the roasted
portobello mushroom with cashews. The pan-seared
lingcod with mustard is outstanding as a main course, as

are the slow-cooked curried goat, the duck biryani roasted in a clay pot and the beef short-ribs braised in coconut milk. My Shanti also does well with vegan and vegetarian dishes like eggplant bharta or curried cauliflower. And on a cold winter's night, the rice pudding is warm and comforting.

Open Sunday to Wednesday 5 pm to 9.30 pm, Thursday to Saturday 5 pm to 10 pm. Licensed. Amex, Master Card, Visa. No reservations. ♿

VANCOUVER　　　　　　　　　　　　**MAP 209**
NICLI ANTICA
62 E Cordova Street　　　　　　　　　　**$90**
(604) 669-6985

Nicli has some of the best pizza in town, wood-fired of course, with a properly thin crust and extravagant toppings. We usually ask for the salame di manzo e funghi, made with roasted mushrooms, organic salami, garlic confit, grana padano and cream, or the pesto BBT (bacon, basil and tomato) with fior di latte and house-smoked bacon. Best of the vegetarian options is probably the cavolo nero e funghi, made with mushrooms, cream and black kale. You can start with a plate of antipasto misto or the crisp rucola salad of fennel, oranges and arugula—a lovely combination of flavours. To follow there's a delicate citrus panna cotta that goes perfectly with a cup of espresso.

Open daily 11.30 am to 11 pm. Licensed. Master Card, Visa. No reservations.

VANCOUVER　　　　　　　　　　　　**MAP 209**
NIGHTINGALE　　　　　　　　　　　　　☆
1017 W Hastings Street　　　　　　　　**$70**
(604) 695-9500

This is David Hawksworth's latest adventure, and it couldn't be more different from his extravagant showplace in the Hotel Georgia. First and foremost, a dinner for two without wine can be had for 50.00, which is pretty much the price of one main course over at Hawksworth. Nightingale is a relaxed and informal place, offering cocktails and small sharing plates from a small but imaginative list. The seasonal menus are the same at lunch and dinner, with additional daily specials. Recent choices include roasted brussels sprouts with pickled grape and sherry vinegar, mushroom pizza topped with confit garlic and arugula pesto, veal tongue tonnato with housemade albacore mayonnaise and anchovy bread-crumbs and grilled Arctic char on a bed of potato-and-artichoke salad. The restaurant is located in the art-deco University Club building, and the spacious high ceilings give a fine sense of occasion.

Open daily 11 am to midnight. Licensed. All cards. Book ahead.
&

VANCOUVER   **MAP 209**
PEACEFUL
2394 W 4 Avenue   **$90**
(604) 559-9533

There are half-a-dozen Peaceful restaurants, but only this one has been consistently good enough to take over from Lin as the go-to Chinese restaurant in Vancouver. Their cuisine is northern, which as a rule means szechuan. We like the braised beef served in chili oil on a bed of greens, the marble pork and the shredded pork with wood-ear fungus and bamboo. Everyone likes the Peaceful beef rolls, which are like Peking duck made with beef—crisp outside, sweet and savoury inside. There's a large selection of vegetarian dishes, including shiitake mush-rooms with minced garlic and szechuan white cabbage with malt vinegar and garlic. Their dim sum features such unusual things as szechuan hot-chili won-tons tossed in chili oil, garlic and vinegar. But note that Peaceful takes nothing but cash.

Open daily 11 am to 9.30 pm (later on Friday and Saturday). Licensed for beer and wine only. No cards, no reservations.

Nobody but nobody can buy his way into this guide.

311

VANCOUVER MAP 209
PEAR TREE ☆
4120 E Hastings Street **$175**
Burnaby
(604) 299-2772

Pear Tree is chic and urbane—a favourite with the faculty at Simon Fraser University. The menu is refreshingly short and full of interesting ideas, and the kitchen is the best in Burnaby. We like to start with the orange-caramelized scallops on double-smoked bacon risotto. Or there's a fine lobster cappuccino with dashi custard or the celebrated gin and tomato soup. Best of the meats is probably the beef short-ribs, braised for 36 hours—you've never had them this tender. There's also a Cornish hen en croute and a braised lamb shank with cauliflower fritters. For sweet try the deconstructed chocolate pudding, with malt crumble, hazelnuts, caramel and ice cream. There's a seasonal table d'hote, but you'll get a more unusual meal from the à la carte. Predictably, prices have crept up and are now near downtown levels.

Open daily 11.30 am to 9 pm. Licensed. All cards. Book ahead.
&

VANCOUVER MAP 209
LA PENTOLA
Opus Hotel **$180**
350 Davie Street
(604) 642-0557

La Pentola used to be known as La Pentola di Quercia, but now it's ready to stand on its own feet without reminding everyone of its Kitsilano parent. Like La Quercia, Pentola is Italian. For *primi* there's squid-ink tagliatelle or beautiful ravioli stuffed with squash, ricotta and chestnuts in brown butter and sage; for *secondi* there are perfectly tender braised short-ribs and pan-roasted lingcod with cauliflower. Either way, the meal will end with panna cotta or a chocolate torte. Since it's in a hotel La Pentola offers three meals a day. Breakfast includes a three-egg omelette with spicy Italian sausage. Weekend brunch is more interesting—try the cold Italian pancakes topped with chantilly cream and fruit. Lunch will remind you of La Quercia, featuring generous helpings of pasta e fagioli. *Open Monday to Friday 7.30 am to 10 am (breakfast), 11 am to 2.30 pm (lunch), 5 pm to 11 pm (dinner), Saturday and Sunday 7.30 am to 10 am, 10.30 am to 3 pm (brunch), 11 am to 2.30 pm, 5 pm to 11 pm. Licensed. All cards.* &

VANCOUVER   **MAP 209**
PHNOM PENH
244 E Georgia Street   **$85**
(604) 682-5777

Phnom Penh is a family-run restaurant serving a mixture of Vietnamese and Cambodian food. The menu is huge, the portions are large, and the food is appealingly spicy—filled with cilantro, mint, lemon grass and chilis. We like to begin with the soup loaded with noodles, bean sprouts, jicama, pineapple and fish, and then go on to deep-fried chicken wings, garlic squid and butter beef (the Cambodian answer to carpaccio). Or you can try the beef luc lac—rare beef on a bowl of fried rice with an egg on top. For sweet, you can't beat the black sticky rice pudding, which is an exotic treat. The service, unfortunately, can be a bit hit-or-miss. And for this they automatically add an 18% tip if you pay by credit card. It's not worth it—bring cash. *Open Monday to Thursday 10 am to 9 pm, Friday to Sunday 10 am to 10 pm. Licensed. Master Card, Visa.* &

VANCOUVER   **MAP 209**
PIDGIN   ★★
350 Carrall Street   **$160**
(604) 620-9400

Pidgin is a fusion language and this is a fusion restaurant, offering French takes on Asian food. The restaurant is also across the road from Pigeon Park at the heart of the city's run-down East Side. When it opened several years ago, there were protests against the intrusion of an up-market restaurant into a neighbourhood where drug addicts and other marginalized people lived in poverty and despair. But Pidgin has survived and become one of the top restaurants on the West Coast. It offers a daily prix-fixe menu for 55.00. For that you get their signature oyster shot (apple granita, horseradish and dashi), their daily pickles, taramasalata with nori paste and onsen egg or sockeye salmon aburi with Korean-style bulgogi beef, followed by a rose-blossom meringue. The à la carte list is broadly similar, but starts with a kohlrabi-noodle salad and excellent grilled octopus in a charred dashi-eggplant purée with feta cheese. For mains, try the beef tataki with bone marrow, the lingcod en papillote with miso butter and shiso, or the duck two ways (ginger glazed breast and leg confit with umeboshi beets). They have a fine selection of sakes and Japanese whiskies. Everything is superb, if expensive.

Open Monday to Thursday 5 pm to midnight, Friday and Satur-day 5 pm to 1 am, Sunday 6 pm to midnight. Licensed. Master Card, Visa. Book ahead if you can.

VANCOUVER   MAP 209

LA QUERCIA   ☆☆

3689 W 4 Avenue   **$175**

(604) 676-1007

For eight years now La Quercia has been our favourite Italian restaurant in Vancouver. Adam Pegg, the owner and chef, cooks in the northern Italian style, offering things like braised rabbit, roast branzino and vitello ton-nato, all of which make frequent appearances on the menu. The seven-course meal costs 60.00 (it's 80.00 for twelve courses), and the kitchen will create dishes around your choice of wine. The menu changes daily. You may find yourself sharing a great charcuterie plate or perhaps a wonderful pair of bone-marrow appetizers. Then there's roasted branzino (European sea-bass), pan-seared duck breast or roast lamb in anchovy sauce. La Quercia is a fine restaurant—it's a pity they only let you stay two hours.

Open Tuesday to Sunday 5 pm to 10 pm. Closed on Monday. Licensed. All cards. Book ahead. ♿

VANCOUVER   MAP 209
RANGOLI
1488 W 11 Avenue   **$70**
(604) 736-5711

Vij's may have moved to Cambie Street, but Rangoli next door is staying put, and offering Vij's level of quality with no wait time and very reasonable prices. Everything at Rangoli is made fresh and without preservatives. Our favourite appetizers are the organic chicken-liver pâté, the potato samosas and the potato pakoras with mango chutney. The vegetarian main courses include a portobello mushroom curry with red peppers and panir and black chickpea cakes with cabbage slaw and a yellow rice pilaf. The best of the meat dishes are the lamb curry with cumin and cream and the pulled pork on sautéed greens. To follow we really like the tangy and thick mango lassi and the rice pudding made with green cardamom and almonds. The restaurant also sells ready-to-eat Indian dishes to take home, Indian spices and Indian cookbooks.
Open daily 11 am to 11 pm. Licensed. All cards. No reservations. ♿

VANCOUVER   MAP 209
SAI WOO   ☆
158 E Pender Street   **$100**
(604) 568-1117

In the last couple of years Sai Woo has significantly raised its game. The inconsistencies that occasionally marred the cooking have been dealt with. And as if to celebrate, a giant neon rooster has been put up outside, a re-creation of the one that marked the original restaurant from 1925 to 1959. The new premises used to be hard to find, but they certainly aren't now. Inside is a huge space with two rooms on two levels: a hundred-seat dining-room and a lower-level lounge. The tables are generously spaced, and conversations can actually be heard. The food is Asian-fusion: start with the Vietnamese pork spring rolls with umami glaze, the pork belly dumplings seasoned with Johnnie Walker and scallions or the Szechuan garlic prawns with crispy shallots, and go on to the Korean scallion pancakes with barbecued pork shoulder, ponzu and kimchi or the Chinese paella filled with prawns, braised chicken, Chinese sausage and coconut broth. There is an imaginative list of cocktails featuring teas and fruits, and a good selection of beers and wines, all at reasonable prices. In fact, with no main course costing more than 25.00, Sai Woo is excellent value.

Open Tuesday to Thursday 4.30 pm to 10 pm, Friday and Saturday 4.30 pm to midnight. Closed on Sunday and Monday. Licensed. All cards. Book ahead. &

VANCOUVER   MAP 209
SALADE DE FRUITS
1555 W 7 Avenue   **$80**
(604) 714-5987

This choice little bistro is one of the city's culinary gems. They've expanded their menu recently, adding fresh seafood (at which they excel) and brunch at weekends (which is the same as lunch). You can have an omelette for brunch if you like, but it's better to go for the mussels (plump and juicy and served with spicy chorizo) or the halibut or sablefish. In the evening they offer frogs' legs, escargots in garlic butter and filet de boeuf Rossini. Or you can try the three-course table d'hôte for 30.00, featuring such things as Peking duck and tarte tatin. The wine-list is limited but well chosen. Bring cash—they accept no credit cards.

Open Tuesday to Friday 11 am to 2.15 pm, 5 pm to 8.30 pm, Saturday and Sunday 10 am to 2.15 pm, 5 pm to 8.30 pm. Closed on Monday. Licensed. No cards. Book ahead. &

Nobody can buy his way into this guide and nobody can buy his way out.

VANCOUVER

MAP 209

SAVIO VOLPE ☆☆
615 Kingsway **$150**
(604) 428-0072

Savio Volpe calls itself an osteria, which is a term used in Italy for a restaurant with local roots and traditional rustic cooking. And this osteria is all of those things. Its ingredients are drawn from nearby lakes, oceans, farms and fields; everything, even the pasta, is handmade fresh every day; the flavours are strong and uncomplicated. But Savio Volpe is much more than that. It starts with its all-star cast of three owners: Craig Stanghetta, who helped design Bao Bei and Pidgin: Paul Grunberg, formerly front of house at Lumière, Chambar, Market and l'Abbatoir; and Mark Perrier, sous-chef at Cibo and executive chef at CinCin. Together they make a formidable team—"savio volpe" means "wise fox." The cooking does sophisticated takes on traditional dishes: pappardelle with chanterelles, pork tonnato (a nice variation on veal), meatballs in lamb neckbone ragu, tripe with pancetta. The grill and rotisserie are wood-fired, and not just with any wood—a blend of grape vine, maple, alder and oak. You can smell the difference when they carry the half chicken with rosemary and lemon to your table—or the roast suckling pig with swiss chard. Sweets run to blood-orange tart, Sicilian cannoli, tiramisu and chocolate tart. There's a long list of craft beers and an interesting wine-list—look for the montepulciano d'Abruzzo, a bargain at 9.00 a glass.

Open Sunday to Wednesday 5 pm to 10 pm, Thursday to Saturday 5 pm to 10.30 pm. Licensed. All cards. Book ahead. ⅋

VANCOUVER

MAP 209

SHANGHAI RIVER
7831 Westminster Highway **$90**
Richmond
(604) 233-8885

Shanghai River still has the best Shanghai-style cooking in Richmond. It's full of Chinese Canadians—always a good sign. One starts with spicy szechuan dumplings, which are bursting with flavour. Or there's thinly sliced cold duck, braised spare ribs and squid salad. Whole rockfish comes next, crisp, deep-fried and topped with bamboo shoots and water chestnuts, black mushrooms and green onions. We also like the szechuan eggplant, sautéed with minced pork and garlic, and the Peking duck. The crispy bananas in caramelized honey sauce make a fine sweet. There are two schools of thought about the xiao long bao: some admire them, others say they don't compare with the lighter ones served at Lin.

Open daily 11 am to 3 pm, 5 pm to 10 pm. Licensed. Master Card, Visa. Book ahead. ♿

VANCOUVER   MAP 209
TACOFINO COMMISSARY
2327 E Hastings Street   **$60**
(604) 253-8226

There are now three Tacofinos: the original in Tofino, a second in Vancouver and a third in Victoria. The Tacofino in Vancouver is popular at lunchtime with the people who work on East Hastings Street, and in the evening with hipsters in love with its tacos and tequila. At noon you can get two tacos for 11.00—pork jowl and cabbage perhaps, or albacore tuna with soy, sesame, ginger and wasabi. They have a few burritos too, with chorizo, cheddar cheese, cabbage and salsa fresca or (for vegetarians) with cabbage, black-garlic mayo and pickled daikon. On a cold day, ask for the green pozole soup, which is crammed with hominy, cilantro, chicken and chili. For sweet, go for the banana churros with dulce de leche and ibarra chocolate.

Open Monday to Thursday 11.30 am to 3 pm, 5 pm to 10 pm, Friday 11.30 am to 3 pm, 5 pm to midnight, Saturday 11.30 am to midnight, Sunday 11.30 am to 10 pm. Licensed. Master Card, Visa.

If you use an out-of-date edition and find it inaccurate, don't blame us. Buy a new edition.

VANCOUVER **MAP 209**
THE TRUFFLE HOUSE
2452 Marine Drive **$125**
West Vancouver
(604) 922-4222

The Truffle House is a popular boutique restaurant that serves mainly truffle-infused dishes. It's a tiny place with only a few tables and chairs. They serve brunch on Saturday and Sunday and dinner on Friday and Saturday. At noon they have a marvellous onion soup, quite the best in the city. The place is packed early in the day for a breakfast of two-egg omelettes with wild mushrooms and black truffles. For dinner they start with truffle gnocchi, a warm scallop-and-spinach salad and dungeness and snow crab with a lemon-and-tarragon aioli, followed by a risotto of wild mushrooms and truffles and roasted sablefish marinated in maple and soy. Afterward there's a variety of crêpes and a really good tarte tatin.
Open Monday to Thursday 8 am to 11 am (breakfast), 11 am to 3 pm (lunch), Friday 8 am to 11 am, 11 am to 3 pm, 5 pm to 9 pm, Saturday 8 am to 3 pm (brunch), 5 pm to 9 pm, Sunday 8 am to 3 pm (brunch). Licensed. Master Card, Visa. No reservations.

VANCOUVER **MAP 209**
L'UFFICIO
3687 W 4 Avenue **$125**
(604) 676-1007

L'Ufficio is like a traditional Italian enoteca, with an extensive wine-list paired with housemade charcuterie and cheeses imported from Italy. In contrast to the clean black-and-white interior of La Quercia next door, l'Ufficio has warm wooden walls that make it feel more like a Piedmontese trattoria than a wine-bar in Kitsilano. We particularly like the three-course chef's special at 36.00, which might bring you something like pork cheeks seasoned with cinnamon and cumin. The sweets are all great, expecially the panna cotta and the lemon cream.

Open Tuesday to Sunday 5 pm to 10 pm. Closed on Monday. Licensed. All cards. No reservations. &

VANCOUVER   MAP 209
VIJ'S   ☆☆
3106 Cambie Street   **$175**
(604) 736-6664

Vij's moved in 2016 to new and larger quarters on Cambie Street near 16 Avenue. The menu is unchanged and the cooking is as good as ever—what is missing is the warmth and intimacy of the original location. And the extra tables don't seem to have made the lineups any shorter. Vikram Vij has never offered traditional Indian food, and he's not about to start now: this is a fusion cuisine designed to appeal to western tastes. He has a fine range of vegetarian dishes—things like shiitake mushrooms with mung beans and rice pilaf, the so-called Monarch butterfly (braised squash with woodear mushrooms) and curried chickpeas served on sweet potato. Meat eaters can start with lamb or beef samosas, sautéed prawns or pork-belly spoons—our favourite—and go on to marinated lamb popsicles in fenugreek curry, grilled venison with a tamarind and date purée or rainbow trout in a coconut and fenugreek masala with wheat-berry pilaf—a dish you'll never see in India. If you have any room left at that point, there's a decadent gulab jamon.
Open daily 5.30 pm to 9.30 pm. Licensed for beer and wine only. All cards. No reservations. &

VANCOUVER   MAP 209
WILDEBEEST
120 W Hastings Street   **$160**
(604) 687-6880

Wildebeest is really for carnivores, though there's nothing wrong with their seafood—try the pan-seared rockfish in an orange-and-chili prawn bisque. Many tables order the bone-in ribeye, a massive 32-ounce steak that has been dry-aged for 30 days. It cost all of

132.00 when we last checked, so you need three or four people to share. The restaurant likes to mix its meats: there's an excellent roast loin of elk, grilled bison steak and a game lasagne layered with braised goat and venison. The most interesting sweet is a crème brûlée with quince purée and roasted parsnip. We didn't dare try the caramelized pears with amaretto cream and boar drippings.

Open Monday to Friday 5 pm to midnight, Saturday and Sunday 10 am to 2 pm (brunch), 5 pm to midnight. Licensed. All cards. Book ahead. &

VANCOUVER MAP 209
YUWA ☆☆
2775 W 16 Avenue **$175**
(604) 731-9378

Yuwa used to be known as Zest. Then the chef, Tatsuya Katagiri, left to open his own restaurant, called Stem, in Burnaby. Zest's owner, Iori Kataoka, nothing daunted, found a new chef and partner in Masahiro Omori, closed for four months of renovations, and reopened as Yuwa. The new space features soft jazz, Japanese wallpaper, walnut tiles and a big slab of Douglas fir for the bar. Omori has replaced Katagiri's fusion cuisine with a more traditional regional menu, but the kitchen's high standards have been rigidly maintained. His sablefish is marinated for 24 hours in a yuzu shoyu sauce, then grilled and dressed with carrot and burdock kinpira and apple compote. His beef suji nikomi is stewed for 48 hours in shoyu stock before being served in a cast-iron bowl. The wine-list has grown considerably, with sakes (Kataoka is a certified sake sommelier) from all over Japan. He'll even recommend sake pairings.

Open Tuesday to Sunday 5 pm to 10 pm. Closed on Monday. Licensed. All cards. Book ahead. &

VANCOUVER
See also GIBSONS.

VIBANK, Saskatchewan (MAP 160)
THE GROTTO ☆
101 2 Avenue **$140**
(306) 762-2010

Located about 30 miles east of Regina, the Grotto occupies the premises of an old convent. Here they offer fresh Mexican dishes as well as several southern barbecues. On Wednesday and Friday they serve a variety of tacos, tamales, smoked ribs and street-style corn. On Saturday it's southern-style barbecues like Carolina ribs, pecan-smoked breast of duck, smoked prime-rib steak and their special show-stopper, which is the Texas Platter. The Texas Platter is a huge tray piled high with brisket, ribs, chicken, baked beans and corn-bread. Dinners end with a chocolate flan, mango-and-pineapple pie or a piece of *tres-leches* cake. You have to book ahead because often all the tables are booked for several weeks (maybe months) at a time.

Open Monday, Tuesday and Thursday 6 pm to 9 pm, Wednesday 9 am to 2 pm, Friday 9 am to 2 pm, 6 pm to 9 pm, Saturday 6 pm to 9 pm, by reservation only. Closed on Sunday. Licensed. Master Card, Visa. You must book ahead.

VICTORIA, B.C. MAP 211
BRASSERIE L'ECOLE ☆
1715 Government Street **$160**
(250) 475-6260

Brasserie l'Ecole never changes—but isn't that the point of a bistro, to offer the warmth and comfort of the famil-iar? Chicken liver and smoked Albacore tuna are two of their best appetizers. Many people choose steak to follow, but on the whole we prefer the Sooke trout, pan-fried in brown butter, which is always on the menu. They do a great job with saltspring mussels, which often come with pernod, with sherry broth and lime gremolata or with ginger and shallots and Japanese rice wine. Duck is also a safe bet. For sweet, you can't go wrong with crème brûlée, which is the best in B.C. The wine-list is full of good buys and especially strong on Belgian beer.

Open Tuesday to Saturday 5.30 pm to 11 pm. Closed on Sunday and Monday. Licensed. Master Card, Visa. No reservations. &

VICTORIA   MAP 211
CAFE BRIO
944 Fort Street   **$150**
(866) 270-5461

Everything at Cafe Brio is prepared in house, from the daily fresh bread to the excellent salumi, the pastas and the sweets. And most of their dishes are available in half-portions if you're looking for a light meal before going on to the Royal Theatre around the corner. The kitchen is good with fish: try the pan-roasted wild salmon with parsnip purée or the sablefish topped with lemon saffron cream. But just as many people come for the perfectly cooked steak served with lemon pepper aioli. Most of the entrées are roasted: the duck breast in cider vinegar, the venison loin with sunchokes, the chicken breast with crispy terrine. There's a very pleasant patio out front in the summer, and a good selection of reasonably priced wines by the glass and the bottle.

Open Tuesday to Saturday 5.30 pm to 10 pm. Closed on Sunday and Monday. Licensed. All cards. Book ahead. &

VICTORIA   MAP 211
CHOUX CHOUX CHARCUTERIE
830 Fort Street   **$75**
(250) 382-7572

Choux Choux is Victoria's best delicatessen, specializing in housemade sausages, pâtés, smoked and cured meats and artisanal cheeses. They also offer very good lunches that are worth every dollar. Try the goulash soup and the chicken-and-brie baguette with pesto mayo. Or check the chalkboard to see the plat du jour. It may be a quiche, a tourtière, steak tartar, grilled bratwurst, Italian sausage or our personal favourite, cassoulet. But you have to look early, because the plat du jour is usually sold out before 1 pm. Choux Choux also makes tasty picnic lunches for 12.00 a head that you can take away to eat wherever you like, which is a tempting idea for at least half of the year. *Open Monday to Saturday 10 am to 5 pm. Closed on Sunday. No liquor, no cards. No reservations.*

VICTORIA MAP 211
FOO
769 Yates Street $60
(250) 383-3111

Little has changed at Foo in the past year or so. It still has an open kitchen and limited seating in front. They still share a parking-lot with a hotel and a liquor store. And the menu still features things like tuna tataki salad with buckwheat noodles and miso vinaigrette. Our favourite dish is the sweet-and-sour pork belly, but others prefer the pad Thai. The butter chicken is also worth trying, as is their laksa—fresh seafood and Shanghai noodles in a curry broth. Check the chalkboard for daily specials, where you may find green-lentil dahl or curried lamb. Foo has recently opened a similar restaurant in Calgary, but we haven't yet tried it.
Open Monday to Saturday 11.30 am to 10 pm, Sunday 11.30 am to 9 pm. Licensed for beer and wine only. Master Card, Visa. No reservations. 占

VICTORIA MAP 211
JAM
542 Herald Street $60
(778) 440-4489

Jam is located at the edge of Chinatown, where it serves modern comfort food. Its big seller is scrambled eggs with spinach, goat-cheese and pesto. You should also try the so-called Charlie Bowl, which means two fried eggs with ham, green onions and cheddar. Or the Herald Street omelette, which comes with hash-brown potatoes and Monterey Jack cheese, spinach, green onions, chopped tomatoes, mushrooms and onion or tomato jam. If you aren't weight-watching, go for the Three Pigs (sausages dipped in pancake batter and served with maple syrup and fruit). They also have deep-fried avocado, pineapple-and-coconut pancakes, French toast with apples and soft tacos with chorizo and tortillas. At lunchtime they offer a nice selection of soups, salads and sandwiches. Expect lineups on weekends.

Open daily 8 am to 3 pm. Licensed. Master Card, Visa. Book ahead.

VICTORIA   MAP 211
LITTLE JUMBO
506 Fort Street: Unit 102   **$100**
(778) 433-5535

Little Jumbo is a favourite restaurant for many people. It caters to a young and trendy crowd, who come for the drinks and stay for the food. It has never been a place for a quiet, intimate meal. Order a bowl of truffled fries, served with garlic aioli, or pan-seared scallops on a bed of saffron risotto. Or there's roast lingcod, or braised lamb shanks, or even a burger with aged farmhouse cheddar. There have been reports of over-salting, which is a fault that is better left to the customers—wash it away with a glass of exceptional merlot from Fairview Winery in Oliver. To find Little Jumbo, look for a purple elephant over the door, and then make your way down the long office hallway inside until you reach the restaurant.

Open Tuesday and Wednesday 5.30 pm to midnight, Thursday to Saturday 5.30 pm to 1 am, Sunday 5.30 pm to midnight. Closed on Monday. Licensed. All cards. &

VICTORIA   MAP 211
MATISSE   ☆☆
512 Yates Street   **$185**
(250) 480-0883

Matisse hasn't raised its prices for at least two years. The prix-fixe dinner still costs only 48.00, which is a pretty good deal. The à la carte opens with a house-made pâté with horseradish and cornichons, or snails braised in red wine, garlic and brandy or one of their wonderful soups (lobster bisque, perhaps). They like to follow that with smoked sablefish, Brome Lake duck with pomegranate port or free-range lamb with rosemary and lemon. Sweets are usually crème brûlée or perhaps a nut tart with maple-walnut ice cream. The wine-list features well chosen local vintages.

Open Wednesday to Sunday 5.30 pm to 10 pm. Closed on Monday and Tuesday. Licensed. Amex, Master Card, Visa. &

VICTORIA   MAP 211
900 DEGREES WOOD-FIRED PIZZA
101-B 2401 Millstream Road   **$60**
(250) 590-4493

There's only one pizza in the Victoria area that can challenge Prima Strada's. This place in Langford has a wood-fired oven that reaches 900 degrees Fahrenheit. Adrian Ortiz-Mena had it handmade in Naples by a master mason, Steffano Ferrara, who used bricks and lava sand from Mount Vesuvius. The result is as close to perfection as it's possible to get. 900 Degrees is 30 minutes away from downtown Victoria, but if you're staying at Bear Mountain Resort, or on your way to Sooke (see above), Langford is only a short detour. Try their Pizza Genovese, which CTV considers Victoria's best pizza. It comes with a house-made pesto sauce, topped with mozzarella, spicy Calabrese salami, pepperoni, house-made fennel sausage, prosciutto and red onions. They make good sweets here too; have their lemon-raspberry panna cotta. The wines are all reasonably priced, and there are some likeable craft beers and a cider.

Open Monday to Thursday noon to 8 pm, Friday and Saturday noon to 9 pm. Closed on Sunday. Licensed. Master Card, Visa. Book ahead if you can.

Every restaurant in this guide has been personally tested. Our reporters are not allowed to identify themselves or to accept free meals.

VICTORIA   **MAP 211**
OLO   ☆
509 Fisgard Street   **$160**
(250) 590-8795

Ulla has changed its name to Olo, but little else has
changed. It's always been known for its inventive menu,
which features Holliewood Zen oysters, sweetbreads
with hot sauce and dry-aged cheddar cheese. They've always cooked well, and this year their clams in dashi broth,
their lingcod with pickled squash, their spelt chitarra
breast of duck and their mashed potatoes with buttermilk—especially the mashed potatoes with buttermilk—
are all great. The service is attentive and concerned. And
their wine-list is fascinating, offering excellent drinking
from Joie Farms, Venturi-Schulze, Tantalus, Black Swift
and Wild Goose, among others, most of them at very
modest prices.
Open daily 5 pm to 11 pm (later on Friday and Saturday).
Licensed. Master Card, Visa. Book ahead.

VICTORIA   **MAP 211**
PRIMA STRADA
230 Cook Street   **$100**
(250) 590-8595

Prima Strada has been undergoing major changes. The
Bridge Street location closed and reopened in Cobble Hill
(see above). But the Cook Street and Fort Street locations
still serve thin-crust pizzas that are about as good as you'd
get in Naples. We ourselves often add on some meatballs
(polpette della casa), which come with shaved parmesan
and good house bread. Or you can get a salad with either
a simple honey dressing or pickled eggplant and pears in
gorgonzola vinaigrette. There are all the usual sweets as
well as one or two unusual things like flourless-chocolate
cake. The espresso is excellent and quite inexpensive.
Open Monday to Thursday 11.30 am to 9 pm, Friday and Sat-
urday 11.30 am to 10 pm, Sunday 11.30 am to 9 pm. Licensed.
Master Card, Visa. ♿

VICTORIA

MAP 211

RED FISH BLUE FISH
1006 Wharf Street   **$90**
(250) 298-6877

Red Fish, Blue Fish is located in a converted shipping container on the dock of the Inner Harbour. It's full of atmosphere, but at peak hours it can get very busy. We like their green salad drizzled with lemon honey and topped with pickled onions, cucumbers and pea shoots, though the traditional battered cod and battered oysters and chips are almost as good. Their whitefish chowder blends whitefish confit and baby corn into a broth of coconut milk. Or you might try the jerk fish, which combines halibut, cod, salmon and tuna, simmered in hot sriracha. The only trouble with Red Fish, Blue Fish is that it's closed in winter and has no liquor.

Open daily 11.30 am to 6.30 pm from mid-February until mid-October. No liquor. Master Card, Visa. No reservations.

VICTORIA   MAP 211

SHINE CAFE
1548 Fort Street   **$60**
(250) 595-2133

Shine is a family operation, and it's open only for breakfast and lunch. It majors in omelettes, the best of which, we think, is the so-called Forager, served on a bed of mushrooms, spinach and avocado. The pancakes with maple syrup is a better dish for lunch, though at noon they also have soup, salads and sandwiches. There isn't much to drink aside from the Bad Apple, which is apple cider spiked with Sailor Jerry's rum. The original location is here on Fort Street, but they now have a branch that's more convenient for visitors to the city. It's at 1320 Blanshard Street (telephone (250) 595-2134). The menus are the same.

Open daily 8 am to 3 pm. Licensed. Master Card, Visa. No reservations.

VICTORIA

MAP 211

STAGE
1307 Gladstone Avenue   **$140**
(250) 388-4222

Stage is a wine bar and small-plates restaurant, very dark and very noisy, and handy for the Belfry Theatre across the street. You can ask for saltspring mussels, crisp-fried pork ribs and pan-roasted brussels sprouts, which have pretty much become Stage's signature dishes, or try one of the outstanding daily specials, like the roasted squash with spiced rum, the duck confit with cranberries or the pork shoulder with crabapples and bacon jam. Over the years most people's favourite dish has been the mussels in coconut curry broth, but we also like the crispy creole cauliflower with Louisiana remoulade and the gnocchi with guanciale, romesco and truffles. Stage has an award-winning wine cellar, and new arrivals and special offers are listed on the chalkboard over the bar.

Open Sunday to Wednesday 5 pm to 10 pm, Thursday to Saturday 5 pm to 11 pm. Licensed. All cards. &

VICTORIA

MAP 211

TACOFINO
787 Fort Street   **$60**
(778) 406-1787

This is one of our three favourite places in Victoria for lunch. (The others are Foo and Choux Choux—see above.) Their fish tacos always seem to us the best. Try the lingcod with chipotle mayo and salsa fresca or the tuna with soy, sesame, wakame, ginger and wasabi. Among the burritos we like the crispy chicken with beans, cabbage, sour cream and salsa, the cod with black beans, cabbage and chipotle mayo and the vegetarian yam, with black beans, salsa and sour cream. The popular tortilla soup is made with ancho chicken broth, sour cream, cheese and cilantro. There's only one sweet, a diablo cookie, but it's ideal for children.

Open daily 11 am to 11 pm. Licensed. Master Card, Visa. No reservations. &

VICTORIA MAP 211
VILLAGE CAFE 🖎
2518 Estevan Avenue **$60**
(250) 592-8311

This is a great place for breakfast. It's located in Estevan village, which is a longish way from the centre of the city. But if you're on your way to Vancouver it's convenient to the Swartz Bay terminal. Its cuisine is Jewish and they do a lot of Montreal smoked meat and a lot of Reuben and Estevan sandwiches. Everyone likes the free-run poached eggs with cumin and garlic and the French toast with maple syrup and fresh fruit. There's a second Village Cafe at 4517 W Saanich Road in Royal Oak (telephone (778) 265-8898. It's open from Wednesday to Sunday 8 am to 3 pm, 5 pm to 9 pm.
Open daily 8 am to 3 pm. Licensed. Master Card, Visa.

VICTORIA MAP 211
ZAMBRI'S ☆
820 Yates Street **$160**
(250) 360-1171

Chefs have a hard time putting a foot right in Victoria, where they have to please a cautious older generation of retired people as well as a younger generation looking for new adventures in eating. At Zambri's they do their best. The new location on Yates Street is crisp and modern, and so, on the whole, is the cooking. For lunch there might be some perfectly al dente penne with peas and gorgonzola, or authentic Italian meatballs with polenta. At night there are things like beef crudo with truffle mayonnaise and horseradish, orecchiette with housemade sausage and a purée of rapini, beef tenderloin with a mushroom duxelle, gorgonzola and polenta and a catch of the day, which may be salmon, halibut or sablefish. There's also a surprisingly good tiramisu, an all-Italian wine-list and a number of grappas.
Open Monday to Thursday 11 am to 3 pm, 5 pm to 9 pm, Friday and Saturday 11 am to 3 pm, 5 pm to 10 pm, Sunday 10.30 am

to 2.30 pm (brunch), 5 pm to 9 pm. Licensed. Amex, Master Card, Visa. ♿

VICTORIA
See also GALIANO ISLAND, SALT SPRING ISLAND, SIDNEY, SOOKE.

VICTORIA-BY-THE-SEA, P.E.I.   (MAP 37)
LANDMARK CAFE   ☆
12 Main Street   **$85**
(902) 658-2286

Eugene Sauvé has been in charge of the kitchen at the Landmark for almost thirty years, and his whole family (including his former wife) now works in the restaurant. Eugene is a great cook and his grilled haddock is as good as anything on the Island, maybe better. The same is true of his meat pies, his lobster rolls and his lasagne. He also makes scallops in garlic butter and a fine Cajun-chicken stir-fry. He has only a couple of wines, Peller and a little-known local wine. (The Peller is the better of the two.) He's a big, friendly man, and he makes sure that everybody has a good time at the Landmark.
Open daily 11.30 am to 2.45 pm, 5 pm to 8 pm from 1 June until 30 September. Licensed. Master Card, Visa. Book ahead. ♿

WAINWRIGHT, Alberta   MAP 213
THE HONEY-POT
823 2 Avenue   **$120**
(780) 842-4094

The Honey-Pot opened in 1979. The idea was to cater to soldiers of Western Command. Three generations later the same family are still in charge—Alex Heath and his daughter Michaela. The soldiers were lucky to find such a place, and so are the travellers of today. The family have never taken anyone or anything for granted. If they couldn't get their usual fresh salmon from Sooke, they'd substitute wild salmon from the Atlantic instead. And pollock may have replaced the haddock they used to serve in their hand-battered fish-and-chips, but the beef in the steak sandwich is still the best you can buy. There are eight cooks in the kitchen, and they're all committed to fresh vegetables and a different homemade soup every day. If you don't feel like soup, ask for jalapeno peppers stuffed with cream cheese and wrapped in bacon. Finish up with nutella mousse or strawberries in chocolate ganache, which they call foggy bottom. They have six beers on tap, including the local Ribstone Creek, which is sold in twenty-ounce British pints.

Open Monday to Saturday 11 am to 9.30 pm. Closed on Sunday. Licensed. Amex, Master Card, Visa. &

WATERLOO, Ontario   (MAP 93)
SOLE   ☆
83 Erb Street W   **$140**
(519) 747-5622

Sole is housed in what was once the Seagram cooperage building. The menu has been shortened, but they've kept their salads and most of their appetizers, as well as a variety of fish. In the evening the most exciting dishes, we think, are the pork belly with (amazingly fresh) scallops on a bed of puréed parsnip, the poached salmon seasoned with lime and the roasted-chicken ballotine stuffed with sausage and sage. The steaks are good too and come with delicate garlic mash. Our longtime favourite sweet is the carrot cake with pecans. There's an extensive list of beer and wine, and the carafes are all excellent buys.

Open Monday to Thursday 11.30 am to 11 pm, Friday 11.30 am to midnight, Saturday 11 am to midnight, Sunday 11 am to 9 pm. Licensed. All cards. &

WELLINGTON, Ontario   (MAP 145)
DRAKE DEVONSHIRE
24 Wharf Street   **$170 ($570)**
(613) 399-3338

Drake Devonshire is an upmarket and expensive boutique hotel (rooms start at $400), but their menus are suprisingly everyday. The hotel calls it "comfort food," and an effort is clearly being made to appeal to families with children. To start there are things like minestrone, Caesar salad, mussels and steak tartar; main courses run from a burger, meatballs amatriciana and a quarter chicken up to Nagano pork chop and Cumbrae's striploin. But within this framework a real effort is made. The Caesar salad comes with kale, bok choy, kohlrabi, pea tendrils, nori and parmesan miso, the mussels with shishito peppers and chorizo verde, and the quarter chicken with fried rice, edamame, charred cabbage, furikake corn and a ginger-scallion sauce. Sweets include apple pie (with calvados and parmesan gelato), bread pudding (with amarena cherries and eggnog zabaglione) and a "PB & J" (peanut-butter ganache, chocolate mousse, saskatoon-berry jam and White Russian gelato). The attractive dining-room faces the lake and is open all week. *Open Monday to Friday 9 am to 2 pm, 5 pm to 9 pm, Saturday and Sunday 8 am to 2 pm (brunch). Licensed. All cards. Book ahead if you can.*

WELLINGTON (MAP 145)
EAST & MAIN
270 Main Street $150 ($350)
(613) 399-5420

East & Main has been serving consistently good food for over a decade, and it's popular with both visitors and locals. The restaurant is an attractive conversion of an old shop, with a central bar and serving station. Appetisers include soup, chicken-liver mousse, crabcake and a good charcuterie plate. Our favourite main courses are the local chicken breast with chorizo and corn polenta, and the pasta with braised rabbit and wild mushrooms. For the more adventurous, there's an African peanut stew, udon soup with spiced shrimp and a creole seafood jambalaya with andouille sausage. To follow, try the pavlova, or the warm apple and berry crumble. The wine-list has more than 20 choices from Prince Edward County, and a good selection by the glass. The restaurant has also recently added a few bedrooms for overnight visitors.

Open Wednesday to Sunday 11.30 am to 2.30 pm, 5.30 pm to 9 pm. Closed on Monday and Tuesday. Licensed. Master Card, Visa. Book ahead.

WEST DUBLIN, N.S. (MAP 100)
PLOUGHMAN'S LUNCH
4645 Highway 331 **$40**
(902) 531-5371

Stefan Kirkpatrick and Desi Gordon own the West Dublin Buffalo Dairy, and have been selling its water-buffalo yogurt and cheese at farmer's markets in the area for some years. They also bake the most amazing French pastries—croissants, pains au chocolat, palmiers, cinnamon twists, tarts and puff pastries of all kinds. In the summer of 2017 they opened Ploughman's Lunch in West Dublin's old general store, which had been closed since 1966. They kept the old counters, stools, display cases and vintage calendars. Here they serve a light lunch of soup, salad, quiche and sandwiches—smoked salmon, lobster, buffalo mozzarella, ham with béarnaise. They also make picnic baskets to go (Crescent Beach is less than five minutes away) and sell some basic groceries and cheese. On Thursdays and Fridays they offer their own buffalo ice cream, which is soft and completely delicious, in a variety of flavours like hazelnut, miso caramel, blackberry lemon, pear chai and chocolate malt.

Open daily 9 am to 5 pm. No liquor. Master Card, Visa.

WEST POINT, P.E.I. (MAP 37)
THE CATCH
159 Cedar Dunes Park Road **$65**
(902) 859-3541

Eric Wagner started out as a lobster fisherman. After 35 years, he and his wife and daughters opened several seaside cottages, a craft brewery and a couple of seafood restaurants, one of which is The Catch. It's a bit out of the way, but one diner thought it worth the trip for the clam

chowder alone. We agree. The restaurant is very picturesque and relatively quiet. You might even be able to take
out one of the canoes parked along the shore—and just
try that anywhere else! The clams on the beach are plentiful, and the kitchen also prepares oysters, mussels and lobster—to say nothing of the burgers, dressed in cheddar
cheese and served with hand-cut, skin-on fries. The
service is very friendly and the prices are modest.
Open daily 11 am to 9 pm. Licensed. Master Card, Visa.

WHISTLER, B.C.   MAP 216

*Whistler is now a world-class resort, and of course that comes at a
price—some of the highest prices in Canada, in fact. If your lift
pass and ski rental didn't leave enough in your budget for Araxi or
Rimrock (see both below), there are still some attractive alterna-
tives. Elements Urban Tapas at 4359 Main Street (telephone
(604) 932-5569) offers bruschetta, slow-cooked pork belly,
mushroom gnocchi, mussels in red curry, crab-and-mushroom
cakes and even a deconstructed ahi tuna taco. They're open for
lunch and dinner every day. Hunter Gather at 4368 Main Street
(telephone (604) 966-2372) serves poutine with roast beef, steelhead chowder, smoked chicken and salad all day every day.
Stonesedge at 4122 Village Green (telephone (604) 962-9292)
has soups, stews, mac'n'cheese, bison short-ribs and venison
poutine available through the day, as well as an excellent
breakfast. Bar Oso at 4222 Village Square (telephone (604)
962-4540) makes great cocktails (try the oso sour) to go with
tapas portions of lamb meat balls, pork jowls, octopus, duck-liver
pâté and lobster and shrimp rolls. They too are open all day every
day. Families with children should try Creekbread at 2021 Karen
Crescent (telephone (604) 905-6666) for one of their organic
wood-fired flatbread pies (tell the kids it's pizza). There are meat,
vegetarian and vegan options, and a 16-inch pie will feed two or
three people. They're open daily from 4 pm to 9 pm.*

The price rating shown opposite the headline of each
entry indicates the average cost of dinner for two with a
modest wine, tax and tip. The cost of dinner, bed and
breakfast (if available) is shown in parentheses.

WHISTLER   **MAP 216**
ALTA   ✪✪
4319 Main Street   **$185**
(604) 932-2582

Alta is that rarity in Whistler, a good restaurant that is not outrageously expensive. Nicholas Cassettari has always been a strong believer in fresh local products, and he's constantly experimenting, even if not always with complete success. The menu is brief, and you should probably stick to things like the charcuterie board, the duck tartar, the elk and the wagyu beef. We've also enjoyed the pan-roasted red snapper and the Arctic char with scallops and Meyer lemon. His beers come from a brewery down the street and many of his wines are local and organic. The service is casual but prompt, the atmosphere lively.
Open daily 5.30 pm to 10 pm (shorter hours in summer). Licensed. All cards. Book ahead. ♿

WHISTLER   **MAP 216**
ARAXI   ✪✪
4222 Village Square   **$200**
(604) 932-4540

Araxi is probably Whistler's best-known restaurant, even if it's not, as Gordon Ramsay once claimed, the best in Canada. James Wait, the chef, introduced the fashion of local ingredients and seasonal menus long before they became clichés in the trade. And he has an astonishing menu, offering such things as citrus-cured steelhead trout, sablefish glazed with sake and soy, pepper-crusted venison loin and sesame-spiced breast of Yarrow duck. His steaks are said to be as good as any in the province, even the twelve-ounce New York for 84.50. To start he has wild albacore tuna tataki, sockeye salmon chirashi, Angus beef tartar and wild side-stripe prawns. A vegetarian menu is also available and all large plates can be made gluten-free. He has 9000 bottles of wine in his cellar, many of them offered at affordable prices. The oyster bar, open daily from 3 o'clock to 5, shucks up to a thousand

oysters of twelve different varieties every day.
Open daily 3 pm to midnight. Licensed. All cards. Book ahead.
&

WHISTLER   **MAP 216**
RED DOOR   ☆
2129 Lake Placid Road   **$180**
Creekside
(604) 962-6262

RD Stewart spent many illustrious years in this guide as
the chef at La Rua, and now he has a place of his own. The
Red Door is small, cozy and warm, seating only 40 people
(reservations are a must). The menu is French with a west-
coast twist: spring rolls filled with duck confit, duck-liver
terrine with star anise, wild-boar chop with mango chutney, juniper-rubbed venison with cherry sauce and chestnuts. The fish is local—cod, halibut, trout—and there's
an excellent bouillabaisse of crab, prawns, mussels and
scallops. Sweets range from a simple vanilla-bean crème
brûlée to the so-called bête noire, a dense chocolate torte
served with raspberry coulis and espresso whipped cream.
The Red Door isn't exactly cheap, but it's certainly better
value than some.
Open daily 5 pm to 10 pm. Licensed. All cards. Book ahead. &

WHISTLER   **MAP 216**
RIMROCK CAFE   ☆☆
Highland Lodge   **$200**
2117 Whistler Road
(877) 932-5589

Rolf Gunther, the long-time owner and chef, has built a
great reputation for both food and service at Rimrock.
Gunther has always been very concerned about the quality of his materials, and trucks still come here all the way
from Vancouver to bring him what he needs. It used to be
oysters; now it's more often game—bison, venison, elk
and caribou. We like to start with the lobster bisque or
the seared scallops, and go on to wild salmon on a bed of

lobster mash, rack of lamb or grilled elk with fig puree and foie-gras butter. If you're lucky enough to be here for a special occasion, the mixed grill of filet mignon, lamb chop and venison makes a memorable spread. The daily specials are more affordably priced: things like braised lamb shank and roasted sablefish with mushroom risotto. We've always been fond of the Rimrock, partly because it was the first restaurant we were able to recommend in Whistler. That was in 1989. Now, almost 30 years later, most people agree that it's still the best restaurant in town.

Open daily 5.30 pm to 9.30 pm (shorter hours in summer). Licensed. All cards. Book ahead.

WHISTLER   **MAP 216**
SPLITZ GRILL
4369 Main Street: Unit 104   **$70**
(604) 938-9300

If you have a family to feed, this is the place for you. They never lower their standards or raise their prices. They play loud music, but if you don't like that, you can always sit in the car. They have beef burgers, chicken burgers, bison burgers and even salmon burgers, all finished with either barbecue or teriyaki sauce. You then get to add any one of at least twenty different toppings. The burgers are huge, but if your children want more to eat, the fries and the onion rings are both first-rate. Then there's a huge choice of ice creams and a chocolate milkshake, which has few equals that we know of. A jumbo hot-dog costs just 4.95, less than that for children. Look for the Splitz Grill in the Alpenglow Hotel, close to the centre of town.

Open daily 11 am to 9 pm. Licensed for beer and wine only. Master Card, Visa.

WHITEHORSE, Yukon   **MAP 217**

If you come to Whitehorse in the daytime, you'll be glad to know about the Baked Cafe and Bakery at 100 Main Street (telephone

(867) 633-6291). Their coffee is so good that people line up for a cup. They have a full range of baked goods and a couple of fine homemade soups. The scones are great and so are the quiches. You go up to the counter for your food, which you then take to a table. They're open on weekdays from 7 am to 7 pm, on Saturday from 8 am to 6 pm, on Sunday from 8 am to 5 pm. They have a licence and take most cards. The Sanchez Cantina at 211 Hanson Street (telephone (867) 668-5858) claims to have the only authentic Mexican food in the Yukon. The owners go home every winter, but regulars think the kitchen is always pretty good, especially with its bean soup and chicken enchiladas. Orlina Sanchez makes nearly everything from scratch. This is a family business and Orlina seems never to stop smiling. They're open for both lunch and dinner every day but Sunday, have a licence and take most cards. Closed January to March.

WHITEHORSE   MAP 217
ANTOINETTE'S
4121 4 Avenue   **$85**
(867) 668-3505

For years we recommended the Wheelhouse over on 2 Avenue in the Waterfront Station. Tourists loved its spectacular fittings, but the locals found it too costly, and in the end there just weren't enough tourists. The best place to eat in Whitehorse now is Antoinette's—and it's certainly not costly. Antoinette describes her food as international with a Caribbean twist. It's that twist—those unfamiliar spices that keep popping up—that makes so many of her dishes appealing. The menu is short, with no more than four or five choices at each course, but there are always a number of specials like Moroccan goat or bison stew. Our favourites have been the halibut TNT (in a light coconut and tomato curry) and the curried chicken stew. Almost every dish is big enough for two, but if you have room left try the chocolate truffle cake or the spiced rum cake. This is a warm and friendly place, and Antoinette is a delightful host.
Open Monday to Saturday 4.30 pm to 9 pm. Closed on Sunday. Licensed. Master Card, Visa. Book ahead if you can.

Jonathan Reaume set high standards at Toscana, both for himself and for his customers. When it all got to be too much, he shut the restaurant down. At about the same time, his closest rivals, Zingara and the City Grill, closed their doors as well. This perfect storm has left a substantial hole in the centre of Windsor's restaurant scene. You might try Nico at 851 Erie Street (telephone (519) 255-7548). They've been around a long time, but the kitchen has improved under new chefs in the last couple of years. There's always a special or two featuring seasonal ingredients, and most things are really very good of their kind. Nico is open Tuesday to Friday 11.30 am to 2 pm, 5 pm to 9 pm, Saturday 5 pm to 9 pm, closed on Sunday and Monday, has a licence and takes all cards. Take Five Bistro at 1068 Erie Street (telephone (519) 962-2991) has capable if somewhat predictable cooking, and their prix-fixe menu at 29.00 (available every evening except Friday and Saturday) is great value. They're open daily 5 pm to 10 pm (or later), have a licence and take all cards. If you'd rather keep it completely casual, Mamo Burger Bar at 1515 Ottawa Street (telephone (519) 973-1234) serves the best burgers in town. Mind you, they still won't cook them rare—they say it's the law. But the meat is local, and they make all the sides: jalapeno slaw, sweet-potato fries and cornbread. Don't expect too much of a wine-list: their customers like beer and there's a large selection of craft ales. Mamo is open Tuesday to Thursday 11 am to 9 pm, Friday and Saturday 11 am to 10 pm, Sunday noon to 8 pm, closed on Monday, has a licence and takes Master Card and Visa.

WINDSOR
See also KINGSVILLE.

WINNIPEG, Manitoba   **MAP 219**
BISTRO DANSK
63 Sherbrook Street   **$100**
(204) 775-5662

Bistro Dansk has been open for more than 40 years now. In all that time, people have been coming here in search of good, authentic food at reasonable prices. And they've been finding it. Paul Vocadlo specializes in pork and chicken schnitzels, several kinds of meatball and a couple of crêpes. The soups are very good too, and as for the sweets, they're enormous. Take our advice and try the lemon soufflé. They have Danish beer as well as some inexpensive wines. The service is excellent and nobody leaves the place hungry.

Open Tuesday to Saturday 11 am to 2.30 pm, 5 pm to 9 pm. Closed on Sunday and Monday. Licensed. Amex, Master Card, Visa. Book ahead. ♿

WINNIPEG   **MAP 219**
CHEW   ☆
532 Waterloo Street   **$150**
(204) 667-2439

Chew is a small, minimalist space with very intelligent cooking. Kristen Chemerika and Kyle Lew both have years of experience in the restaurant trade, and over those years they learned to cook simple. At noon they serve vegetable burgers and soups—beet, for example, with cardamom. In the evening their menu runs strongly to steaks and fish, followed by some great sweets, like choco-late terrine and sea-salt pudding. The breads are marvellous and the service has wit. The wines are carefully chosen and fairly priced. Parking is on-street, but it's close and comfortable.

Open Tuesday to Sunday 11 am to 11 pm. Closed on Monday. Licensed. Master Card, Visa. Book ahead. ♿

WINNIPEG   **MAP 219**
DEER AND ALMOND
85 Princess Street   **$150**
(204) 504-8562

At Deer and Almond old favourites come in new clothes. The trouble with this is that prices here are pretty high and, worse still, some things tend to work better than others. Bread and butter, for instance, costs 8.00. Raw-tuna salad costs twice that. As for new experiences, panna cotta, usually made with sweet cream, is made at Deer and Almond with buttermilk topped with puffed rice and bee pollen. Their risotto is flavoured with Spanish manchego cheese instead of the customary Italian parmesan. The sweet they call the salt of the earth—beet ice cream with pickled blueberries, feta, mushrooms and cocoa—is, however, genuinely novel and usually pretty good. There is, of course, something to be said for originality and chef Mandel Hitzer has always been known for it. We all remember his winter dinners on the frozen river, and not just for the price (100.00 a head). There was more to it than that, which is why Deer and Almond is now in *Where to Eat in Canada*.

Open Monday to Friday 11 am to 2 pm, 5 pm to 11 pm, Saturday 5 pm to 11 pm. Closed on Sunday. Licensed. Amex, Master Card, Visa. Book ahead. &

WINNIPEG   **MAP 219**
EAST INDIA COMPANY   ☆
349 York Avenue   **$80**
(204) 947-3097

There are many restaurants in Winnipeg with all the traditional samosas, pakoras, biryanis and vindaloos.The East India Company is the best of them, if only because of their lovely interior and their gorgeous list of sweets. They have many vegetarian dishes, as well as a first-class bar serving Indian beers like Kingfisher and Cheetah. The East India Company is a genuine find, and there's even free on-street parking after 5 pm. Remember it.

Open Monday to Friday 11 am to 10 pm, Saturday 5 pm to 10 pm, Sunday noon to 9 pm. Licensed. Amex, Master Card, Visa. Book ahead. &

Every restaurant in this guide has been personally tested. Our reporters are not allowed to identify themselves to the management or to accept free meals. We accept no advertisements. We accept no payment for listings. We depend entirely on you. Recommend the book to your friends.

WINNIPEG   **MAP 219**
529   ☆☆
529 Wellington Crescent   **$200**
(204) 487-8325

529 is a mansion manqué that has become one of Winnipeg's
most lavish restaurants. Built in 1912 on a baronial scale, its
rooms are dark and elegant, its prices high, and its service
attentive. The menu is very New York: seared foie gras, oysters, smoked salmon, a couple of scallops wrapped in prosciutto for 48.00, steaks and ribs from 40.00 to 70.00,
potatoes and vegetables on the side at 10.00 each. But the
execution is good, especially with fish. Sweets are what you'd
expect—chocolate cake, cheesecake, crème caramel. The
wine-list is elaborate, with of course plenty of reds. There is
ample parking, the neighbourhood is quiet, and in summer
you can eat on the terrace out back surrounded by flowers.
Open Monday to Friday 11.30 am to 2 pm, 5 pm to 11 pm, Sat-
urday 5 pm to 11 pm, Sunday 5 pm to 9 pm. Licensed. All cards.
You must book ahead. ♿

WINNIPEG   **MAP 219**
IGI BBQ AND SUSHI BISTRO   🍴
1875 Pembina Highway: Unit 10   **$75**
(204) 477-9909

At IGI you sit in front of a gas-fired grill, which is right on
the table. You choose what you want and cook the meal
yourself. They have all sorts of fresh ingredients—vegetables, chicken, fish and lobster—as well as kimchi, sushi
and dragon rolls. The place is full of students, who like the
rush and the noise. You pay 23.00 on weekdays for all you
can cook, 31.00 on weekends, plus a tip of ten percent.
We like the place for the fun and the low prices, to say
nothing of the quality of the raw material and the will-
ingness of the staff to help beginners get into the game.
Just be careful not to cook more than you can eat!
Open Monday 11.30 am to 3 pm, Tuesday 4.30 pm to 10.30
pm, Wednesday to Sunday 11.30 am to 3 pm, 4.30 pm to 10.30
pm. Licensed. Master Card, Visa. Book ahead. ♿

WINNIPEG   MAP 219
NORTH GARDEN   🍴
33 University Crescent: Unit 6   **$65**
(204) 275-2591

The North Garden may be in the south end of town and it
certainly has no garden, but it's probably the best Asian
restaurant in Winnipeg. The menu has a few Indonesian
satays and Indian curries, but is largely Chinese—hot-
and-sour soup made to order, terrific hot-pots, vegetarian
specialties, fresh fish from the tank at the door—and the
place is usually packed with Asian students from the University of Manitoba nearby. Sweets are limited, but the
morning dim-sum is not. There's lots of free parking, and
lots of room inside.
*Open Monday to Saturday 11 am to 11.30 pm, Sunday 11 am to
10.30 pm. Licensed. All cards. Book ahead.* &

WINNIPEG   MAP 219
THE PALM ROOM
Fort Garry Hotel   **$120**
222 Broadway Avenue
(204) 942-8251

The Palm Room is a masterly restoration. It's meant to
look like a grand dining-room of the Edwardian era,
which is when the hotel opened. The current owners are
Richard Bel and Ida Albo. They bought the hotel many
years ago and have been restoring it at great cost ever
since—adding a Turkish spa and refurbishing its gorgeous public rooms. One of these is the restaurant known
as the Palm Room, where they serve roast chicken and
pot roast, hamburger and meatloaf, Italian antipasti—and
even a Reuben sandwich. Their sweets are superb and
their whisky as good as any in town. Everything comes
to the table with deliberate ceremony, which is a rarity
in Winnipeg.
*Open Monday to Thursday 11 am to midnight, Friday 11 am to
1 am, Saturday noon to 1 am, Sunday noon to midnight.
Licensed. Amex, Master Card, Visa. Free indoor parking.* &

PEASANT COOKERY
283 Bannatyne Avenue: Unit 100   **$95**
(204) 989-7700

At Peasant Cookery they cook French—or maybe we
should say French Canadian, given their baked chicken
with maple syrup, their poutine and their tourtière. The
menu is long, running from salads to onion soup, from
pasta with bacon and clams to mussels with chorizo. But
it offers a plate of cold cuts for just 19.00 or beef brisket
for 27.00. There's a lovely bar next door and a terrace in
summer. The service is good, though parking is not. You
come here for the atmosphere as much as the food and you
pay for what you get. But in Toronto you'd pay twice as
much and be thankful.
Open Monday to Thursday 11.30 am to 2.30 pm, 5 pm to 11
pm, Friday 11.30 am to 2.30 pm, 5 pm to midnight, Saturday 5
pm to midnight, Sunday 5 pm to 10 pm. Licensed. Amex,
Master Card, Visa. Book ahead. &

RAE & JERRY'S
1405 Portage Avenue   **$150**
(204) 783-6155

Rae & Jerry's is pure 1960. It looks it and the menu proves
it. Nothing changes. There's still shrimp cocktail, herring
in sour cream and Caesar salad. They do beef in ten different ways, they serve chicken by the platter, ribs, lobster,
pickerel, halibut and salmon. They have first-class bread
and all the pecan pie you can eat. The restaurant is not for
vegetarians, or indeed anyone worried about their
arteries, but the rest of us can enjoy the beef, the service
and the prices. (Lunch is about half the cost of a typical
dinner.) On-site parking is plentiful and free, and no-one
ever says they haven't had enough to eat.
Open Monday to Wednesday 11 am to 10 pm, Thursday to Sat-
urday 11 am to 11 pm, Sunday 11 am to 8.30 pm. Licensed.
Amex, Master Card, Visa. Free parking. Book ahead. &

WINNIPEG

MAP 219

LA SCALA
725 Corydon Avenue   **$110**
(204) 452-2750

Perry Scaletta used to race bicycles, but for many years now he's been a chef, creating Asian-Italian dishes here with considerable aplomb. He's famous for his pork-and-ginger dumplings, but he's also good with pasta of all sorts, pizzas, osso buco and cioppino. Often he waits on the tables himself, and he's always friendly and helpful. The dining-room is hung with colourful local art, and in summer there's an outdoor terrace that is usually packed. The wine-list is modestly priced, and features an unusual selection of Italian cabernet-sauvignons. This is a good restaurant, and Scaletta makes a charming host.

Open Monday to Thursday 5 pm to 10 pm, Friday and Saturday 5 pm to 2 am, Sunday (except in winter) 5 pm to 10 pm. Licensed. Amex, Master Card, Visa.

WINNIPEG

MAP 219

TRE VISI
926 Grosvenor Avenue   **$125**
(204) 475-4447

Some time ago Tre Visi moved from its rough lunch-crowd location to an upscale address where the biggest problem is finding somewhere to park. But they still cook Italian, helpings are big and the prices are fair. They cut and trim their own squid and make the tomato sauce to go with it. Their excellent crostini is served with fig jam and gorgonzola. The soup is usually minestrone, and of course there are the inevitable pizzas (our favourite is the puttanesca with capers and olives). Their pasta, expecially the Adriatica with scallops, mussels and shrimps, is about as good as it gets. They have a short list of sweets, among them tiramisu and a chocolate hazelnut bombe. The wines are good and quite modestly priced; the service is gracious. We like Tre Visi.

Open Tuesday to Friday 11.30 am to 2.30 pm, 5 pm to 9 pm,

Saturday and Sunday 5 pm to 10 pm. Closed on Monday. Licensed. Amex, Master Card, Visa. Book ahead. ⅃

WOLFVILLE, N.S.   MAP 220
BLOMIDON INN   ☆☆
195 Main Street   **$160 ($325)**
(877) 542-2291

Donna Jackson is in charge of the kitchen at Blomidon again this year, assisted by James Freiman from Fresh. And innkeeper Michael Laceby is still in charge of the wine-list, which is as remarkable as ever, featuring most of the great French and Italian labels, to say nothing of local bot-tlings from Grand Pré, Benjamin Bridge, Gaspereau and Luckett's. The big news this year is that Michael's mother Donna, the original cook in the family, has left her giftshop and become the inn's full-time gardener. She's even acquired a greenhouse where she grows herbs for the kitchen all winter. All the established dishes at the restau-rant are still in place: the lobster, the beef tenderloin, the free-range chicken and, in summer, the tuna. And both the food and the service are still all they should be. One diner told us that his praline-apple cheesecake was "an absolute killer."

Open daily 11.30 am to 2 pm, 5 pm to 9.30 pm. Licensed. Master Card, Visa.

WOLFVILLE   MAP 220
CELLAR DOOR   ☞
Luckett Vineyards   **$50**
1293 Grand Pré Road
(902) 542-2600

Pete Luckett has now sold the last of his stores in Halifax and Wolfville so he can concentrate on his vineyard, and on the vineyard's restaurant. The Cellar Door is a mixed blessing: the panoramic view from the top of the hill overlooking the Midas Basin is spectacular, the food is simple but good, and the service is not. They offer soup, Italian-style sandwiches (try the ham with figs) and several charcuterie platters. There's also a fine steak-and-mushroom pie. And there's nothing whatever wrong with the wines, which are getting better and better every year as the vines mature.

Open daily 10 am to 5 pm from 1 June until 31 October. Licensed. Amex, Master Card, Visa. Book ahead if you can.

WOLFVILLE   MAP 220
TROY   ☆
12 Elm Avenue   **$145**
(902) 542-4425

Erkut Surmeli learned his trade in Turkey, which is why there's a Turkish restaurant in Wolfville. He left Troy after a year or so, but his menu is still in place. Daniel Franck and Wil Lang met at Acadia University, and when they graduated they decided to stay in town and bought Troy. The menu may still be Turkish, but most of the ingredients come from just down the road. Meals start with an array of mezze, and then go on to appetizers (a lentil soup with mint, perhaps) and a plethora of kebabs, at least one of which is vegetarian. Our favourite main course is the lamb shank on the bone with eggplant sauce. The wines are mostly from Nova Scotia. Troy is an exotic experience: the high ceiling is hung with herbs, and on the outdoor patio there's even a replica of the Trojan Horse.

Open daily 11 am to 9 pm. Licensed. All cards. ♿

WOLFVILLE
See also GRAND PRE.

WYEBRIDGE, Ontario   MAP 222
MAD MICHAEL'S   ☜
8215 Highway 93   **$90**
(705) 527-1666

For years we recommended Explorers in Midland. Explorers still has some fine cooking and a great wine-list, but after a few readers sent us critical letters we started going down the road to Mad Michael's in Wyebridge. It's a barbecue joint, but (you won't believe this) all the ingredients are fresh and local. They even make their own tomato ketchup. They have Texas-style pork ribs with lots of meat and little bone, sliced beef brisket, jerk chicken and smoked lamb with jalapeno jelly, as well as some irresistible things for vegetarians. They have pies for 6.00 and butter tarts for 2.00, and you'll never find a better piece of pie, or a better butter tart for that matter. They have a licence, but you shouldn't leave without trying the homemade lemonade or ginger beer. One diner describes Mad Michael's as beyond excellent—his words. *Open Thursday to Sunday noon to 8 pm from mid-May to mid-October. Closed Monday to Wednesday. Licensed. Amex, Master Card, Visa.*

YARMOUTH, N.S.   MAP 223
OLD WORLD BAKERY
232 Main Street   **$45**
(902) 742-2181

Ferries come and go, but the Old World Bakery just keeps on getting better and better. Nathan Bain, who trained here and bought the place three years ago—when the Bar Harbor ferry shut down—has built a business able to stand on its own feet. He has come to stay, and expects to be here 40 years from now. His bread—rye, whole-grain, sourdough and sweet-potato—is fantastic, and every morning at 7 o'clock six kinds of freshly-baked muffins get put out on the counter. There's a different homemade soup every day as well as big, filling sandwiches. (Our favourite is the smoked lamb.) The lamb, like the turkey and the sausage, is smoked on the premises. The coffee is fairly traded and it's always wonderful. And they're so Old World they even sell vinyl records. *Open Tuesday to Friday 7 am to 6 pm, Saturday 7 am to 4 pm. Closed on Sunday and Monday. No liquor, no cards.* &

Our website is at www.oberonpress.ca. Readers wishing to use e-mail should address us at oberon@sympatico.ca.

YARMOUTH

THE RED SHED MAP 223

81 Water Street ☞

(902) 740-6697 **$40**

The Red Shed sits on a small trailer on the Yarmouth docks, a few feet from the water and a stone's throw from the Portland ferry. The local boats can pretty much toss their catch through the door as they land, and the fish is the freshest in town. Everything is handmade and cooked to order, from the seafood to the burgers, tacos and fries. In the last few years they've won awards for best fish-and-chips, best burger, best poutine and best customer service. There are a lot of gourmet burgers—fajita burgers, aloha burgers, dill burgers, donair burgers—but what you really come for is the fish. There are three or four tables at the edge of the wharf, two with red umbrellas, and it's a surprisingly pleasant place to pass some time.

Open Monday to Thursday 11.30 am to 3.30 pm, Friday 11.30 am to 7.30 pm, Saturday 11.30 am to 3.30 pm from 15 May to 15 September. Closed on Sunday. No liquor. Master Card, Visa. No reservations.

YARMOUTH

See also MIDDLE WEST PUBNICO.

YELLOWKNIFE, N.W.T. MAP 224

BULLOCK'S BISTRO ☆

3534 Weaver Drive **$150**

(867) 873-3474

Bullock's may be crowded and noisy, but it's outlasted all its competitors. That's not because of its low prices, because its prices aren't low. (If you want low prices, we suggest the cafe in the Prince of Wales Museum at 4750 48 Street, telephone (867) 873-7570—it's only open on weekdays and has a very small menu, but there's lovely fresh fish, several daily specials, big helpings and a nice view.) Bullock's used to be a working fish shack and still looks it from the outside. Inside, the walls are plastered with graffiti and bumper stickers. But everyone agrees, the fish is about as good as it gets. Most of it—and all the whitefish, pickerel and trout—comes in fresh every day from Great Slave Lake, and you can have it grilled, pan-fried or deep fried in beer. If bison is on the menu, be sure to ask for it. (They have a combination plate of perfectly cooked bison and Arctic char fried in big dollops of butter.) There are no sweets, but the fish chowder makes up for that—the chowder, the bison, the pickerel, the cin-namon rolls on Saturday, and the salad dressings. If you want a beer, help yourself from the cooler.

Open Sunday and Monday 4 pm to 9 pm, Tuesday to Saturday 11 am to 9 pm. Licensed. Master Card, Visa. Book ahead if you can.

YELLOWKNIFE   MAP 224
WILDCAT CAFE
3904 Wiley Road   **$100**
(867) 873-4004

The Wildcat is a long way from almost anywhere, but nobody comes to Yellowknife without stopping at the Pilot Monument and this log shanty nearby. The Wildcat was built in the nineteen-thirties and since then it's been extensively restored more than once. Apparently the town is determined to keep the place on its feet, and it has to be said that the food remains good year after year. Sometimes breakfast is the highlight; sometimes it's the fish chowder. This year it's been the bison and the tacos. Everyone is friendly, even the tourists off the buses. In fine weather there are tables outside, where you can watch the sun set over Back Bay.

Open Monday to Friday 11.30 am to 10 pm, Saturday and Sun-day 10.30 am to 9 pm. Licensed. Master Card, Visa.

We will soon be preparing the next edition of this guide. To do that, we need the help of our readers, many of whom routinely send us information and comments on restaurants that interest them, whether or not they are already in the guide. Please address us by mail at 145 Spruce Street: Suite 205, Ottawa, Ontario K1R 6P1, by fax at (613) 238-3275 or by e-mail at oberon@sympatico.ca

First published July 1971. Reprinted September 1971, November 1971, January 1972. Second edition published June 1972. Reprinted July 1972. Third edition published June 1973. Reprinted July 1973. Fourth edition published June 1974. Fifth edition published June 1975. Book-of-the-Month Club edition published July 1975. Sixth edition published June 1976. Seventh edition published June 1977. Eighth edition published June 1978. Ninth edition published June 1979. Tenth edition published June 1980. Eleventh edition published June 1981. Twelfth edition published June 1982. Thirteenth edition published June 1983. Fourteenth edition published June 1984. Fifteenth edition published June 1985. Sixteenth edition published June 1986. Seventeenth edition published June 1987. Eighteenth edition published June 1988. Nineteenth edition published June 1989. Twentieth edition published June 1990. Twenty-first edition published June 1991. Twenty-second edition published June 1992. Twenty-third edition published June 1993. Twenty-fourth edition published June 1994. Twenty-fifth edition published June 1995. Twenty-sixth edition published June 1996. Twenty-seventh edition published June 1997. Twenty-eighth edition published June 1998. Twenty-ninth edition published June 1999. Thirtieth edition published June 2000. Thirty-first edition published June 2001. Thirty-second edition published June 2002. Thirty-third edition published June 2003. Thirty-fourth edition published June 2004. Thirty-fifth edition published June 2005. Thirty-sixth edition published June 2006. Thirty-seventh edition published June 2007. Thirty-eighth edition published June 2008. Thirty-ninth edition published June 2009. Fortieth edition published June 2010. Forty-first edition published June 2011. Forty-second edition published June 2012. Forty-third edition published June 2013. Forty-fourth edition published June 2014. Forty-fifth edition published June 2015. Forty-sixth edition published June 2016. Forty-seventh edition published June 2017. Forty-eighth edition published June 2018.